THE COMPLETE PRICE GUIDE TO BASEBALL CARDS WORTH COLLECTING

THE COMPLETE PRICE GUIDE TO BASEBALL CARDS WORTH COLLECTING

PAUL M. GREEN

CONTEMPORARY
BOOKS

CHICAGO

Library of Congress Cataloging-in-Publication Data

Green, Paul (Paul M.)
    The complete price guide to baseball cards worth collecting
/ by Paul M. Green.
       p.   cm.
   ISBN 0-8092-3793-8
    1. Baseball cards—Collectors and collecting—United
States.   2. Baseball cards—Prices—United States.   I. Title.
GV875.3.G743   1994
796'.49796357'0973—dc20   93-37637
                                           CIP

Author's note

Readers' comments and criticisms are welcome. Comments about what you find most useful as well as suggestions to improve later editions are most welcome. Please address your comments to the author in care of the publisher.

    The information provided in this book is the personal opinion of the author based on his own experience and is provided only for the enjoyment of readers. No information presented in this book should be construed as advice for investment or any other purpose. The author neither warrants nor represents that the information presented in this book can be used for financial gain. Consequently, the author and publisher disclaim responsibility for any loss, monetary or otherwise, that might result from the use of any information contained herein. The author recommends collecting baseball cards for the joy of collecting and does not recommend that the information in this book be used for investment purposes.

Copyright © 1994 by Paul M. Green
All rights reserved
Published by Contemporary Books, Inc.
Two Prudential Plaza, Chicago, Illinois 60601-6790
Manufactured in the United States of America
International Standard Book Number: 0-8092-3793-8
10   9   8   7   6   5   4   3   2   1

Dedication

To Teri,

They won't understand Alfred, but they certainly can understand that you are the most kind, understanding and loving person I have ever known. Without you this wasn't possible, but with you this book and everything else seem not only possible but likely.

All my love,
Paul

Contents

Acknowledgments

THIS BOOK REPRESENTS the labors of a variety of people. First on that list is Kit Kieffer. In fact, the book is half Kit's, and that's almost certainly the better half. Had it been possible, his name would have appeared as coauthor, for surely he deserves it.

Bill Corsa not only spent months working out the deal for this book, but in conjuction with Clarice McElsy and others worked out the technology to turn a massive undertaking into a large, but possible, undertaking.

When the pressure was at its worst, Hal Hintze, one of the real baseball-card experts, produced the material we needed to get this done near deadline.

Finally, to friends, family, and loved ones from Ridgeway, Wisconsin, to New York, to California, and at the end of the road in Key West, Florida, goes my thanks for their understanding and tolerance during what was a short but intense period.

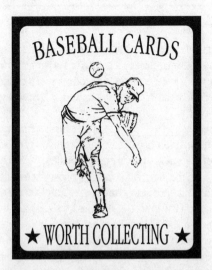

BASEBALL CARDS

★ WORTH COLLECTING ★

Introduction:
A Perspective

BASEBALL CARDS aren't a new idea. Your father probably had cards as a boy, and his father before him. They're not as old as Roman ruins or fossils, but cards from the 1950s are considered old to most of today's collectors. The first baseball cards from all the way back in the 1880s are fossils in their own right.

It stands to reason that if cards date back to the 1880s the same would be true for card collecting. Consider for a moment what cards and baseball were like in the 1880s.

There were no companies—let alone a half dozen or more—producing high-quality cards, update sets, traded sets, and autographed insert cards in 1887. To begin with, cards did not come in packs or complete sets. They came one at a time in cigarette packs. The major baseball card set of the period was a premium on Old Judge cigarettes. If your parents smoked a pack a day you might complete a set in about two years, assuming on each pack there was a new card not yet in your collection. It wasn't the ideal situation for avid collectors (or nonsmokers).

There were other baseball cards being produced in the 1880s, but they were either small sets or had only a small number of baseball players as part of a larger card set featuring other important sports of the day such as boxing, rowing, wrestling, and even walking. Today's collectors are not partial to sets of mixed sports, and the same was probably true in the 1880s.

Early collecting

There is some limited evidence (in the form of early-day checklists) that companies were encouraging people to acquire all the cards in a given set. Based on the fact that complete early sets, with a few exceptions, exist today it seems clear that even if people weren't trying to get all the cards from a set they were at least saving all the cards they got.

Proof positive of early collecting can be found in certain premium cards. These large-size cards, which required proof of purchase and sometimes a small amount of money, are solid evidence of collecting. A typical example of these big and beautiful cards was the premium issue from the American Tobacco Company known as the T3 or Turkey Red. You didn't get a Turkey Red in a cigarette pack like most of the cards of the day. To get a Turkey Red card you had to send in coupons from various brands of cigarettes. It wasn't an insignificant number of coupons either. It took 10 Turkey Red coupons or 25 of other brands to get just one card. The complete T3 set included boxers and totaled 125 cards. In addition, there were variations such as Vic Willis,who was placed with Pittsburgh or sometimes with Pittsburgh and St. Louis. So if you smoked Turkey Red brand cigarettes it took 125 cartons to get a complete set of premium cards.

While we have no actual proof of anyone smoking their way to a complete set, existing numbers of T3s suggest that people were attempting to put complete sets together. Otherwise, given the option of using your coupons for Ty Cobb or Hooks Wiltse, why would anyone besides the immediate Wiltse family order a Hooks over a Ty Cobb? The conclusion has to be that people were collecting all kinds of cards — and the proof is that impressive numbers of cards of such common players as Wiltse remain today.

Additional proof of early card collecting lies in the fact that the use of cards to promote other products expanded. In 1914 the popular Cracker Jacks candy featured a card. Soon other candy companies, and later gum companies, joined in using cards to promote their products.

Baseball-card history clearly shows some important dividing lines. Prior to 1900, card sets were generally small in number with limited production levels. From 1900 to about 1914 the tobacco companies continued to be the major source of cards. The number of cards printed increased during the period as did the number of players in a complete set, although sets containing more than 200 different cards were still the exception.

Just as the candy companies were beginning to use cards, World War I broke out. These two events might seem unrelated, but the fact is that wars tend to bring baseball card production to a grinding halt. This was true during World War I, but once the war was over cards returned right along with the troops.

Bubble gum

It was not until the 1930s that the combination of cards and bubble gum appeared, and for a logical reason: it was not until then that bubble gum was invented. Admittedly, the creation of bubble gum doesn't rank in the history of the planet along with the discovery of electricity or the invention of the wheel, but where baseball cards are concerned it is incredibly important. Bubble gum needed promotion, and bubble gum companies chanced on cards as a way to encourage little customers to chew gum, not to annoy teachers and parents.

The 1930s were dominated by the National Chicle Company, Gum Inc., and the Goudey Gum Company. Goudey cards in particular are favored by collectors of 1930s cards today. In 1939, Gum Inc. of Philadelphia introduced Play Ball gum and cards. If World War II had not intervened, Play Ball cards would probably be better known today than any other type of card, and would certainly have dominated collecting during the 1940s. Instead, Play Ball cards became a transitional pre-World War II card, with cards featuring players such as Joe DiMaggio and Ted Williams taking the early 1940s lead.

Modern card companies

At the end of World War II, Gum Inc. became Bowman Gum Inc., the first of what are considered the modern card companies. From 1948 to 1952 Bowman had little competition. Bowman combined the progress made in card production during the 1930s and 1940s, such as informative card backs, with regularity of production and an eagerness to experiment with design. Consequently the company produced some of the best and most interesting cards of the 1950s. Many of Bowman's important rookie cards include stars of the 1950s such as Mickey Mantle and Willie Mays.

Bowman did more than produce important cards. Its success almost certainly helped to foster the 1952 arrival of the first real cards from Topps. As anyone who has collected baseball cards over the past 40 years can verify, the arrival of Topps changed baseball cards and baseball-card collecting forever.

When Topps entered the baseball-card market, collecting was still in its infancy. Baby Boomers were just reaching the age when they might stop in the penny candy store on their way home from school and plunk down a penny or nickel for a pack of cards. Throughout the 1950s Topps encouraged that practice with checklists, with larger-than-ever card sets, and by offering new cards every year. Occasionally Topps produced some awful-looking cards with bad airbrushed pictures, but the company was on its way to becoming a monopoly, so perfection didn't seem to matter. Topps bought out Bowman in 1955 and stood alone in hooking a generation of youngsters on card collecting. For the next 25 years Topps was a monopoly.

For most of those 25 years there was little reason for serious challenge. Baseball-card collecting remained a hobby for children. Kids bought cards, flipped cards, traded cards, and even tortured them in bicycle spokes. Most cards were lost, thrown out, or destroyed by gum-chewing little leaguers (or more frequently by their parents). It probably never crossed the minds of anyone then that those stacks of baseball cards would be worth a lot of money someday.

During the 1970s interest in baseball cards as a serious collectible gradually grew. At first just a few individuals were offering to pay money for older cards. As time passed their numbers increased, and that process was promoted by publications and other forms of publicity. Then in 1981 a federal court opened the doors for competition and Topps was quickly joined by Fleer and Donruss as major card producers.

A recession slowed collecting for a few years, but by the mid-1980s baseball cards were a rage among the young and not a laughing matter among adults. Publications, card shows, and shops abounded. Whereas a decade earlier it would have been hard to find anyone who cared about cards, now everyone seemed to care. The continued growth in collecting as a hobby in the '90s is due in part to public awareness of the incredible value of some baseball cards. That public awareness has been heightened by the national publicity of six-figure prices achieved by some cards at auction. Increasing public awareness has, of course, strained the available supply, causing prices to rise. With higher prices, a real market has developed. This market flourishes because of modern technology. A dealer on one coast can get price quotes from dealers thousands of miles away. Big deals are struck that would have been impossible a few years ago.

Card price guides

In the current baseball-card market pricing information is critical. Unfortunately, getting a price fast is impossible under the current system. Most baseball-card price guides attempt to price every card whether it's a Mickey Mantle or a Darrell Porter, and those guides try to price them in a variety of grades. Think about that. Hundreds of thousands of cards are already in circulation. Each year half a dozen companies issue new sets adding tens of thousands more to the market. All of these new cards need to be priced. Imagine you are the editor of a price guide and you attempt to price every known card. You work 40 hours a week, 52 weeks a year, take no vacations, and never talk on the phone or take a break. Assuming you are such a super worker you can devote one minute per card per year to price all the cards in all the grades. That's approximately 125,000 cards. But of course by the time you are done the prices from the first cards are now a year old; the market is changing day by day.

All of that effort is made in the name of having a complete price guide. Such guides are now becoming impossible to carry due to their weight, and are hopeless for use at a card show due to their size. Truthfully, most collectors and dealers do not need that much information, and especially that much old information.

How this guide is different

What we have done in this book is give you almost as much information, but have vastly reduced the number of individual cards priced. This strategy enables us to give you a book you can carry to shows and shops and give you the individual card prices you are most likely to want. How does it work?

Consider cards for players like Reggie Jackson or Mickey Mantle. Both are now in the Hall of Fame. In fact, every player in the Hall of Fame is an important player, so their cards are all priced individually. Simply look up the player in the Hall of Famers section and you'll find a sampling of information about that player and his cards and the prices of his most important cards. Other prominent stars, such as Shoeless Joe Jackson or Ken Griffey Jr., who have not yet been elected to the Hall of Fame, have cards that are in demand that you are likely to want to buy or sell. Look for those players in the Key Players section, and again they are listed with a sampling of information and pricing of their most important cards.

So who's missing from this price guide, you want to know? The answer is common players like Bob Mabe, Carlos May, and Luis Aguayo. They are among the hundreds of thousands of "commons" currently priced individually in other guides. Actually, we haven't completely left them out of our guide. We just have not given them separate, individual listings. Instead, we have put them in the section entitled Major Modern Card Sets. There you will find both set and common-player prices. This way, you can look up the 1959 Topps set, find the common-player price, and safely assume that's the price for Bob Mabe's '59 card and scores of other commons from that set. If the Luis Aguayo card you have in mind is a 1989 Upper Deck, then you simply look up that set, find the common-player price, and you can safely assume that's what you would pay for Luis Aguayo and hundreds of others like him.

We have nothing against Bob Mabe and other common players. It's just that most people do not need to know the prices of those cards. And if you do, we think you can safely find them under one common listing a lot faster than you can by looking up 1959 Topps or 1989 Upper Deck and scanning the list of hundreds of cards. Moreover, by doing it this way, this book is portable enough for you to carry with you to card shows. It also has current and expanded information about a player's cards that you are likely to need to price them.

Arrangement

There's another advantage to this approach. By arranging the pricing information alphabetically by player name rather than by manufacturer and year, it's easier for you to find the important rookie card and other early card prices for the player you want to collect without guesswork. To give you an example, let's assume that you want to find the Donruss rookie card of Danny Tartabull. The problem is you don't know what year Donruss made its first Danny Tartabull card. This is not an insignificant problem. Let's say you can narrow it down to between 1984 and 1987. Somewhere in those thousands of cards you'll find the Danny Tartabull rookie, but where? Organized by manufacturer and year, you will have to read through each year until you find the first Tartabull. With this book, knowing that rookie cards bring more money and have more collectors, you can save time scouring through listings by simply turning to the Key Players section (since he isn't in the Hall of Fame yet) and looking up Danny Tartabull alphabetically. It's quick and easy to do.

With those words of advice, good luck in your collecting and enjoy the book!

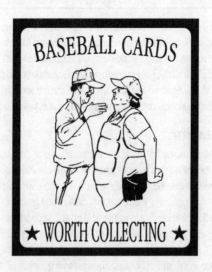

BASEBALL CARDS

★ WORTH COLLECTING ★

How Cards Become Valuable

HOW DO CARDS become valuable? This basic question is one that many collectors seem to ignore. In fact, many collectors are content to simply accept prices assigned by so-called experts, often their local dealers. Collectors can make repeated buying and selling mistakes that might cost them a good deal of money.

Cards are not priced by some deep mystical process. It's not applied science. Actually, sometimes it's not even logical. That's because cards are priced according to supply and demand. Many factors can influence the supply (and more often the demand) for a given card, but ultimately the price of every card rises or falls based on the delicate balance between the supply of that card and the demand for it.

Factors affecting supply

While not as dramatically as demand, the supply of a given card can change. Every time you read of the discovery of a new T206 Honus Wagner card, the supply has increased. But that doesn't mean the price drops, because demand for the card is still well in excess of the number available. The same thing can happen when unopened cases of cards from the 1950s are discovered. Increases in supply are offset by all kinds of natural events, from fires to floods to poor handling.

No cards are immune to supply changes. In warehouses across the country there are thousands of unopened cases of modern cards. They represent a supply change waiting to happen, and if you want to be dramatic, they represent a dagger aimed right at the heart of prices for cards issued in the last decade. The reason for that, once again, is that card prices are determined by supply and demand. Cards still in packs are not part of the existing market supply. If all the packs were opened tomorrow, card prices would almost certainly drop. But that scenario is unlikely since all of the owners of the unopened packs and cases are unlikely to open their treasures at the same time.

The rookie factor

Let's take a look at some of the factors that influence demand. A generation of collectors grew up believing that rookie cards are worth the most money and that other cards are almost worthless. Because of that, the rookie-card market is not likely to disappear, and that has generally made the first card of any given player one of his most valuable. But not all rookie cards are valuable. And the second-, third-, and tenth-year cards of a given player might also have little or no value. And remember, zero times one million is still zero. If a player is not a star (star quality creates demand for his cards), then none of his cards are worth much because the available quantity of them will far exceed the small demand. What a rookie card has going for it—as opposed to a fifth-year card — is that the card value is based on the historically higher price rookie cards bring if the player becomes a star or achieves the ultimate honor: induction in the Hall of Fame. So collectors tend to collect, buy, and speculate on rookie cards for that reason.

Additionally, a player's rookie card is almost always available in smaller quantities than his later cards. There are two reasons for this: first, card production has increased over the years, so that the 1948 card of a player was probably produced in smaller quantities than his 1956 card (a secret closely guarded); second, until the past decade no one really cared about rookie cards. The kids growing up in the 1950s lived in something perilously close to the Dark Ages in terms of information about rookies. They treasured their Mickey Mantle and Willie Mays cards but thought little about their Frank Robinson or Yaz rookie cards because they were just rookies. When they became stars they wanted their Robinson and Yaz cards.

That gives us some concrete reasons for the higher values of rookie cards. They have a short but very real history of higher prices and smaller available supplies — both of which create demand in the card market.

Does that mean that by definition rookie cards must go up in price? The answer is no because demand does not remain the same and, to a lesser degree, neither does supply. Examples abound of rookie cards that soared in price only to drop equally fast. A great deal depends on how the player succeeds on the field. One year Mark McGwire hit 25 home runs and didn't have a batting average greater than his weight, so his cards collected dust on dealers' shelves waiting for buyers. To create some interest, dealers dropped prices until they reached a level where someone, anyone, would buy McGwire's cards. The next year, McGwire had 25 home runs by July and suddenly everyone wanted his cards, so prices rose. The same thing happens to dozens of players and their cards each year. And how would you predict which green rookie is going to be in the Hall of Fame 20 years down the line?

Other factors affecting demand

Although supply can change, the real pricing drama occurs on the demand side of the equation. It would be difficult, if not impossible, to list all the potential factors that can change the demand for a given card, but a few stand out. Geography is becoming less of an influence on demand, but it still remains a factor. The cards of players from bigger cities tend to bring higher prices. If you look at two players with identical records, one of whom plays for Montreal while the other is on a team from New York, chances are the cards of the player from New York will bring higher prices. The reason is that many collectors are seeking cards from their home teams. Big-city teams are often promoted by "superstations" and develop fans all over the country and even the world. Sheer population numbers mean greater demand for big-city teams, and it's not just limited to New York City. Boston is a large enough city in its own right to produce somewhat higher prices, but with most of New England viewing the Red Sox as their home team, the Boston premium is one of the highest of all. In recent years there has been some change in the geographical influence on demand. Money does not have a favorite team, and with more people buying cards for their profit potential instead of their team loyalty, the geographical influence has lessened.

Race is another factor that influenced demand in the past — white players brought higher prices. Old pricing patterns die hard, but things have changed. Today, race doesn't matter to the investor who wants to own the top rookie of 1994. Collectors want the stars, and nothing better illustrates that point than Ken Griffey, Jr. cards — the best cards of the past few years. The ability to hit or throw a curve is not determined by race, and that ability (or lack thereof) goes a long way toward determining card prices.

Publicity and demand

The most significant single factor in creating demand may be publicity. Examples abound. Robin Yount labored for years and although his success was noted, his card prices rose as he neared 3000 hits. Collectors seem to discover a player all at once. Magazines pick the top rookies for the upcoming year, and their cards hit the market at price levels a number of times higher than lesser-known players with the same teams. When a player is elected to the Hall of Fame, prices rise. The demand creates publicity which creates more demand. Winning a league MVP or Cy Young award or starring in a World Series will have a similiar effect. It's a nice little cycle, but it doesn't last long as the publicity switches to another star on another team.

Publicity for current players comes with success on the field. In the case of retired players, publicity must come from other factors, and there is very little national media attention being paid to the players of the 1930s. Shoeless Joe Jackson is an exception. Banished from baseball for alleged participation in the "Black Sox" 1919 World Series scandal, the legendary Joe Jackson is probably as well known today as at any time since 1920. Joe Jackson is the stuff of legends, and that hasn't been lost on generations of authors or Hollywood. The combination of books and movies about Joe Jackson makes him one of the biggest names in baseball and makes his card more expensive than virtually any other card. The demand remains high while the supply of Jackson cards is static, and rather low.

The most valuable card of them all, the T206 of Honus Wagner, represents a clear case of how publicity creates demand and dwarfs an already very small supply. Many collectors believe that the T206 Honus Wagner is the rarest card around. The fact is there are thousands of cards that are tougher to find than a T206 Wagner. If you ignored the demand factor, then these other cards would be higher priced than the Wagner, but they don't receive the attention the Wagner does and consequently have neither the demand nor the six-figure price tag of the Wagner. When a card of which only one or two are known sells for $1000 while a Wagner of which there may be 60 known examples can bring over $400,000, you can readily see that publicity can be worth a great deal — because it creates demand.

Error cards

The most confusing aspect of pricing for most new collectors comes in the form of errors on cards. Even cards with errors are subject to supply and demand. Many collectors incorrectly assume an error card is automatically rare and valuable. Errors on modern cards are often too insignificant to attract collector attention, so with little demand, prices remain low. When errors are not corrected, supplies can equal that of cards without errors, and therefore the error cards have no special value. There are a few exceptions. Perhaps the most memorable in recent times came when an obscenity was found on a bat being held by Billy Ripken. Fleer, which produced the card, naturally stopped production immediately and put out a Billy Ripken card without the wording. By the time that was done, however, a fairly large number of the cards containing the offensive words were in packs of cards all over the country. Moreover, once discovered, the cards received national media attention, and that caused the demand for them to mushroom. The price jumped from under a dollar to over $100.

The problem was that the initial outburst of demand was not long lasting. In fact, where many would pay a dollar or two for such a card, the market thinned out significantly at the higher prices. Soon, the Billy Ripken with the obscenity was priced well below its one-time peak. Even today the price of that card continues to drop; it is often found for under $10.

So many card errors occur each year that errors do not generally account for a large collector market. Although many collectors would like to think that printing the wrong age or hometown on a card is consequential, there is no support among the various collector magazines and price guides to list and catalog every possible mistake. A general rule in evaluating errors is that to have any value the errors must be significant and they must be produced in limited numbers. That means the company that produced the card must cease production and replace it with a correct version. Finally, the error must be widely recognized by collectors and dealers. In the absence of those factors, the error card might still be interesting, but its potential value is limited. In fact, it tends to have the same price as any correct card for the player.

Condition

The majority of collectors believe that the single most important factor in determining price is condition. Logically speaking, the nicer the card the more someone is willing to pay for it. A nearly perfect T206 of Honus Wagner might be a $500,000 card while a badly beaten example of the same card is probably worth $40,000. That's a big difference. The vast difference in price based on condition is also related to supply and demand. There may be only 2 or 3 known T206 Honus Wagners in top condition while the remaining 50 or so known to exist are not nearly so well preserved. No Wagner is common, but it's much easier to find one of the well-worn examples available for sale than it is to find one in excellent condition.

Demand is also affected by condition. Just as people would prefer a nicer house or car to one of lesser quality, the same is true of baseball cards and all other collectibles. Collectors are willing to pay substantial premiums for quality in the case of older cards while cards of the past few years must be perfect or their price is sharply reduced, as is their potential for sale.

In this guide you will find prices for cards in the three most widely used states of preservation. You may hear of enormous prices paid for cards in so-called Mint condition, but the reality is that very few older cards could ever legitimately meet the rigid standards for Mint. There are few older cards (1950s and earlier) that trade regularly even in Near Mint condition. Most older cards will be in Excellent or Very Good condition and their prices will reflect that vastly greater supply.

Condition depends on the specific nature of the problems that might move the card into a lower category. While two cards may be technically in the same condition, a card with a mustache drawn on the player's face will probably bring a lower price than one that has a small amount of writing on the back. Mint cards from just about any year before 1980 will bring substantial premiums. As a rule, the older the Mint card, the greater its premium over the Near Mint price.

That holds true, as do all items influencing pricing, because of their impact on either supply or demand, as those forces and nothing else determine prices and trends.

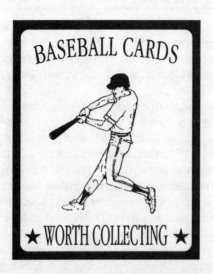

BASEBALL CARDS

★ WORTH COLLECTING ★

The Baseball-Card Market Today

THE 1992 AND 1993 baseball card buzzword has been stratification. Stratification was the plan card companies felt they had to adopt to remain competitive, so in 1992 the baseball card market "stratified." There were more types and brands of cards for collectors to buy in 1992, but fewer available cards in each brand than in previous years. The days of truly wretched excess, when Upper Deck would crank out as many cards as the market would bear and then some, ended with a thud in late 1991 and did not revive in time for the 1992 baseball card year (which runs, incidentally, from November to November).

How wretched were the days of excess in 1991? Actually, things were pretty good if you were a card maker and the people you sold your cards to didn't have the privilege of returning product that didn't sell. You made a lot of money that year. And if you were a dealer you probably made money selling a particularly popular product — Topps Stadium Club Baseball. But the regular card products from each of the major manufacturers (and this is the important point) were extravagantly overpriced and did not come anywhere close to selling through, i.e., selling completely from the manufacturer to the distributor to the dealer to the consumer. Distributors, dealers, and manufacturers were stuck with products they could not sell and could not repackage and try to sell again.

How much product? Let's take a close look at 1992 Upper Deck as an example of overproduction. In 1992 just about anything that happened in baseball cards happened to Upper Deck, and out of all proportion to other card makers. Upper Deck started out in 1989 as the first high-end card company and made huge amounts of money in 1989 and 1990 by over producing and selling to the average market. At the same time, the manufacturer promoted the image that Upper Deck was a limited-production product. It's a tough combination to pull off, but Upper Deck managed it like no company before or since.

In 1989 Upper Deck made approximately 65,000 cases of foil packs (about 7.2 billion cards) and about 3.5 billion cards in factory-collated sets. In 1990 production was up to about 120,000 cases, although the number of baseball cards and collectors increased by less than 10 percent. In 1991 production increased to a reported 240,000 cases with the same increases in factory-set production, although the increase in collectors by this time was incremental. Collectors weren't buying twice as many cards in 1991 as they were in 1990, so what possessed Upper Deck to make so many more cards? Greed? That had something to do with it. But there was a battle for market share and shelf space occurring among the five major baseball card manufacturers in 1991, and it was being fought with numbers — sheer numbers of cards being printed and rushed into the market as fast as possible. The more cards of one company's brand on the market, the less room there is for another company's. When the battle wound down in 1992 nothing had really changed. Topps was still on top, and Fleer, Donruss, Upper Deck, and Score still trailed. But one lesson was learned: Upper Deck was never going to make the mistake of printing 240,000 cases of baseball cards again. So in 1992 Upper Deck cut back. As it had quadrupled production over the previous three years, it just as easily cut production and settled in at about 120,000 cases. Yet even at that level, Upper Deck failed to sell through. Ironically, if the company had made 120,000 cases of its 1991 product, it would have sold through with no problem. As it was, Upper Deck languished.

An unfortunate year

It was an unfortunate year for that to happen because 1992 was shaping up as Upper Deck's breakout year. It was the first company since Topps (the old Topps) to have licenses in all four major sports (baseball, football, basketball and hockey), with Reggie Jackson, Joe Montana, Michael Jordan, and Wayne Gretzky, as its spokesmen. The company had gone to great lengths to secure a minor league baseball license, anticipating (accurately, as it turned out) that Major League Baseball would be banning card companies from making cards of minor-league players who had not yet played in the major leagues. Upper Deck was planning to expand its Comic Ball series, a line that featured Looney Tunes characters and live baseball and football players. A high-tech waterless printing technique that produces more vibrant, true-to-life colors was implemented. The company planned to roll out two revolutionary products: a line of autographed and guaranteed-genuine memorabilia cards called Upper Deck Authenticated and an ultra-high-end series of cards called the Heroes Collection.

Upper Deck Authenticated specialized in mail-order memorabilia. Its line of signed plaques, photos, jerseys, helmets, sweaters, and card sets even boasted holographic anticounterfeiting technology with prices to match. The second phase of its plan included Authenticated kiosks in shopping malls that sold Upper Deck cards and

Authenticated memorabilia. This strategy served to blur the line between manufacturer and dealer in a unique way.

The Heroes Collection cards were planned to be made in small sets of 12 to 15 cards, each set devoted to a particular player and sold in editions of a few thousand each. Several sets a year were planned for release, with multiple sets released over a period of several years. These sets planned to feature Upper Deck's marquee players — Joe Montana, Michael Jordan, Ted Williams, and Wayne Gretzky. The cards were to be marketed with leather binders, hand-laid paper, state-of-the-art printing techniques, and hand-signed letters of authenticity and original artwork. The price per set was to run from several hundred dollars to several thousand dollars.

The Heroes Collection and Upper Deck Authenticated would do what Upper Deck had done so well three years before: ignore the existing market and create an entirely new market above and beyond it. It would expand the audience and blur the line between card and collectible art, between manufacturer and dealer. Great ideas. Too bad only one of the two ideas actually made it past the prototype stage.

Uprising at Upper Deck

There were major internal changes at Upper Deck in late 1992 that affected both the personnel and the products. There were lawsuits and counter-suits. When the dust cleared, the Upper Deck Authenticated set stayed but the Heroes Collection bit the dust.

Upper Deck was on the litigation offensive against other manufacturers as well. It sued Topps over the right to make cards of some Russian hockey players Topps claimed it had exclusive rights to, and sued National Football League Properties and its players' association over what it claimed were double payments for the right to certain football players whose card-reproduction rights were in dispute. Upper Deck languished and lost its focus in 1992, but managed to bring some issues to a close. Upper Deck forced the NFL and the NFLPA to kiss and make up over the issue of cards, if only briefly.

Okay, but what about Upper Deck's baseball cards? Could you get the rookie of the year card in a 1992 Upper Deck baseball set? Yes, you could, sort of. Upper Deck's Final Edition set of 1991 was crammed with minor-league prospects like Dmitri Young, Ryan Klesko, Rondell White, Jim Thome, Kenny Lofton, and Frankie Rodriguez, and the set came out of the blocks hot. People were excited about it. The 1992 Upper Deck baseball set followed the '91 Final Edition set by only a few months and had a much less exciting player list. It had planned to include cards of Brien Taylor, Mike Kelly, and Frankie Rodriguez, but couldn't. Classic had Kelly and Taylor signed to exclusive contracts, and Front Row had Rodriguez locked up. The best cards in the Upper Deck set were the first cards of the draft picks David McCarty and Manny Ramirez and rookies Bob Wickman, Dave Fleming, and Brian Jordan. There were curious cards of Mark Smith and Joe Vitiello that featured manipulated photos and no major-league logos anywhere, front or back. Upper Deck's high numbers added A.L. Rookie of the Year Pat Listach, but the total package was not a set to make anyone turn back flips. It was a muddle of a set for a muddle of a year.

Topps still tops

Fortunately, not everything was this chaotic in baseball cards in 1992. Topps was still Topps and still capable of turning out tacky mass-market cards. The company's '92 Triple Headers test issue featured Chinese-made mini baseballs with three awful little player portraits attached. It was a product for which the ultimate destination was next to Thumb Fun bubble gum and Ring Pops at the local variety store. It was pure unadulterated junk with no aspirations whatsoever — the old Topps in all its glory.

Stadium Club '92 represented the new Topps: state-of-the-art exterior, bubble gum at the center. Topps tried to build on the 1991 success of its high-end brand the only way Topps knows how to build on anything — by making more. But it didn't work. The notion behind Stadium Club in 1991 was precisely the same idea that drove Upper Deck in 1989: ordinary cards at a premium price. People were willing to pay a lot for the '91 Stadium Club phenomena, right up there with '89 Upper Deck and '84 Donruss and the rest of the card phenomena of the recent past. In 1992 the Stadium Club design was slightly tweaked and wholly uninspired. The photos showed some nice variety but were not up to Upper Deck's standards. The fit and finish was high-test, the packs were expensive from the word go, but the passion was gone. The novelty had worn off somewhere between Stadium Club football and Stadium Club hockey. There were three series of Stadium Club baseball, 900 cards in all, and by the time Topps got to the end of the third series it was definitely sucking wind. Third-series Stadium Club featured a neat No. 1 draft pick chase subset featuring Chipper Jones, Brien Taylor, and Phil Nevin. Otherwise it contained lots of cards of players filling slots 38 - 40 on the 40-man roster and lots of cards of draft picks leaning up against trees and not wearing uniforms (the High School Graduation Photo subset). As Upper Deck did with its Final Edition set, Topps produced a special Stadium Club SkyDome set at the end of '91 containing most of the top draft picks, and that cut into early sales of '92 Stadium Club. But Stadium Club would have lacked momentum of its own even without a '91 Final Edition set.

Regular Topps baseball was a curious creature. Its trademark, choppy gray card stock, was history, replaced by a bleached-white board, and the gum was gone! Otherwise the cards were virtually indistinguishable from any regular Topps set of the last decade. As a bonus to pack buyers, Topps gold-leafed the player team name on each of the 792 cards for its regular set, and then inserted one of these ToppsGold cards into each '92 pack, along with a "Match the Stats" scratch-off game card with additional ToppsGold cards as prizes. Card collectors were anxious to cash in on the prizes, so they found a way to beat the game. Collectors found that by shining a bright light through the back of the game card they could see where the matching stats were and could push their chances of winning on a given card into the 100 percent range. Topps was totally unprepared for the onslaught of winning tickets and had to cancel the game, but not without first redeeming several hundred thousand winning tickets. However, they had the last laugh in the whole silly affair by stamping each of the gold cards won in the promotion with "WINNER."

Topps embraced the idea of stratification wholeheartedly in 1992. The company's sets not only covered the low end (regular Topps), the mid-priced end (Bowman), and the high end (Stadium Club), but also the ultra-low end (a nostalgic end). Bowman continued to be a major irritant for the hobby press and an extremely slow seller on the retail end in 1992, despite getting a face-lift and a bump up on quality. Topps' philosophy, that Bowman cards take shelf space away from other manufacturer's products, continued to keep Bowman in the Topps mix for '92 and '93.

Topps Kids was a much more interesting product: a 35-cent pack of cards with a stick of bubble gum and 10 cartoony cards designed to appeal to five-to-eight-year-olds. Topps determined it was missing this audience with its existing card lines in which prices started at 55 cents a pack and went up steeply from there. The artwork front and back was simple, goofy, and altogether winning — the product was a success, albeit a limited one. Topps Kids may have shown that a product designed explicitly with no collector value can make a profit, and that the youngest collectors have not yet become jaded by the idea that baseball cards have to be worth money to be valued.

Topps' final niche product, Topps Archives, played on one of the company's unique strengths: history. No other card maker has been in business for more than 40 years except Topps. The number of surviving sets from Topps' first years in business falls far short of the number of collectors who want them, so the opportunity has long existed for Topps to reprint its early sets and sell them to collectors in such a way that it would not jeopardize the value of its original sets. Topps Archives was just such a way. Topps reprinted its 1953 set in modern-size card form (the original cards were an oversized $2^5/_8$" x $3^3/_4$"), created horrid new cards for players who were omitted from the original set, and then sold the cards in high-end-priced wax packs.

The concept was a winner from the word go. Collectors drove the prices for packs up over $2, and sets sold for better than $100. Mickey Mantle cards were $25 items, and all this for a set that wasn't even original. Even a correction in price later in the season couldn't put a damper on the soundness of the Archives concept in today's market. In 1993 Topps announced its next Archives project: a set of basketball cards for which there had been no originals — covering the years from 1983 to 1991 when Topps was not even in the basketball-card business. In a lot of ways, Archives is Topps' best product, and most definitely the one that says the most about the current card market.

Fleer Ultra — which way is up?

If you're looking for cards that say a lot about the card market, '92 Fleer Ultra gets its share of words in, too. '92 Fleer Ultra should have been no hotter than '91 Fleer Ultra; i.e., not very hot at all. Ultra's '91 debut set had all the earmarks of a me-too product, a high-end set rushed onto the market so Fleer could say it had a high-end set. The '92 version was prepared with a little more attention to detail, but not enough of the right sorts of details to turn around the market. Nice, in other words, but not fabulous. But collectors did get excited about Fleer Ultra, more than any other baseball card set of 1992, and the reasons why are fascinating. '92 Fleer Ultra was so popular because '91 Fleer Ultra football was so unpopular. The cards were overproduced and overpriced and dealers soured on Fleer's late shipping and mediocre customer service. In fact, Fleer

Ultra football burned so many dealers that when the solicitations came around for '92 Fleer Ultra baseball, many dealers simply threw them right in the garbage.

The fact that only a few card dealers ordered Fleer Ultra baseball worked magic on the business of collecting. All of a sudden dealers — the same dealers who has spurned Fleer Ultra only a few months before — wanted the product and were willing to go to whatever lengths it took to get it. That forced them to candy and tobacco wholesalers and newsstand distributors, who ordered the product and were happy to sell it to dealers at a nice premium. This self-induced clamor for Fleer Ultra drove up prices to astronomical heights, at least by 1992 standards. Complete Ultra sets sold for $75 and up, a pleasant change from the 1991 product, which sold for $35 and less.

The lesson from this adventure in the modern baseball card market is this: Give the card market something it wants and it won't want it. Give the card market something it doesn't want and it still won't want it. But give some other market something the card market doesn't want and the card market will want it.

An improved Fleer Ultra line didn't spell any improvement for Fleer's regular line of cards. It became a mid-priced product without any of the concomitant increases in quality and decreases in production, and was not a big seller for that reason. The exception was Fleer's Rookie Sensation subset, which was packed in its newsstand-only cello packs and was a huge success for two very basic reasons: the set had Frank Thomas in it and dealers couldn't get it without a struggle. Again, the combination was magic. Rookie Sensations sets sold for $175 and up.

At the same time Fleer was enjoying unprecedented sales gains, the company was experiencing a transformation. In the summer of 1992 it bought ProCards, one of the country's largest makers of minor-league cards. Several months later, Fleer was bought out by Marvel, the giant comic-book manufacturer. The two events were unrelated, but their timing made the symbolism hard to miss. In ProCards, Fleer bought into the minor-league market, the last frontier in baseball cards, the one arena in which there still appeared to be a profit in market expansion. In Fleer, Marvel bought into the burgeoning card market, brought a lot of cash and an attractive bottom line, and was able to diversify its product line without greatly expanding its distribution and sales costs. The decisions of Fleer to buy ProCards and Marvel to buy Fleer were business decisions; there was nothing haphazard about them.

Score shakeups

Score, meanwhile, went through some corporate shakeups of its own. Optographics, one of the original partners in Score and the holder of Score's card licenses, ceased to exist in 1992. The new partners changed the name to The Score Group, but little else changed at Score besides the names of the partners. The company still produced great-looking cards at an affordable price and had trouble convincing people to buy them. The regular Score brand may also have been hurt by the No. 1 draft picks it couldn't show (Brien Taylor, Dmitri Young, Joe Vitiello, et al.) and its lack of enticing chase cards. Its high-end Pinnacle brand was hit hard by the glut in the high-end card market and did not sell well, despite some interest in its Team Pinnacle and Pinnacle 2000 randomly inserted chase cards. Late in the year the company reacted to an internal squabble over whether to launch a low-end kids' product or launch a mid-range youth product called Score Select for 1993. Compared to other card companies, Score made the fewest waves in 1992.

Donruss quiet

Business was quiet at Donruss as well, although the company had some initial success moving its base-level cards to a 99-cent price point. The company's long-time favorite Diamond Kings were transformed successfully into limited-edition insert cards, but beyond that, its rookies were nothing exclusive to Donruss and its design and photography did not break new ground. The cards were just one more set of cards that in a less-crowded landscape might actually have stood out. Among all the card companies, Donruss is the only maker to have two high-end products: Studio and the Leaf Set. In 1991, the two sets were able to coexist; each found a niche in the market and was able to exploit it successfully. But 1992 was not a good year to be selling two high-end sets. The silver-bordered Leaf Set suffered from a tired design and a lack of solid chase cards. While the late-season Studio portrait set was a marked improvement design-wise, it's sales were worse. Collectors were simply tired of high-end baseball cards in August and September. Even a set that promised such delights as Paul Molitor in a Seattle Pilots uniform and Kirby Puckett in a Senators jersey couldn't get collectors to part with $30 again. Donruss had one new product in 1992, a kids-only niche product called Triple Play. The Donruss Triple Play featured horrible photos, lame special cards, indifferent card backs, and a tolerable insert set. It sold almost in spite of itself, but unlike Topps Kids, which came off as a genuine kids' product, Triple Play seemed to be a kids set meant for adult collectors. It was no one's "set of the year."

Classic comes into its own

Classic seemed to be coming into its own in 1992. The company produced its best and most extensive set of minor-league cards under the Classic-Best brand and also cornered the baseball draft-pick market by signing most of the top picks to exclusive and lucrative contracts. It locked up Dmitri Young, Brien Taylor, David McCarty, Joe Vitiello, and others from the 1991 draft. It also signed on overall No. 1 draft pick Phil Row and Jeffrey Hammonds from the 1992 draft. It eventually drove competitors Front Row and Star Pics out of the draft-pick card business and made a name for itself that can't be scorned. In its niches, Classic is every bit as formidable as Topps or Upper Deck.

New in 1993: More, bigger, better…
and more expensive

Early 1993 saw a continuation of the stratification of the baseball-card market with a listing of sets that included Donruss, Fleer Ultra Series I, Topps, Score Select, Pinnacle Series I, 1993 Stadium Club Murphy Stadium, and Upper Deck Series I. But this was not enough for manufacturers who sought new set ideas and price levels. In a climate of increasing competition, the numerous sets already on the market did not seem sufficient. Taking a cue from Upper Deck successes a few years previous, all manufacturers decided the way to go in 1993 was up. So up they went in all phases of the market: up in quality, up in price, and, of most interest, up in the claims of limited production. The prevailing theory? Higher quality with advertised limited availability would translate into big bucks very fast for the manufacturers. Of course, the collector would be left to find out how this would affect the aftermarket.

Topps, in something of a rare move, seemed to take the lead with a set called Topps Finest. They introduced the set with an announcement that only 4,000 cases would be produced. The cards feature a multicolored look and enhanced depth and dimension. The suggested price — a mere $3 per 5-card pack. Early demand actually pushed prices higher. Lawsuits (becoming a staple in the baseball-card market) followed from dealers who ordered sets but did not receive any of the limited number of sets produced.

Fleer followed Topps' lead with Fleer Flair. With a production level pegged at 15% of the production of Fleer Ultra Baseball, Fleer Flair has the requisite claim of scarcity. It, too, has production enhancements, as the cards are double the normal thickness. Further, the set includes 20 projected rookies from the minors. Prices for Fleer Flair were announced at $3.99 for a 10-card pack.

Fleer, Topps, and Upper Deck usually set the pace for the baseball-card market, with an ever growing group of manufacturers following their lead. As the 1993 season was winding to a close, the prospect of the card market shutting down for the off-season — as had been the case in past years — seemed rather remote. Instead, the off-season held out the promise of even more sets in even higher quality at even higher prices from even more companies. As this is being written, it appears that these new sets will be heavily promoted by card dealers and embraced by card collectors. The stratification of the market, like other trends, has taken firm hold. We may be in for a production blitz until we find out what the collector's saturation point really is.

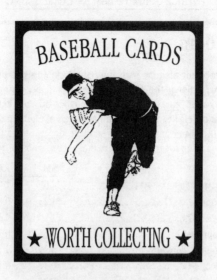

BASEBALL CARDS

★ WORTH COLLECTING ★

Key Players

A note about the listings

NOT ALL OF a player's cards are listed. Cards not listed for a given player may be considered "common" and worth less than $1.00 in Near Mint condition. A player not listed in either the Hall of Famers or Key Players sections can safely be assumed to have card values common to all cards of a given issuer in a given year. Refer to the Major Modern Card Sets section and find the values for common players listed by year, manufacturer, and set.

Rick Aguilera

Rick Aguilera spent his time with the New York Mets complaining about not starting. Since joining the Minnesota Twins and becoming one of the top relievers in the A.L., those complaints have fallen off a bit. Aguilera followed in the footsteps of Jeff Reardon, but unlike Reardon, Aguilera doesn't strike you as being Hall of Fame material; too much to do, too little time. But the way things are changing for relief pitchers these days, who knows?

	NM	EX	VG
1985 TCMA Tidewater #11	4.00	1.75	0.75
1986 Donruss #441	1.25	0.55	0.25
1986 Fleer #74	1.00	0.45	0.20
1986 Topps #599	0.65	0.30	0.12
1986 Topps Tiffany #599	3.25	1.25	0.60
1987 Fleer #1	0.30	0.12	0.04
1987 Fleer Glossy Tin #1	0.25	0.10	0.03
1990 Topps Big #284	0.08	0.03	0.01
1991 Topps Desert Shield #318	4.25	2.00	0.85
1992 Leaf Gold #34	0.40	0.15	0.05
1992 Topps Gold #44	0.75	0.30	0.12

Roberto Alomar

Probably the best of the Alomar father and sons, Roberto is the quintessential all-around ballplayer: he hits for average, with home-run power, speed on the basepaths, and outstanding defensive abilities. Young for a player with four major-league seasons under his belt, Alomar is far from peaking offensively and is emerging as an old-fashioned team leader of the sort that usually winds up in Cooperstown. Because Alomar plays in Toronto he is not in the limelight as much as many players of similar or lesser abilities, and as a result his cards are undervalued. Alomar's rookie cards carry a buy recommendation across the board, and his first high-end cards are likewise solid buys.

	NM	EX	VG
1987 Team Wichita Pilots (set) #14	22.00	10.00	4.00
1987 Texas League All-Stars #8	7.00	3.00	1.25
1988 Donruss #34	5.25	2.50	1.10
1988 Donruss Rookies #35	8.25	4.00	1.25
1988 Fleer Update #122	9.50	4.50	2.00
1988 Score Traded #105	60.00	27.50	13.00
1988 Topps Traded #4	8.25	4.00	1.75
1989 Bowman #458	1.50	0.60	0.25
1989 Classic #127	1.00	0.40	0.15
1989 Upper Deck #471	5.25	2.50	1.00

1990 Leaf #75 .... 5.75	2.75	1.25
1991 O-Pee-Chee Premier #1 .... 0.65	0.30	0.12
1991 Studio #131 .... 1.25	0.50	0.20
1991 Topps Desert Storm #315 .... 5.00	2.50	1.25
1991 Topps Stadium Club #304 .... 5.00	2.25	1.10
1992 Fleer Ultra #143 .... 1.00	0.45	0.20
1992 Fleer Ultra Award Winners #20 .... 9.00	4.25	2.00
1992 Kenner Starting Lineup 22.50	10.00	4.00
1992 Score Pinnacle Team 2000 #48 .... 1.50	0.60	0.25
1992 Upper Deck Ted Williams' Best		
Hitters #11 .... 3.75	1.75	0.80

Sandy Alomar Jr.

One of the odd and definitely irregular things about baseball cards is that while
Roberto Alomar is clearly the superior baseball player of the Alomar brothers,
Sandy Jr. is actually the more ballyhooed from a baseball-card standpoint.
Perhaps part of the reason for that is that Roberto plays in Toronto and Sandy
plays in ... well, Cleveland. The larger reason is there is no reason. Whenever
the card makers have an open slot in any of their sets they simply slap in a card
of Sandy Alomar Jr., figuring they can't go wrong. Maybe they can't, though we
are getting a little tired of seeing Sandy Jr. at every turn. And one more thing:
the Padres used to have him, too.

	NM	EX	VG
1986 ProCards Beaumont (set) 32.00	15.00	6.50
1987 Team Wichita (set) 45.00	21.00	10.00
1987 Texas League All-Stars #10 .... 3.50	1.50	0.65
1989 Bowman #454 .... 0.25	0.10	0.04
1989 Bowman #258 (w/Roberto and		
Sandy Sr.) 0.35	0.15	0.05
1989 Donruss #28 .... 0.20	0.08	0.03
1989 Donruss Rookies #21 .... 0.15	0.05	0.01
1989 Fleer #300 .... 0.20	0.08	0.03
1989 Score #630 .... 0.20	0.08	0.03
1989 Topps #648 .... 0.20	0.08	0.03
1989 Topps Tiffany #648 .... 1.00	0.45	0.20
1989 Upper Deck #5 .... 0.75	0.35	0.15
1990 Fleer Update Glossy Tin #89 .... 0.35	0.15	0.05
1990 Leaf #232 .... 0.50	0.20	0.08
1990 Score Traded #18 .... 0.20	0.08	0.03
1990 Topps Traded #2 .... 0.10	0.04	0.01
1990 Upper Deck #655 .... 0.15	0.05	0.01
1990 Upper Deck #756 .... 0.10	0.04	0.01
1991 Donruss Diamond King #13 .... 0.12	0.04	0.01

1991 Fleer Ultra #105	0.10	0.04	0.01
1991 O-Pee-Chee #2	0.20	0.08	0.03
1991 Score #694	0.10	0.04	0.01
1991 Score #793	0.10	0.04	0.01
1991 Score All-Star #400	0.10	0.04	0.01
1991 Score Dream Team #879	0.10	0.04	0.01
1991 Score Franchise #851	0.10	0.04	0.01
1991 Topps Stadium Club #61	0.40	0.15	0.05
1991 Upper Deck Final Edition #81	0.10	0.04	0.01
1992 Donruss Triple Play #227	0.05	0.01	0.01
1992 O-Pee-Chee Premier #164	0.05	0.01	0.01
1992 Topps Kids #71	0.05	0.01	0.01
1992 Upper Deck FanFest #12	0.20	0.08	0.03

Moises Alou

Moises Alou didn't intend to wind up playing for his father; it just worked out that way. His father, Felipe Alou, was coaching for the Expos when manager Tom Runnels was fired. Felipe was named manager, and all of a sudden Moises started seeing more playing time. And all of a sudden he really started hitting. Alou finished the season hitting .282 with nine homers, and that's really just a taste of what Alou is capable of. And if you ever want to rub it into the Pirates, remember this: Alou was stolen from Pittsburgh in the Zane Smith deal. Outside of Alou's Gold Leaf Rookie card and his '91 Stadium Club card, everything else is affordable and somewhat attractive. There are some nice long-term buys here.

	NM	EX	VG
1988 ProCards Augusta (set)	18.00	7.50	3.50
1989 Star Co. Salem (set)	10.00	4.50	2.00
1990 Bowman #178	0.40	0.15	0.05
1990 Bowman Tiffany #178	2.50	1.00	0.45
1990 Score #592	0.50	0.20	0.06
1990 Topps Major League Debut #5	0.35	0.15	0.05
1991 Classic-Best Minor-League Wax #360	0.50	0.20	0.08
1991 Donruss #191	0.50	0.20	0.06
1991 Donruss #38	0.20	0.08	0.03
1991 O-Pee-Chee #3	0.15	0.05	0.01
1991 Score #813	0.25	0.10	0.04
1991 Topps #31	1.75	0.75	0.30
1991 Topps #526	0.15	0.05	0.01
1991 Topps Desert Storm #526	35.00	16.50	7.50
1991 Upper Deck #665	0.30	0.12	0.04
1992 Donruss Phenoms #1	1.25	0.50	0.20

1992 Fleer Ultra #511	0.50	0.20	0.08
1992 Leaf #426	0.30	0.12	0.05
1992 Leaf Gold Inserts #426	1.25	0.50	0.20
1992 Score Pinnacle Rookies #16	0.35	0.15	0.05
1992 Topps #519	0.15	0.05	0.01
1993 Fleer #70	0.15	0.05	0.01
1993 Score Select Stars #2	5.00	2.25	1.00
1993 Topps Gold Inserts #123	0.25	0.10	0.04
1993 Upper Deck #297	0.15	0.05	0.01

Brady Anderson

Once thought to be the logical successor to Fred Lynn, Anderson was dealt to Baltimore in 1988 with Curt Schilling as part of the Mike Boddicker deal and spent most of the next three seasons trying to live up to his clips, with little success. But Anderson finally blossomed in 1992, hitting with power and running with abandon and doing all that good stuff everyone knew Brady was capable of. Because of his checkered past it's hard to unequivocally recommend Anderson and his cards, though he makes a nice buy as part of that star-studded Topps Traded set. Or try the Tiffany version if you're feeling adventuresome.

	NM	EX	VG
1986 ProCards Winter Haven (set)	15.00	6.50	2.50
1987 ProCards New Britain (set)	15.00	6.50	2.50
1988 Topps Tiffany Traded #5	10.00	4.25	1.75
1989 Bowman Tiffany #18	1.50	0.50	0.20
1991 Topps Desert Storm #97	20.00	9.50	4.25

Kevin Appier

Kevin Appier is the American League's version of Sid Fernandez: great ERA and strikeout numbers, but never as many wins as the secondary numbers would suggest. Is that Appier's fault? To an extent. He tends to lose concentration now and again. Does it affect the values of his cards? Yes. Should it? Yes. Appier's cards aren't going anywhere until he learns how to become a consistent winner.

	NM	EX	VG
1988 Star Baseball City Royals (set)	16.00	7.50	3.50
1989 CMC Omaha Royals (set)	7.25	3.50	1.50
1989 Fleer Glossy Tin Update #35	2.50	1.00	0.45
1989 Topps Major League Debut #6	0.45	0.20	0.08
1990 Mother's Cookies A's #17	0.55	0.25	0.10
1992 Topps Desert Storm #454	16.00	7.50	3.25

Steve Avery

Steve Avery was the best high-school pitcher to come out of Michigan in years, and has done his best to live up to the hype. Forced to do a lot of learning and growing up on major-league mounds, Avery came of age during the 1991 World Series and is now close to being the complete pitcher the Braves envisioned when they made him a first-round draft pick in 1988. Avery is still young enough to craft a very substantial career; however, the jury at this point is out on both him and his cards.

	NM	EX	VG
1989 Bowman #268	1.75	0.75	0.30
1989 Bowman Tiffany #268	6.50	3.00	1.25
1989 Star Co. Durham Bulls #1	12.50	6.00	2.50
1989 Star Co. Minor League Wax #68	8.50	4.00	1.75
1989 Topps #784	1.75	0.75	0.30
1989 Topps Tiffany #784	7.50	3.50	1.50
1990 CMC Richmond Braves #1	15.00	6.50	2.75
1990 Donruss #39	0.75	0.30	0.12
1990 Donruss Rookies #42	1.00	0.45	0.20
1990 Fleer Glossy Update #1	4.50	2.00	0.85
1990 Fleer Update #1	1.00	0.45	0.20
1990 Leaf #481	12.50	5.75	2.75
1990 Score Traded #109	1.50	0.65	0.30
1990 Topps Traded #4	1.25	0.50	0.20
1990 Upper Deck #65	2.25	1.00	0.45
1991 Fleer Ultra #1	1.10	0.50	0.20
1991 Leaf Studio #141	1.25	0.50	0.20
1991 Topps Stadium Club #48	6.75	3.25	1.50
1991 Topps Stadium Club Dome #9	1.00	0.45	0.20
1992 Fleer Ultra #157	1.20	0.50	0.20
1992 Leaf Gold #59	2.50	1.10	0.50
1992 Score Impact Player #12	0.45	0.20	0.08
1992 Topps Gold #574	2.00	0.85	0.40
1992 Topps Stadium Club #60	1.25	0.60	0.25
1992 Topps Stadium Club Members Choice #594	1.00	0.45	0.20

Carlos Baerga

While you can have a swell old time listing all the outfielders who used to be with the Toronto Blue Jays, you can have just as good a time listing all the infielders who used to be with the San Diego Padres, starting with Ozzie Smith and going right through Ozzie Guillen, Joey Cora, Dave Hollins, Roberto Alomar, and stopping at this guy. Baerga is the real deal, a stumpy-looking infielder with power and the ability to hit for average. He can even steal bases, a fact you wouldn't guess by looking at him. He was the youngest player in Triple-A when the Indians nabbed him as part of the Joe Carter deal; that should have told you something right there. As it stands his cards are undervalued, but they won't be for long.

	NM	EX	VG
1989 ProCards Las Vegas Stars (set)	7.50	3.50	1.50
1990 Bowman #339	1.50	0.65	0.30
1990 Bowman Tiffany #339	6.50	3.00	1.25
1990 Donruss Rookies #19	1.50	0.65	0.30
1990 Fleer Update #90	1.50	0.65	0.30
1990 Leaf #443	9.25	4.50	2.00
1990 Score Traded #74	1.50	0.65	0.30
1990 Upper Deck #737	3.00	1.25	0.55
1991 Bowman #69	0.35	0.15	0.05
1991 Fleer #360	0.25	0.10	0.04
1991 Leaf #225	1.00	0.45	0.20
1991 Score #74	0.35	0.15	0.05
1991 Topps #147	0.25	0.10	0.04
1991 Topps Stadium Club #115	3.25	1.50	0.65
1991 Upper Deck #125	0.50	0.20	0.08
1992 Bowman #531	0.65	0.25	0.10
1992 Donruss Triple Play #235	0.15	0.05	0.01
1992 Fleer #104	0.20	0.08	0.01
1992 Fleer Ultra #46	0.70	0.30	0.10
1992 Leaf Gold #202	1.75	0.75	0.30
1992 Pinnacle Team 2000 #56	1.00	0.45	0.20
1992 Studio #163	0.40	0.15	0.05
1992 Topps Gold #33	2.00	0.85	0.35
1992 Upper Deck #231	0.35	0.15	0.05
1993 Donruss Diamond Stars #13	3.00	1.25	0.55
1993 Topps Gold #221	1.50	0.65	0.25
1993 Upper Deck #174	0.20	0.08	0.03

Jeff Bagwell

A young hitter with surprising power — even in the Astrodome — Bagwell has been described as "a right-handed Don Mattingly." Does that mean back problems are on his horizon? Maybe. But that could also mean a plateauing of his cards three or four years down the line.

	NM	EX	VG
1990 Best minor-league #132 .... 22.50		12.00	7.00
1990 CMC minor-league #739 .... 22.50		12.00	7.25
1991 Classic Collectors' Edition #90 .... 2.00		0.90	0.30
1991 Donruss Rookies #30 .... 2.00		1.00	0.45
1991 Donruss Studio #172 .... 4.50		2.50	1.00
1991 Fleer Ultra Update #79 .... 5.00		2.25	1.00
1991 Fleer Update #87 .... 2.00		1.00	0.45
1991 Leaf Gold #14 .... 12.00		6.00	2.50
1991 Score Traded #96 .... 2.25		1.00	0.45
1991 Topps Major League Debut #7 .... 1.50		0.75	0.25
1991 Topps Stadium Club #388 .... 16.00		8.00	3.00
1991 Topps Traded #4 .... 2.00		1.00	0.45
1992 Fleer Rookie Sensations #4 .... 22.50		12.00	6.00

Derek Bell

So how many Toronto Blue Jays outfielders who were supposed to be stars were traded away by the team before they became stars and then never got to be stars? Let's see ... there was Sil Campusano ... Rob Ducey ... Geronimo Berroa ... Mark Whiten ... Ryan Thompson ... Pedro Munoz ... Francisco Cabrera can play a little outfield ... and now Derek Bell. The Blue Jays wanted to trade Derek Bell so badly they could taste it, and it ended up tasting like Darrin Jackson. Bell looks like a player but also thinks like a Blue Jay outfielder, which is not good. He'll have his chance in San Diego, but he'll have to have a Gary Sheffield-like renaissance for his cards to justify their values.

	NM	EX	VG
1989 Best Knoxville (set) 14.00		0.65	2.50
1990 CMC Minor League #340 .... 1.50		0.65	0.25
1990 CMC Syracuse (set) 25.00		10.50	4.50
1990 ProCards Syracuse (set) 10.00		4.50	2.00
1990 Score Traded #81 .... 0.60		0.25	0.10
1991 Donruss #32 .... 0.35		0.12	0.04
1991 Fleer #168 .... 0.25		0.10	0.04
1991 Topps Traded #7 .... 0.35		0.12	0.04
1991 Upper Deck Final Edition #26 .... 40.00		0.15	0.05
1992 Bowman #237 .... 0.20		0.08	0.03
1992 Bowman #559 .... 1.00		0.45	0.20
1992 Bowman Gold #237 .... 1.00		0.45	0.20
1992 Fleer Ultra #448 .... 0.50		0.20	0.08
1992 Pinnacle #250 .... 0.35		0.15	0.05
1992 Score Impact Player #23 .... 0.30		0.12	0.04

	NM	EX	VG
1992 Topps Gold #121	4.00	1.75	0.65
1992 Upper Deck Scouting Report #4	1.25	0.55	0.20

George (Jorge) Bell

George (or Jorge, depending on whether or not you're Topps and whether or not it's 1984) Bell is an excellent hitter with a big-time head on his shoulders. If Bell spent his entire career playing in New York City that might be viewed as an asset, but playing where Bell has played — Toronto and Chicago — it's caused him to be labeled as a loudmouthed troublemaker who just so happens to be able to hit the heck out of the ball. You could also argue that the same things that make Bell the less-than-perfect teammate also make him the less-than-perfect card buy. Considering Bell's numbers — a .282 career batting average going into 1993, better than 250 homers — you'd expect his rookie card to be worth more than nine bucks, tops. But it's not, and it's probably best it's not, but realize that with a little change in attitude it could all be changed around.

	NM	EX	VG
1982 Donruss #54	5.00	2.25	1.00
1982 Fleer #609	4.00	1.50	0.65
1982 O-Pee-Chee #254	10.00	4.50	0.20
1982 Topps #254	7.50	3.45	1.75
1984 Donruss #73	2.50	2.20	0.45
1984 Fleer #148	2.25	1.00	0.40
1984 Nestle #278	6.00	2.50	1.00
1984 O-Pee-Chee #278	2.75	1.15	0.50
1984 Police Blue Jays #11	1.50	0.65	0.25
1984 Topps #278	1.25	0.50	0.20
1984 Topps Tiffany #278	6.75	3.00	1.00
1985 Donruss #146	0.75	0.30	0.12
1985 Fleer #100	0.75	0.30	0.12
1985 O-Pee-Chee Posters #18	0.75	0.30	0.12
1985 Police Blue Jays #11	1.25	0.50	0.20
1985 Topps #698	0.50	0.20	0.08
1985 Topps Stickers #360	0.08	0.03	0.01
1985 Topps Tiffany #698	2.50	1.00	0.40
1986 Donruss #71	0.60	0.25	0.10
1986 Donruss Diamond King Supers #4	0.30	0.12	0.04
1986 Leaf #4	0.35	0.15	0.05
1986 Police Blue Jays #11	1.25	0.50	0.20
1986 Sportflics #102	0.35	0.15	0.05
1986 Topps #338	0.40	0.15	0.05
1986 Topps Tiffany #338	1.25	0.50	0.20
1987 Classic #56	0.40	0.15	0.05

1987 Fleer #220	0.30	0.12	0.05
1987 Fleer All-Stars #9	0.50	0.20	0.08
1987 Fleer Baseball's Best #3	0.20	0.08	0.03
1987 Fleer Star Stickers #9	0.35	0.15	0.05
1987 Police Blue Jays #11	1.00	0.40	0.15
1987 Topps Coins #3	0.20	0.08	0.03
1988 Drake's Panel #9	3.00	1.25	0.50
1988 Fleer All-Stars #5	0.75	0.30	0.12
1988 Fleer Baseball Award Winners #2	0.20	0.08	0.03
1988 Hostess Potato Chips Panel #12	1.75	0.75	0.35
1988 Kenner Starting Lineup	12.00	5.00	2.00
1988 Topps Stickers #158	0.30	0.10	0.04
1989 Fleer Baseball All-Stars #2	0.12	0.05	0.01
1990 Leaf #185	0.50	0.20	0.08
1990 Score McDonald's #20	4.00	1.50	0.50
1991 Topps #504	0.50	0.20	0.08
1992 Donruss Diamond Kings #7	1.00	0.40	0.15
1992 Leaf Gold Inserts #462	0.40	0.15	0.05
1992 Topps Gold Inserts #320	2.00	0.80	0.35

Albert Belle

Belle is one of those unusual baseball players (Lester Buster Narum being the other that comes to mind) who can't decide what his first name actually is. As Joey Belle, he was a troublemaker who was sent down to the minors repeatedly for disciplinary reasons. As Albert Belle, he's kept his temper in check a little more and has become one of the majors' most feared power hitters. His cards haven't quite caught up to his accomplishments, and his checkered past definitely has something to do with that. As it stands, many of his cards are undervalued and recommended.

	NM	EX	VG
1985 McDag LSU (set)	17.50	7.50	3.50
1988 Star Co. Kingston Indians #4	11.50	5.00	2.25
1990 Leaf #180	7.50	3.50	1.50
1990 Topps #283	0.60	0.25	0.10
1991 Bowman Tiffany #81	0.75	0.30	0.12
1991 Fleer Ultra #107	0.35	0.15	0.05
1991 Fleer Update #107	0.30	0.12	0.05
1991 Leaf #239	1.00	0.45	0.20
1991 O-Pee-Chee #8	0.25	0.10	0.04
1991 Topps Stadium Club #465	2.75	1.30	0.60
1991 Upper Deck #764	0.30	0.12	0.04
1992 Fleer Ultra #47	0.60	0.25	0.10

1992 O-Pee-Chee Premier #100 .... 0.05	0.01	0.01
1992 Score Pinnacle Team 2000 #18 .... 0.50	0.20	0.08
1992 Topps Gold #785 .... 2.00	0.85	0.40
1992 Topps Kids #73 .... 0.05	0.01	0.01
1992 Upper Deck Home Run Heroes #13 ..... 2.00	0.85	0.40
1992 Upper Deck Ted Williams' Best #13 ..... 3.00	1.25	0.55
1993 Score Select #50 .... 0.15	0.05	0.01

Andy Benes

Being the first player chosen in the 1988 baseball draft and a former member of the U.S. Olympic Baseball Team to boot meant there was a lot of pressure for Andy Benes to succeed from the get-go, and basically, he hasn't disappointed. His stuff would suggest a better won-loss record, but he hasn't had the best or most consistent support from his teammates, and he's really still refining what he can do. Benes could be around for quite a while and win quite a few games. Looking at him for the long term, he looks solid.

	NM	EX	VG
1988 Topps Tiffany Traded #14 .... 7.25		3.50	1.50
1989 Bowman Tiffany #488 .... 3.00		1.25	0.50
1989 Rock's Dugout Highlight (set) 10.00		4.50	2.00
1989 Rock's Dugout Stadium (set) 13.00		6.00	2.50
1989 Rock's Dugout Update (set) 9.50		4.00	1.50
1989 Rock's Dugout Wichita regular (set) ... 13.00		6.00	2.50
1989 Topps Tiffany #437 .... 2.00		0.80	0.30
1990 Leaf #56 .... 2.50		1.15	0.50
1990 Sportflics #90 .... 0.50		0.20	0.08
1990 Upper Deck #55 .... 0.75		0.30	0.12
1991 Topps #51 .... 1.50		0.60	0.25
1992 Fleer Smoke'n Heat #9 .... 0.75		0.30	0.12
1992 Leaf Gold Inserts #74 .... 1.00		0.40	0.15
1992 Topps Gold Inserts #682 .... 2.00		0.80	0.30

Craig Biggio

Craig Biggio is one of the most unusual baseball mutants: a successful catcher who was moved successfully to second base. Before that move, Biggio was a sometimes leadoff hitter and sometimes center fielder and an all-the-time threat to steal bases, which must have been too much for baseball purists to handle. It's hard for us to handle sometimes, too, especially when we consider Biggio's cards. We suppose they're moderately priced for cards of a catcher-turned-second baseman. Let's just say if you buy Biggio's cards you're not going to really know what you're getting for another couple of years.

	NM	EX	VG
1989 Fleer Glossy Tin #353	1.50	0.65	0.30
1989 Score Young Superstar II #33	0.35	0.15	0.05
1990 Bowman Tiffany #78	0.75	0.35	0.15
1990 Sportflics #22	0.70	0.30	0.12

Greg Blosser

Greg Blosser is one of the Boston Red Sox two top outfield prospects, Jeff McNeely being the other. For their shared status, the two are about as dissimilar as prospects get in the Red Sox system. McNeely is a speed guy with occasional power, and Blosser ... well, Blosser swings for the fences, misses more often than he makes contact, and is your basic butcher in the field. All of which are certainly in the Boston tradition and should endear him hugely to the Boston faithful when Blosser finally arrives in the bigs in 1994.

	NM	EX	VG
1990 Bowman #278	0.15	0.05	0.01
1990 Bowman Tiffany #28	1.00	0.45	0.20
1990 Score #681	0.15	0.05	0.01
1991 Bowman #115	0.10	0.04	0.01
1991 Classic-Best #226	0.25	0.10	0.03
1991 Upper Deck #70	0.25	0.10	0.04
1992 Bowman #251	0.10	0.04	0.01
1992 Classic #194	0.05	0.01	0.01
1992 Classic-Best New Britain (set)	5.00	2.25	1.00

Wade Boggs

From the word "Go" Boggs' cards rate Cooperstown consideration, though Boggs is quite a ways from being a lock for the Hall of Fame. He's too old, he doesn't hit for power, he doesn't run well, and while he's a better fielder than he used to be, that's damning him with faint praise. His first year as a Yankee was an improvement over his last year as a Red Sox, but still far short of his late '80s seasons. All that said, there's no reason why Wade Boggs couldn't be an older version of George Brett, doing practically everything that Brett did, only three or four years behind. It's just not as likely as his card prices would have you believe, that's all.

	NM	EX	VG
1981 TCMA Pawtucket #15	125.00	61.50	30.00
1983 Donruss #586	22.50	11.00	5.00
1983 Fleer #179	22.50	11.00	5.00
1983 Topps #498	37.50	18.00	8.50

1984 Donruss #1561	13.50	6.50	3.00
1984 Fleer #392	7.50	3.50	1.50
1984 Topps #30	4.00	1.75	0.75
1984 Topps Tiffany #30	30.00	13.50	6.50
1985 Donruss #172	4.25	2.00	0.85
1985 Fleer #151	4.25	2.00	0.85
1985 Fleer Limited Edition #3	0.65	0.30	0.12
1985 Topps #350	2.00	0.85	0.40
1986 Donruss #371	2.00	0.85	0.40
1986 Fleer #341	2.00	0.85	0.40
1986 Fleer Star Stickers #8	1.00	0.45	0.20
1986 Sportflics #3	1.50	0.65	0.30
1986 Topps #510	1.00	0.45	0.20
1986 Topps Tiffany #510	5.00	2.25	1.00
1987 Classic #105	1.50	0.65	0.30
1987 Donruss #252	0.60	0.25	0.10
1987 Donruss Opening Day #181	0.75	0.30	0.10
1987 Donruss Pop-Ups (1)	0.55	0.25	0.10
1987 Fleer #29	1.25	0.60	0.25
1987 Topps #8	2.50	1.15	0.55
1988 Fantastic Sam's #8	1.25	0.55	0.20
1988 Fleer All-Star #8	2.50	1.15	0.55
1988 Score #2	0.25	0.10	0.04
1989 Bowman #32	0.25	0.10	0.04
1989 Bowman Tiffany #32	1.25	0.50	0.20
1989 Upper Deck #389	1.00	0.45	0.20
1990 Leaf #51	1.75	0.75	0.30
1991 Donruss Elite #9	100.00	48.50	23.50
1991 Fleer Ultra #27	0.25	0.10	0.04
1991 Score #894	1.50	0.60	0.20
1991 Studio #11	0.50	0.35	0.15
1991 Topps Desert Storm #450	30.00	13.50	6.50
1992 Donruss Diamond Kings #9	2.25	1.00	0.45
1992 Fleer Team Leaders #13	1.50	0.65	0.30
1992 Fleer Ultra Award Winners #4	4.00	1.75	0.75
1992 Leaf Gold #286	2.00	0.85	0.35
1992 Studio Heritage Series #3	2.50	1.10	0.50
1992 Upper Deck Ted Williams' Best Hitters #1	3.00	1.25	0.55
1993 Upper Deck Then & Now #1	3.50	1.50	0.65

Barry Bonds

He may be the best player in baseball, but he is certainly not the most popular despite a stellar season in San Francisco last year. Barry Bonds plays to please himself, and while his standards of performance are high, his standards of conduct aren't. The result? Bonds is easily the most disagreeable great player this side of the retired Willie Mays. That image hasn't helped his cards any, which is actually a boon for collectors. You can pay a lot more for cards of inferior players with less potential for continued greatness than Barry. A bonus: The 1987 Donruss Opening Day card of Bonds that shows teammate Johnny Ray (Ray wears a dark jersey on the card) is one of the great rarities of this or any age and a recommended buy. The rest of his cards aren't bad, either.

	NM	EX	VG
1986 Donruss Rookies #11	14.00	6.50	3.00
1986 Fleer Update #U14	8.50	4.00	1.75
1986 Topps Tiffany Traded #11T	35.00	16.50	7.50
1986 Topps Traded #11T	5.50	2.50	1.10
1987 Classic Baseball #113	5.00	2.25	1.00
1987 Donruss #361	8.00	3.50	1.50
1987 Donruss Opening Day #163A (error)	125.00	55.00	25.00
1987 Donruss Opening Day #163B (correct)	0.55	0.20	0.08
1987 Fleer #604	15.50	7.50	3.50
1987 Fleer Tin Glossy #604	16.50	8.00	3.50
1987 Topps #320	2.75	1.25	0.55
1987 Topps Tiffany #320	7.50	3.50	1.50
1987 Toys 'R' Us #4	0.50	0.20	0.08
1988 Donruss #326	0.50	0.20	0.08
1988 Fleer #322	1.25	0.55	0.20
1988 Fleer Tin Glossy #322	2.00	0.85	0.30
1988 King-B #11	1.00	0.45	0.20
1988 Score Glossy #265	5.50	2.50	1.10
1988 Topps American Baseball Glossy #5	0.75	0.30	0.12
1988 Topps Big #89	0.20	0.08	0.03
1989 Kenner Starting Lineup	8.00	3.25	1.25
1989 Upper Deck #440	1.75	0.65	0.25
1990 Ames #5	0.40	0.15	0.05
1990 Leaf #91	3.25	1.50	0.65
1990 Upper Deck #227	0.50	0.20	0.08
1991 Donruss Elite #2	140.00	65.00	30.00
1991 Fleer All-Star #5	2.00	0.85	0.40
1991 Topps Stadium Club #220	3.00	1.25	0.55
1991 Upper Deck Silver Slugger #5	4.50	2.00	0.85

1992 Fleer All-Star #3 .... 2.25	1.00	0.45
1992 Fleer Lumber Co. #8 .... 2.50	1.10	0.45
1992 Fleer Ultra All-Star #16 .... 6.50	3.00	1.25
1992 Fleer Ultra Award Winners #11 .... 7.50	3.50	1.50
1992 Leaf Gold #275 .... 2.50	1.10	0.45
1992 Score Team Pinnacle #8 .... 45.00	21.50	10.00
1992 Topps Gold #380 .... 2.00	0.85	0.35
1992 Topps Gold #380 .... 2.00	0.85	0.35
1992 Upper Deck Home Run Heroes #21 ..... 1.75	0.75	0.35
1992 Upper Deck Ted Williams' Best Hitters #2 .... 3.25	1.50	0.65

Bobby Bonilla

Boy, those were the days, when Bonds and Bonilla formed a one-two punch for the Pirates and played in the outfield with Andy Van Slyke between them. At least, that must be the way Bonilla feels about things. It's unlikely that Bonilla will ever again be able to re-create the situation or rekindle the power he had hitting right next to Barry Bonds, though Bonilla's the type of player who'll try very hard to do it. A dreadful season like the Mets had in '93 could wipe out a lesser talent. New York may be the wrong place for his career, but it doesn't hurt his cards. They're premium-priced, which would be justifiable if Bonilla were a little more of an all-arounder. As it stands now, though, Bonilla doesn't do enough to live up to his reputation, and neither do his cards.

	NM	EX	VG
1983 TCMA Alexandria (set) 140.00	65.50	30.00
1986 Donruss Rookies #30 .... 4.50	2.00	0.80
1986 Fleer Update #15 .... 4.50	2.00	0.80
1986 Sportflics Rookies #26 .... 2.50	1.00	0.40
1986 Topps Traded #112 .... 2.00	0.40	0.08
1986 Topps Tiffany Traded #12 .... 13.50	6.50	3.00
1987 Donruss #558 .... 2.75	1.25	0.50
1987 Fleer #605 .... 4.00	1.50	0.60
1987 Fleer Glossy Tin #605 .... 7.75	3.50	1.50
1987 Topps #184 .... 1.00	0.40	0.15
1987 Topps Tiffany #184 .... 7.50	3.50	1.50
1988 Classic Blue #236 .... 1.25	0.50	0.20
1988 Fleer #323 .... 0.75	0.30	0.12
1988 Fleer Tin #323 .... 2.00	0.80	0.30
1988 Kenner Starting Lineup 13.00	5.50	2.25
1988 Score Glossy #116 .... 4.50	2.00	0.80
1989 Fleer All-Stars #1 .... 1.25	0.50	0.20
1989 Topps Big #1590 .... 0.08	0.03	0.01
1989 Upper Deck #578 .... 0.60	0.20	0.08

1990 Leaf #196	1.25	0.50	0.20
1991 Topps #139	1.00	0.40	0.12
1991 Upper Deck Silver Sluggers #15	1.50	0.60	0.20
1992 Donruss Gallery of Stars #1	1.00	0.40	0.15
1992 Fleer Team Leaders #9	1.00	0.40	0.15
1992 Fleer All-Stars #4	1.00	0.40	0.15
1992 Score Pinnacle Slugfest #6	2.00	0.80	0.30
1992 Topps Gold Inserts #160	2.00	0.80	0.30
1993 Topps Gold Inserts #52	0.50	0.20	0.08

Bret Boone

There's a lot of fuss being made over the fact that Bret Boone is the first third-generation major leaguer — Bret's father is Bob Boone and his grandfather is Ray Boone — but there'd be a fuss made over Bret even if he wasn't third-generation stock. Bret is a second baseman with one of the qualities you always find in a second baseman — spunk — along with one of the qualities you don't always find — power. He's had a little trouble adjusting to the major-league way of doing things, but he's learning quickly. His cards are moving up, too, which ought to be expected considering all the hoopla. The hoopla will wear off eventually, though, and fortunately, underneath it all you're left with a pretty darn good major-league prospect.

	NM	EX	VG
1991 Bowman #261	1.00	0.40	0.15
1991 ProCards Jacksonville Suns (set)	9.00	4.25	2.00
1991 ProCards Tomorrow's Heroes #142	1.00	0.40	0.15
1992 Bowman #511	1.25	0.50	0.20
1992 Fleer Update #54	0.75	0.30	0.12
1992 Leaf Gold Leaf #12	5.50	2.50	1.10
1992 Upper Deck #771	0.60	0.25	0.10
1993 Score Select #326	0.50	0.20	0.08
1993 Score Select Stars #21	7.50	3.50	1.50

George Brett

Brett is undoubtedly one of the best hitters to play the game, but he also is going to be responsible for leaving behind some of the game's most unusual memories. What other future Hall of Famer can you think of whose two most memorable moments revolve around pine tar and hemorrhoids? Be that as it may, Brett has been a superb hitter and a credit to the game, and his cards are worth every penny of their asking price, though not a whit more. They'll go up some over the next five years — maybe not 20 percent a year, but 5 percent to 10 percent. Brett's legend is not going to go away anytime soon. He has

announced his intention to retire after the '93 season which would make him
eligible to be elected to the Hall of Fame in '98. How much is that rookie card?

	NM	EX	VG
1975 O-Pee-Chee #228	210.00	100.00	45.50
1976 Hostess Panel #3B	14.00	6.00	2.50
1976 O-Pee-Chee #190	15.00	5.50	2.25
1977 Hostess Twinkie #33	10.00	4.50	2.00
1977 Kellogg's #6	8.25	4.00	1.50
1977 O-Pee-Chee #170	9.00	4.25	2.00
1978 Hostess Panel 9	15.00	6.50	2.75
1978 Kellogg's #6	5.00	2.25	1.00
1978 O-Pee-Chee #215	3.50	1.50	0.65
1979 Kellogg's #50	3.50	1.50	0.65
1979 O-Pee-Chee #167	4.00	1.75	0.75
1979 Topps Comics #9	0.50	0.20	0.08
1980 Burger King Pitch Hit & Run #13	1.50	0.65	0.30
1980 Kellogg's #9	4.00	1.75	0.75
1980 O-Pee-Chee #235	3.25	1.50	0.65
1981 Fleer Star Stickers #116	1.00	0.45	0.20
1981 Kellogg's #8	1.25	0.50	0.20
1981 O-Pee-Chee #113	2.00	0.85	0.35
1981 Perma-Graphics All-Star Credit Card #10	2.00	0.85	0.35
1982 Kellogg's #3	1.00	0.45	0.20
1982 O-Pee-Chee #200	1.25	0.85	0.35
1983 Donruss Action All-Stars #42	0.70	0.25	0.10
1983 Topps Stickers #83	0.25	0.10	0.04
1984 Cereal Series #13	0.60	0.25	0.10
1984 Topps Super #13	0.90	0.40	0.15
1985 General Mills	1.50	0.65	0.25
1986 Donruss Pop-Ups (6)	0.40	0.15	0.05
1986 Fleer Baseball's Best #3	0.30	0.12	0.05
1986 Kitty Clover Royals #20	3.50	1.50	0.65
1986 Meadow Gold Milk #6	5.00	2.00	0.85
1987 Classic #47	1.00	0.45	0.20
1987 Jiffy Pop #5	2.50	1.00	0.45
1988 Kenner Starting Lineup	12.00	5.00	2.00
1988 Panini Stickers #104	0.25	0.10	0.04
1988 Topps Big Baseball #157	0.30	0.10	0.04
1989 Bowman Tiffany #121	1.25	0.50	0.20
1989 Donruss All-Stars #11	0.12	0.05	0.01
1990 Ames All-Stars #2	0.25	0.10	0.04
1990 Score McDonald's #19	15.00	6.50	2.50
1991 Topps Box Bottoms	0.20	0.08	0.03

Ellis Burks

Mishandled and oft-injured in Boston, Ellis Burks has found a new home for his talents in Chicago. His talents are considerable, too: speed, power, and all that good stuff. If he finally lives up to his press clippings the White Sox will be happy and loads of people will be surprised. If he falters —well, it's just because he got hurt too much and his head messed with in Boston. His cards have come way down since his glory year and a half and are actually pretty affordable.

	NM	EX	VG
1986 ProCards New Britain (set)	70.00	32.50	15.00
1987 Donruss Rookies #5	0.25	0.10	0.04
1987 Fleer Update #15	0.25	0.10	0.04
1987 Sportflics Rookies #5	1.00	0.45	0.20
1988 Classic Travel Blue #229	1.00	0.45	0.20
1988 Fleer #348	0.60	0.25	0.10
1988 Kenner Starting Lineup	25.00	12.00	5.00
1988 Leaf #174	0.85	0.35	0.15
1988 Score Young Superstars I #37	0.60	0.20	0.08
1988 Sportflics #144	0.75	0.30	0.12
1989 Donruss Baseball's Best #9	0.30	0.10	0.04
1989 Kenner Starting Lineup	9.00	4.00	1.50
1989 Sportflics #191	0.50	0.20	0.08
1990 Leaf #261	0.25	0.10	0.04
1990 Topps Big #107	0.25	0.10	0.04
1991 Denny's Grand Slam #1	2.00	0.85	0.35
1991 Pepsi Red Sox #11	0.30	0.10	0.04
1991 Topps #108	0.25	0.10	0.04
1991 Upper Deck Silver Sluggers #10	1.00	0.40	0.15
1992 Leaf Gold Inserts #314	0.40	0.15	0.05
1992 Topps Gold Inserts #416	2.00	0.80	0.35
1993 Topps Gold Inserts #351	0.25	0.10	0.04

Jeromy Burnitz

There were almost universal shouts of puzzlement when the Mets drafted Jeromy Burnitz, an outfielder out of Oklahoma State, with their first pick in the 1990 draft, and while people understand a little better now, there are still times when Burnitz makes them shake their heads. He has excellent power, good speed, and a fantastic attitude, but sometimes it all goes sour and no one can get him straightened out for a time. Fortunately, those funks don't last long. Burnitz is slated to arrive in 1994. Look for a slow start but steady improvement after that. And don't feel any rush to load up on his cards. They're going to plateau for a while.

	NM	EX	VG
1991 Bowman #474	0.25	0.10	0.04
1991 Classic-Best Minor-League #68	2.50	1.10	0.50
1991 ProCards Tomorrow's Heroes #280	2.00	0.85	0.40
1991 Score #380	0.25	0.10	0.04
1992 Bowman #189	0.60	0.25	0.10
1992 Upper Deck Minor League #130	0.25	0.10	0.04
1993 Donruss #787	0.25	0.10	0.04
1993 Fleer #69	0.25	0.10	0.04

Tom Candiotti

Candiotti is one of the few remaining knuckleball pitchers and the surest bet of the bunch to hang around as long as Charlie Hough. Candiotti has been pretty good with good teams (Toronto) and bad teams (Cleveland, Los Angeles), which leads you to believe that being pretty good is his lot in life. Candiotti could be a pretty good knuckleball pitcher and make it into the Hall of Fame, but he'd have to pitch until he's 60 to do it. His cards are priced appropriately for his outlook.

	NM	EX	VG
1984 Nestle's #262	0.80	0.30	0.10
1984 Topps Tiffany #262	4.00	1.50	0.65
1988 Fleer Tin #604	0.25	0.10	0.04
1989 Fleer Glossy Tin #488	0.30	0.12	0.05

Jose Canseco

Jose Canseco is one of the dominant baseball-card figures of the last five years. Ken Griffey Jr. and Frank Thomas have given him a run for his money recently, but neither one can match Canseco's combination of longevity and ubiquitousness. Canseco is not the force he once was, either on the diamond or in card stores, but just by sheer numbers he has enough of a presence to severely affect the market if he goes into a prolonged slump or on a spree. At this point his cards aren't worth the prices they're fetching and it's likely to be a long time before they are. The injury from his ill-fated pitching exploit in 93 could keep him inactive a long time and how well will he play when he does return?

	NM	EX	VG
1986 Mother's Cookies A's #90	18.00	8.50	4.00
1987 Classic #46	38.50	16.50	7.50
1987 Fleer Baseball All-Stars #6	1.00	0.45	0.20
1987 Fleer Baseball Game Winners #8	1.00	0.45	0.20
1987 Fleer Baseball's Exciting Stars #7	1.00	0.45	0.20

1987 Fleer Limited Edition #6	1.00	0.45	0.20
1987 Fleer Record Setters #3	1.00	0.45	0.20
1987 Fleer Star Stickers #18	1.00	0.45	0.20
1987 Mother's Cookies A's #26	3.00	1.35	0.55
1987 Topps Coins #6	1.00	0.45	0.20
1987 Topps Glossy All-Star (60) #59	2.25	1.00	0.45
1987 Topps Glossy Rookies #3	3.00	1.25	0.50
1987 Topps Stickers #164	0.75	0.35	0.15
1988 Bazooka #3	1.00	0.45	0.20
1988 Classic Red #165	3.00	1.25	0.50
1988 Donruss A's Team Book #256	1.75	0.75	0.35
1988 Fleer Baseball's Exciting Stars #8	0.75	0.35	0.15
1988 Fleer Star Stickers #54	1.00	0.45	0.20
1988 Kenner Starting Lineup #16	42.50	20.00	9.00
1988 Mother's Cookies A's #7	3.00	1.35	0.55
1988 Score Young Superstar #30	1.00	0.45	0.20
1988 Topps American Baseball Glossy #10	4.00	1.75	0.75
1988 Topps Big #13	1.25	0.50	0.20
1988 Topps Stickercards #48	0.10	0.04	0.01
1989 Classic #103	1.10	0.50	0.20
1989 Donruss Pop-Ups	0.75	0.35	0.15
1989 Fleer Baseball MVP #6	0.85	0.40	0.15
1989 Kenner Starting Lineup #95	18.00	8.50	3.50
1989 Mother's Cookies Jose Canseco (set of 4)	15.00	6.50	2.50
1989 Scoremasters #40	1.00	0.45	0.20
1989 Topps Big #190	1.00	0.45	0.20
1990 Ames #29	0.50	0.20	0.08
1990 Bowman Tiffany #460	2.50	1.10	0.50
1990 Donruss Learning Series #6	7.50	3.50	1.50
1990 Mother's Cookies Jose Canseco (set of 4)	18.50	8.50	3.50
1991 Topps Desert Storm #700	95.00	40.00	17.50

Steve Carlton

Steve Carlton will be an automatic Hall of Fame selection. A 20-year-plus career has produced a lot of Carlton cards extending all the way to 1987. You won't need a second mortgage to buy a Carlton unless it's from his first few years. His later cards have little upward potential due to their heavy production. All Carlton cards not listed are 25¢ or less in Near Mint condition.

	NM	EX	VG
1965 Topps #477	495.00	200.00	95.00
1967 Topps #146	110.00	40.00	17.50
1968 Topps #408	45.00	20.00	7.50
1969 Topps #255	45.00	20.00	7.50
1970 Topps #220	30.00	12.50	5.00
1971 Topps #55	45.00	12.50	5.00
1972 Topps #420	17.50	6.00	2.50
1972 Topps #751	45.00	17.50	8.00
1973 Topps #300	14.00	5.00	2.00
1974 Topps #95	9.50	3.50	1.50
1975 Topps #185	9.00	3.50	1.50
1976 Topps #355	6.50	2.25	1.00
1977 Topps #110	7.50	2.50	1.50
1978 Topps #540	4.50	1.75	0.95
1979 Topps #25	3.50	1.25	0.50
1980 Topps #210	3.35	1.00	0.50
1981 Donruss #33	1.00	0.30	0.10
1981 Fleer #6	1.00	0.30	0.10
1981 Fleer #660	0.95	0.25	0.10
1981 Topps #630	1.65	0.50	0.15
1982 Donruss #42	0.75	0.25	0.10
1982 Fleer #243	0.75	0.25	0.10
1982 Topps #480	0.75	0.25	0.10
1983 Donruss #219	0.75	0.25	0.10
1983 Fleer #155	0.75	0.25	0.10
1983 Topps #70	0.95	0.25	0.10
1984 Donruss #111	2.75	1.25	0.50
1984 Fleer #25	1.50	0.50	0.15

Joe Carter

Joe is an underrated all-around ballplayer who his finally getting his due — even if it took two world championships by Toronto for him to get it. Strong Canadian demand has helped drive up the price for Carter's early cards, though his more recent cards are very affordable, especially for a player who is putting up close-to-Cooperstown numbers. If Carter doesn't make the Hall, the prices for his early cards will seem out of line and the prices for his more recent cards will be in line. If he continues to drive in runs like he has the last several seasons, though, watch for a price explosion for some of his near-common current cards.

	NM	EX	VG
1983 TCMA Iowa Cubs #90	85.00	42.00	20.00
1984 Donruss #41	47.50	23.00	11.00
1985 Donruss #616	5.25	2.50	1.10
1985 Fleer #443	9.25	4.50	2.10
1985 Topps #694	5.25	2.50	1.10
1985 Topps Tiffany #694	45.00	22.00	10.00
1986 Donruss #224	1.50	0.70	0.30
1987 Classic #127	1.00	0.45	0.20
1987 Fleer #244	0.75	0.35	0.15
1987 Fleer League Leaders #9	0.15	0.06	0.01
1987 Fleer Star Stickers #21	0.25	0.12	0.05
1987 Leaf #133	0.70	0.30	0.10
1987 Sportflics #176	0.15	0.07	0.01
1987 Topps Coins #7	0.12	0.05	0.01
1988 Topps American Baseball Glossy #12 ...	0.50	0.20	0.08
1988 Topps Big #78	0.15	0.06	0.01
1989 Upper Deck #190	0.65	0.30	0.12
1990 Leaf #379	3.25	1.50	0.65
1990 Score Traded #19	0.30	0.12	0.05
1990 Topps All-Star Glossy (60) #33	0.15	0.06	0.01
1991 Topps Stadium Club #513	3.00	1.45	0.70
1992 Donruss Elite #10	110.00	50.00	22.00
1992 Fleer Team Leaders #14	1.00	0.40	0.15

Andujar Cedeno

Another overtalented, underachieving shortstop. Cedeno has more power than the rest of the bunch and excellent range and arm at shortstop. He just hasn't been able to do it at the big-league level. Maybe he's pressing; maybe he just can't get the job done. His cards run the gamut, but basically they're reasonably priced.

	NM	EX	VG
1984 Nestle #182	70.00	32.50	15.00
1990 Best Columbus (set)	12.00	5.00	2.00
1990 Best Minor-League #72	4.00	1.75	0.75
1990 Bowman Tiffany #77	0.85	0.35	0.15
1990 ProCards A&AA Minor-League #58	2.00	0.85	0.35
1991 Bowman Tiffany #563	0.75	0.35	0.15
1991 Topps Desert Shield #646	30.00	12.50	5.50

Raymond Chapman

Ray Chapman's name went down in baseball history in the most tragic way possible. He is still the only player to die from an injury received during a major-league game, when he was struck and killed by a Carl Mays pitch on August 17, 1920. The incident is periodically reviewed by historians, and each time, Chapman's few cards go up in price.

	NM	EX	VG
M101-4	45.00	20.00	10.00
M101-5	45.00	20.00	10.00
M101-6	60.00	25.00	15.00

Harold Chase

A lot of people must think that Hal Chase is in the Hall of Fame since his cards always bring premium prices. But he is not enshrined at Cooperstown, and he's not going to be. That makes his cards a questionable investment unless you believe you can keep fooling most of the people most of the time.

	NM	EX	VG
Turkey Red (T3) #6	475.00	150.00	50.00
D303 General Baking	125.00	50.00	20.00
D304 General Baking	115.00	40.00	15.00
E101	375.00	150.00	65.00
E102	375.00	150.00	65.00
E103 Williams Caramel	550.00	175.00	75.00
E106 American Caramel	275.00	100.00	35.00
E254 Colgan's Chips	65.00	20.00	10.00
E270	65.00	20.00	10.00
E300 Plow's Candy	550.00	175.00	75.00
E90-1 American Caramel	175.00	55.00	15.00
E92 Croft's Candy	225.00	75.00	25.00
E92 Croft's Cocoa	225.00	75.00	25.00
E92 Dockman	150.00	50.00	20.00
E93	275.00	100.00	35.00
E98	325.00	125.00	50.00
M116 (blue background)	750.00	200.00	75.00
M116 (pastel background)	400.00	150.00	50.00
T202 Hassan	325.00	125.00	45.00
T205 (only one ear showing)	725.00	150.00	75.00
T205 (with both ears showing)	250.00	75.00	25.00

	NM	EX	VG
T206 (holding trophy)	350.00	135.00	50.00
T206 (portrait blue background)	225.00	75.00	25.00
T206 (portrait pink background)	400.00	125.00	50.00
T206 (throwing, black cap)	175.00	65.00	20.00
T206 (throwing, white cap)	175.00	65.00	20.00
T210 Mecca	100.00	35.00	15.00
T213 Type 1	175.00	75.00	25.00
T213 Type 2	150.00	65.00	20.00
T213 Type 3	150.00	65.00	20.00
T216	150.00	65.00	20.00

Edward Cicotte

Eddie Cicotte is one of the three members of the 1919 Chicago White Sox who, had it not been for the scandal, might have made the Hall of Fame. As it is, he's one of the better known of the eight players who were banished. Of the eight who appeared on cards, his cards are fairly popular. Normally you won't find his cards at common prices. With current demand, prices are likely to climb.

	NM	EX	VG
M101-4	50.00	20.00	10.00
M101-5	50.00	20.00	10.00
M101-6	60.00	20.00	10.00
M116	250.00	100.00	40.00
1914 Cracker Jack #94	995.00	125.00	50.00
1915 Cracker Jack #94	175.00	75.00	35.00
E270	55.00	25.00	10.00
E286 Ju Ju Drums	375.00	200.00	100.00
E94	235.00	85.00	25.00
E95	235.00	85.00	25.00
T201 Mecca	90.00	35.00	15.00
T202 Hassan	275.00	85.00	30.00
T204 Ramly	435.00	125.00	50.00
T205	175.00	75.00	25.00
T206	200.00	75.00	20.00
T207	225.00	75.00	20.00

Will Clark

While "The Natural" hasn't been a natural disaster the last couple of years, he hasn't been the dominant hitter he was expected to be. The off seasons have slowed the appreciation of his cards somewhat, but they still carry generally higher value than those of new teammate Barry Bonds (another one for the go-figure department). Clark is a superb hitter driven to perfection, but that dedication is stripped of some of its importance if his play isn't up to snuff. Get the red flag ready for Will, but don't wave it yet; he still has plenty of time to turn it around.

	NM	EX	VG
1986 Donruss Rookies #32	12.50	6.00	2.50
1986 Fleer Update #U25	9.50	4.50	2.00
1986 Mother's Cookies Giants #7	10.00	4.50	2.00
1986 Topps Tiffany Traded #24T	35.00	16.50	8.00
1986 Topps Traded #24T	8.75	4.00	1.75
1987 Donruss #66	10.50	5.00	2.25
1987 Fleer #269	27.50	13.50	6.50
1987 Fleer Limited Edition #9	1.00	0.45	0.20
1987 Fleer Tin Glossy #269	29.50	14.50	7.00
1987 Mother's Cookies Giants #2	4.50	2.00	0.85
1987 Topps #420	2.00	0.85	0.40
1988 Donruss #204	0.55	0.25	0.10
1988 Donruss #21 (Diamond King)	0.30	0.12	0.05
1988 Fleer #78	2.75	1.25	0.55
1988 Fleer Mini #116	0.80	0.35	0.15
1988 Leaf #170	0.80	0.35	0.15
1988 Mother's Cookies Giants #2	3.50	1.50	0.55
1988 Score Glossy #78	8.50	4.00	1.75
1988 Score Young Superstar #25	1.00	0.45	0.20
1989 Donruss Pop-Ups (11)	1.00	0.45	0.20
1989 Fleer All-Star #3	3.00	1.25	0.55
1989 Mother's Cookies Will Clark (set of 4)	10.00	4.50	2.00
1989 Scoremasters #10	1.00	0.45	0.20
1989 Upper Deck #155	2.00	0.85	0.35
1990 Fleer All-Star #2	2.00	0.85	0.40
1990 Leaf #172	3.50	1.60	0.65
1990 Mother's Cookies (set of 4)	16.00	7.50	3.50
1990 Score McDonald's #1	25.00	12.00	5.75
1990 Upper Deck #556	0.45	0.20	0.08
1991 Classic III #9	0.15	0.05	0.01
1991 Donruss Elite #11	135.00	60.00	27.50
1991 Leaf #238	0.85	0.40	0.15
1991 Leaf Studio #254	1.50	0.65	0.30
1991 Topps Stadium Club #5	3.00	1.25	0.55
1992 Donruss Diamond Stars #2	4.00	1.75	0.75

1992 Fleer All-Stars #13	3.00	1.25	0.55
1992 Fleer Ultra #287	1.25	0.55	0.25
1992 Fleer Ultra All-Stars #11	6.50	3.00	1.25
1992 Fleer Ultra Award Winners #14	7.00	3.25	1.50
1992 Leaf Gold #241	3.75	1.75	0.75
1992 Leaf Studio Heritage #8	4.50	2.00	0.85
1992 Score Pinnacle Slugfest #12	2.75	1.25	0.55
1992 Score Superstar #4	0.35	0.15	0.05
1992 Score Team Pinnacle #4	95.00	45.00	21.50
1992 Topps Gold #330	4.00	1.75	0.75
1992 Upper Deck Ted Williams' Best Hitters #4	3.75	1.75	0.75

Royce Clayton

Clayton is one of a quartet of young N.L. shortstops — Jose Offerman, Wilfredo Cordero, and Andujar Cedeno being the other three — who could redefine the position for the next decade and beyond if they could only stick on the major-league roster for longer than six weeks at a crack. Clayton might be the most exciting of the bunch. His line-drive bat has a little bit of sock to it, he runs well, and he's flashy afield. Errors are a problem, as is consistency at the plate. But his 1989 Bowman card, among others, make both the regular and Tiffany versions of this scourged set worth considering. When you look at Clayton's wide array of cards you think that he must be something pretty special, but when you look at what he's done to date you wonder what all the fuss is about.

	NM	EX	VG
1989 Bowman #472	0.40	0.15	0.05
1989 Bowman Tiffany #472	2.25	1.00	0.45
1991 Bowman #641	0.25	0.10	0.04
1991 Classic Best Minor-League #251	2.75	1.25	0.55
1991 ProCards Shreveport (set)	9.00	4.25	0.20
1991 Upper Deck #61	0.75	0.35	0.15
1992 Bowman #212	0.40	0.15	0.05
1992 Donruss #397	0.20	0.08	0.03
1992 Donruss The Rookies #123	0.10	0.04	0.01
1992 Fleer #632	0.15	0.05	0.01
1992 Fleer Ultra #288	0.60	0.25	0.10
1992 Leaf Gold #272	2.25	1.00	0.45
1992 Pinnacle Team 2000 #34	0.50	0.20	0.08
1992 Score #841	0.15	0.05	0.01
1992 Score Impact Players #24	0.35	0.15	0.05
1992 Score Pinnacle #268	0.20	0.08	0.03
1992 Score Pinnacle Rookie Idols #15	30.00	14.50	6.50

1992 Studio #115	0.40	0.15	0.05
1992 Topps Gold #786	3.00	1.25	0.55
1992 Topps Stadium Club #630	0.80	0.35	0.15
1992 Upper Deck #2	0.20	0.08	0.03
1992 Upper Deck FanFest #5	0.25	0.10	0.04
1992 Upper Deck Final Edition #4	0.35	0.15	0.05
1992 Upper Deck Scouting Report #6	1.25	0.55	0.20
1993 Donruss #208	0.10	0.04	0.01
1993 Fleer #155	0.10	0.04	0.01
1993 Upper Deck #151	0.15	0.05	0.01

Roger Clemens

Pitchers are such fickle creatures that you almost hate to speak of any of them, no matter how good they are, as being sure things of any sort. There are two exceptions to this: Nolan Ryan and Roger Clemens. Roger Clemens is not likely to eclipse any of Ryan's records, nor is he a threat to Cy Young or Warren Spahn in any regard. However, Clemens is the best pitcher of this era, which may not seem like much now, considering his competition, but will eventually be a big deal. Clemens' cards are priced on par with those of the best contemporary hitters, which is right. As investments per se they're not much, but there certainly are a lot of them. Kudos in this regard go to Fleer and its 12-card Roger Clemens chase set inserted into its '92 base-brand product.

	NM	EX	VG
1984 Fleer Update #27	425.00	210.00	100.00
1985 Donruss #273	63.50	31.00	15.00
1985 Fleer #155	62.00	30.00	14.50
1985 Topps #181	27.50	13.50	6.50
1985 Topps Tiffany #181	150.00	72.50	32.50
1986 Donruss #172	12.50	6.00	2.75
1986 Fleer #345	12.50	6.00	2.75
1986 O-Pee-Chee #98	2.50	1.10	0.50
1986 Topps #661	4.75	2.25	1.10
1986 Topps Tiffany #661	25.00	12.00	5.25
1987 Classic #84	5.00	2.25	1.00
1987 Donruss #276	2.50	1.10	0.50
1987 Fleer #32	4.00	1.75	0.75
1987 Fleer All-Star #11	4.00	1.75	0.75
1987 Fleer Glossy #32	4.25	2.00	0.85
1987 Fleer World Series #3	0.70	0.30	0.12
1987 Topps #1	0.30	0.12	0.05
1987 Topps Coins #8	0.35	0.15	0.06
1988 Donruss #51	0.45	0.20	0.08

1988 Fleer #349	1.10	0.50	0.20
1988 Fleer All-Star #4	4.25	2.00	0.85
1988 Leaf #56	0.80	0.35	0.15
1988 Score #110	0.50	0.20	0.08
1988 Score Glossy #110	5.75	2.75	1.25
1988 Topps Big Baseball #118	0.35	0.15	0.05
1989 Bowman #26	0.30	0.12	0.05
1989 Bowman Glossy #26	4.50	2.00	0.85
1989 Fleer Superstars #9	0.25	0.10	0.05
1989 Scoremasters #20	1.00	0.45	0.20
1989 Sportflics #3	0.40	0.15	0.05
1989 Topps All-Star Glossy (60) #23	0.40	0.15	0.06
1989 Topps American Baseball #16	0.30	0.12	0.05
1989 Upper Deck #195	1.75	0.75	0.35
1990 Fleer For The Record #2	1.25	0.55	0.25
1990 Leaf #12	4.00	1.75	0.75
1990 Score McDonald's #18	18.00	8.50	4.00
1990 Upper Deck #323	0.45	0.20	0.08
1991 Fleer Ultra #31	0.50	0.20	0.08
1991 Pepsi Red Sox #21	1.00	0.45	0.20
1991 Post #12	0.80	0.35	0.15
1991 Studio #14	1.15	0.55	0.25
1991 Topps Desert Storm #530	95.00	45.00	22.00
1991 Topps Stadium Club #309	3.75	1.75	0.75
1992 Fleer Autographed Card	125.00	55.00	25.00
1992 Fleer Set (12)	25.00	12.00	5.00
1992 Fleer Ultra Award Winner #6	8.00	3.75	1.75
1992 Leaf Gold #19	3.75	1.75	0.75
1992 Topps Gold #150	3.00	1.25	0.55
1992 Topps Gold All-Star #405	2.00	0.75	0.35
1992 Topps Stadium Club #80	1.25	0.55	0.25
1992 Topps Stadium Club Members Choice #593	1.25	0.55	0.25
1993 Donruss Diamond Kings #3	7.00	3.25	1.50

Vince Coleman

Perhaps the ugliest single piece of sports memorabilia ever made is the Vince Coleman "Catch Me" statue, produced by a company called Kondritz Collectibles. You wanted to catch it like you wanted to catch cholera. Unfortunately, that's a fitting piece of memorabilia for the card career of Vince Coleman. There's really no more up side for Coleman's cards; a player with bad hamstrings who lives and dies by speed is not any sane person's idea of an ideal investment. Known to have made some pretty bad throws from the outfield, the firecracker thrown from Eric Davis' jeep which injured a young fan has probably killed any demand for his cards. He may not appear in this guide as a Key Player next year as his card values could possibly drop to common levels.

	NM	EX	VG
1986 Donruss #181	1.75	0.75	0.30
1986 Fleer #31	1.00	0.40	0.15
1986 Fleer #637	0.70	0.30	0.12
1986 Fleer Star Sticker #25	0.20	0.08	0.03
1986 Kas Potato Chips Cardinals #1	1.75	0.75	0.35
1986 Schnucks Milk Cardinals	1.75	0.75	0.35
1986 Sportflics #24	1.25	0.50	0.20
1986 Topps #370	0.75	0.30	0.12
1987 Donruss Opening Day #60	0.15	0.05	0.01
1988 Fleer Baseball's Exciting Stars #11	0.45	0.20	0.08
1989 Smokey Bear Cardinals	0.75	0.30	0.12
1992 Fleer Ultra #229	0.50	0.20	0.08
1992 Topps Gold Inserts #500	2.00	0.80	0.35

Jeff Conine

A world-class racquetball player who also happens to be a world-class hitter, Conine was supposed to be the next George Brett until a wrist injury put those thoughts on hold. Once the wrist healed Conine found himself behind Wally Joyner at first and Phil Hiatt at third, and so the Royals let Conine walk to the Florida Marlins, where he and his line-drive bat have found happiness in the outfield. Of all the players on both expansion teams, Conine bears the most watching over the next couple of years. Right now his cards aren't very expensive and are a good gamble. They may not stay that way for long.

	NM	EX	VG
1990 Best Memphis Chicks (set)	9.00	3.75	1.50
1990 ProCards A&AA Minor League Stars #48	0.45	0.20	0.08
1990 ProCards memphis (set)	9.00	3.75	1.50
1990 Star Co. Memphis (set)	9.00	3.75	1.50
1990 Star Minor League Wax #85	0.60	0.25	0.10
1990 Topps Major League Debut #34	0.15	0.05	0.01
1991 Bowman #184	0.20	0.08	0.03
1991 Bowman Tiffany #184	1.00	0.45	0.20
1991 Donruss #63	0.50	0.20	0.08
1991 Fleer Ultra #145	0.35	0.15	0.05
1991 Impel Line Drive AAA #332	0.60	0.25	0.10
1991 Score #722	0.20	0.08	0.03

1991 Score Rookies #19	0.20	0.08	0.03
1992 Donruss Phenoms #3	0.15	0.05	0.01
1992 Topps #683	0.15	0.05	0.01
1993 Score Select Stars #12	3.00	1.25	0.50

Wilfredo Cordero

The Expos quit waiting for Wilfredo Cordero to be ready to take over the shortstop's job in 1993; they flat-out gave it to him. Now everyone will be able to see whether Fantasy Baseball's 1991 minor-league Player of the Year is everything he's cracked up to be. Supposedly Cordero has 15-homer power to go along with a lively line-drive bat, good speed, and more consistent fielding than the Andujar Cedenos and Jose Offermans of the world. He could be the glue holding together a wonderful young Expos infield, but at this point he hasn't shown it. The values of his cards reflect quite accurately the expectation as well as the uncertainty.

	NM	EX	VG
1989 Star Co. West Palm Beach (set)	11.50	5.50	2.50
1990 Best Jacksonville Expos (set)	9.00	4.00	1.50
1990 Best Minor League Baseball #128	1.50	0.65	0.25
1990 ProCards Jacksonville Expos (set)	9.00	4.00	1.50
1991 Impel Line Drive AAA #179	0.75	0.30	0.10
1991 Leaf Gold Leaf #3	6.00	2.75	1.25
1991 ProCards Indianapolis (set)	6.00	2.50	1.00
1991 ProCards Tomorrow's Heroes #254	1.25	0.50	0.20
1992 Bowman #194	1.00	0.40	0.15
1992 Bowman Gold #194	2.50	1.15	0.50
1992 Fleer Update #97	1.00	0.40	0.15
1993 Score Select Stars #18	3.00	1.25	0.50
1993 Topps Gold Inserts #256	0.50	0.20	0.08

Tim Costo

When Tim Costo was drafted in the first round of the 1990 draft by the Cleveland Indians, he was compared to Cal Ripken Jr. Those comparisons aren't being made much anymore, both because Costo doesn't play shortstop these days — first base is his position now — and because he's yet to make it to the major leagues for more than a handful of games. Costo does have power, and the potential to be a very productive hitter, but he hasn't come close to turning that potential into anything more. Because of that, he has to remain a speculative buy.

	NM	EX	VG
1990 Classic Draft Pick #8	0.50	0.20	0.08
1990 Sportsprint Kinston (late-issue set)	13.00	6.25	0.30
1991 Bowman #79	0.25	0.10	0.04
1991 Classic-Best Minor-League #431	0.50	0.20	0.08
1991 Gold Leaf Rookies #18	2.25	1.00	0.45
1991 ProCards Tomorrow's Heroes #51	0.45	0.20	0.08
1991 Score #680	0.15	0.05	0.01
1991 Topps #103	0.15	0.05	0.01
1991 Upper Deck #62	0.40	0.15	0.05
1992 Bowman Gold #489	1.25	0.55	0.25
1992 Classic-Best #70	0.20	0.08	0.03
1992 Donruss The Rookies #29	0.15	0.05	0.01
1993 Donruss #270	0.15	0.05	0.01
1993 Upper Deck #11	0.15	0.05	0.01

Midre Cummings

Midre Cummings is the key prospect the Pirates have to show from the John Smiley-to-the-Twins deal. He's already won one minor-league batting title and may win another by the time he makes it to the Pirates in late 1994 or '95. He has a quick bat and quicker feet, not a lot of power yet, but that will come. His few cards are relatively inexpensive and shouldn't be going up in the next year or so. Considering the direction the Pirates are headed in, Cummings' cards might be a very good buy.

	NM	EX	VG
1991 Classic-Best #318	0.40	0.15	0.05
1991 Classic-Best Kenosha Twins (set)	7.00	3.00	1.25
1991 ProCards Kenosha Twins (set)	6.00	2.50	1.00
1991 ProCards Tomorrow's Heroes #98	0.35	0.15	0.05
1992 Classic Best Minor #240	0.15	0.05	0.01
1992 Salem Buccaneers (set)	5.00	2.00	0.80
1992 Upper Deck Minor League #277	0.20	0.08	0.04
1992 Upper Deck Minor League POY #18	3.00	125.00	0.50
1993 Fleer #90	0.25	0.10	0.04

Chad Curtis

Chad Curtis is the perfect complement to Tim Salmon in the Angels outfield in that he can get on base and can run. Probably the best way to describe him is as a Brett Butler type but with a little more sock. Heady outfielders with good speed and little power don't do it for the card-buying community, so his cards don't have much potential.

	NM	EX	VG
1990 Grand Slam Quad City Angels (set)	7.50	3.25	1.50
1991 ProCards Edmonton Trappers (set)	7.00	2.50	1.00
1992 Bowman Gold #627	2.50	1.10	0.50

Darren Daulton

Talk about your late bloomers! Daulton bounced around from minors to majors, barely hitting his weight, until 1990, when he (a) started lifting weights seriously (b) signed an immense contract and (c) married one of the Hooters girls. In no time Daulton wound up in the minors again. But he was hurt and on rehab, and when he got off rehab in 1992 he went out and won himself an RBI title. Daulton is a huge catcher who can hit. He's a quality player on a Phillies league championship team but he's not Lenny Dykstra. He's not Cooperstown material, and there's no reason for his cards to be priced where they are, but he is better now than ever, and that's got to count for something. Just don't drop six bucks for his '85 Fleer Update card if you can avoid it.

	NM	EX	VG
1984 Cramer Portland Beavers (set)	11.00	5.00	2.25
1985 Fleer Update #33	6.00	2.75	1.25
1986 Donruss #477	2.25	1.00	0.40
1986 Fleer #438	2.50	1.10	0.50
1986 Tastykake Phillies #10	0.15	0.05	0.01
1986 Topps #264	1.50	0.60	0.20
1986 Topps Tiffany #264	6.50	2.50	1.00
1987 Donruss #262	0.35	0.25	0.05
1987 Fleer #172	1.00	0.40	0.15
1987 Fleer Tin Glossy #172	1.40	0.60	0.25
1987 Topps Tiffany #636	0.75	0.30	0.10
1988 Topps Tiffany #468	0.30	0.10	0.04
1989 Tastykake Phillies #10	0.15	0.05	0.01
1990 Bowman Tiffany #158	0.35	0.15	0.05
1990 Leaf #369	0.50	0.20	0.08
1991 Bowman Tiffany #507	0.25	0.10	0.04
1991 Donruss Elite #33	45.00	21.00	10.00
1991 Topps #4	0.40	0.15	0.05
1992 Bowman Gold #440	0.50	0.20	0.08
1992 Leaf Gold Inserts #335	0.40	0.15	0.05
1992 Leaf Studio Heritage #13	0.75	0.25	0.10
1992 Topps Gold Inserts #244	0.75	0.25	0.10
1993 Donruss MVPs #11	0.75	0.25	0.10

1993 Donruss Diamond Kings #17 .... 1.50	0.65	0.25
1993 Fleer NL All-Stars #9 .... 1.00	0.45	0.20
1993 Score #5 .... 3.00	1.25	0.50
1993 Topps Black Gold Inserts #3 .... 3.00	1.25	0.50
1993 Upper Deck Iooss Collection #17 .... 1.50	0.65	0.25

Glenn Davis

Once a feared power hitter with the Astros, injuries and a squirrelly attitude
have taken most of Davis' game. Now he's just another blocky first baseman
who can occasionally poke out a long ball. Needless to say, most of the
momentum that had built up in his cards has long since dissipated. Will it ever
return? Don't bet on it.

	NM	EX	VG
1984 Cramer Tuscon (set) 15.00	6.50	2.50
1987 Donruss Opening Day #16 .... 0.15	0.05	0.01
1987 Fleer Baseball Game Winners #12 .... 0.15	0.05	0.01
1987 Fleer Star Stickers #31 .... 0.20	0.08	0.03
1987 Mother's Cookies Astros #10 .... 1.00	0.40	0.15
1988 Fleer Baseball's Best #11 .... 0.12	0.05	0.01
1988 Fleer Star Stickers #86 .... 0.20	0.08	0.03
1988 Kenner Starting Lineup 13.00	6.00	2.50
1989 Score Superstar #46 .... 0.10	0.04	0.01
1990 Topps Big #122 .... 0.15	0.05	0.01

Andre Dawson

Despite a change of teams and leagues, the "Hawk" is still the Hawk, and is still
one of the toughest outs in the game. Dawson has managed to maintain a
package of speed, power, defense, and excellent batting average despite several knee injuries. Dawson's intensity rivals Dave Stewart's, but his endurance
is better. Andre and Willie Mays are the only major-leaguers to have more than
300 homers and 300 steals. If that isn't a ticket to Cooperstown, nothing is.
Dawson's rookie card is priced in with a pack of fairly certain Hall of Famers:
Yount, Brett and Winfield have more expensive cards, Molitor and Morris have
cheaper. His card is priced about the same as Eddie Murray's, and undervalued,
too.

	NM	EX	VG
1977 Redpath Sugar #10 .... 10.00	4.75	2.25
1977 Topps #473 .... 75.00	36.50	17.50
1978 Topps #72 .... 20.00	9.50	4.50
1979 Topps #348 .... 14.00	6.75	3.25

1980 Topps #235	10.00	4.75	2.25
1981 Donruss #212	2.00	0.85	0.40
1981 Fleer #145	2.00	0.85	0.40
1981 Topps #125	3.50	1.75	0.85
1982 Donruss #88	1.75	0.85	0.40
1982 Fleer #187	1.75	0.85	0.40
1982 Squirt #17	0.35	0.15	0.05
1982 Topps #540	3.00	1.45	0.70
1982 Zeller's #4	1.00	0.45	0.20
1983 Donruss #518	1.50	0.70	0.30
1983 Fleer #280	1.50	0.70	0.30
1983 Topps #680	2.25	1.10	0.50
1984 Donruss #97	6.00	2.75	1.25
1984 Fleer #273	3.25	1.55	0.75
1984 Milton Bradley	0.35	0.15	0.05
1984 Nestle #200	4.50	2.25	1.10
1984 Stuart #11	2.00	0.90	0.35
1984 Topps #200	1.25	0.60	0.25
1984 Topps Tiffany #200	10.50	5.00	2.25
1985 Donruss #421	1.75	0.85	0.40
1985 Fleer #394	1.75	0.75	0.35
1985 Topps #420	1.00	0.45	0.20
1986 Donruss #87	1.25	0.55	0.25
1986 Fleer #246	1.00	0.45	0.20
1986 Topps #760	0.40	0.15	0.05
1987 Classic #124	0.45	0.20	0.08
1988 Score #4	0.15	0.06	0.01
1988 Score Glossy #4	1.25	0.55	0.25
1989 Upper Deck #205	0.75	0.30	0.10
1990 Leaf #177	1.00	0.45	0.20
1991 Donruss Elite #4	75.00	36.50	18.00
1991 O-Pee-Chee Premier #31	0.25	0.10	0.04
1991 Topps Stadium Club #310	1.00	0.45	0.20
1992 Donruss #422	0.08	0.03	0.01
1992 Topps Gold #460	2.00	0.85	0.40

Carlos Delgado

Some scouts are calling Delgado the best-hitting catcher to come along since Roy Campanella, which probably isn't true. While Delgado is an amazing hitter (.324-30-100 in the Florida State League in a year when everyone else in that league struggled to crack the .300 mark), he's no Campy. And about the best thing you can say about his catching is that it compares favorably to Hector

Villanueva's. But a super stick can take you places, especially in the A.L., and right now it appears that Delgado's stick is going to take him to Toronto sometime in 1994.

	NM	EX	VG
1992 Bowman #127	2.75	1.25	0.55
1992 Classic-Best #90	1.25	0.55	0.20
1992 Upper Deck Minor League #264	0.75	0.30	0.12
1992 Upper Deck Minor League #4	1.25	0.55	0.12
1992 Upper Deck Minor League #53	0.75	0.30	0.12

Delino DeShields

A little-known fact about Delino DeShields: He was supposed to be Rollie Massamino's point guard at Villanova, but turned his back on a scholarship at the last minute to sign with the Expos. Okay, now here's a little-known baseball-card fact about Delino DeShields: His real rookie card is in the '88 O-Pee-Chee set. It's worth searching out, because DeShields is a real talent. Speed, power, fielding ability — he's got it all. And he's going to get better. DeShields' cards are undervalued, starting with his rookie card and moving up. They're worth having; their values are going to increase.

	NM	EX	VG
1988 O-Pee-Chee #88	9.50	4.50	2.00
1988 Team Rockford Expos (set)	23.00	11.00	5.00
1989 Best Jacksonville (set)	17.00	8.00	3.50
1990 Bowman #119	0.75	0.30	0.12
1990 Bowman Tiffany #119	4.50	2.00	0.85
1990 Classic III #95	0.30	0.12	0.04
1990 Donruss Rookies #6	0.50	0.20	0.08
1990 Donruss Learning Series #47	1.00	0.45	0.20
1990 Fleer Update #27	0.50	0.20	0.08
1990 Score #645	0.75	0.30	0.12
1990 Topps #224	0.55	0.20	0.08
1990 Topps Big #231	0.50	0.20	0.08
1990 Upper Deck #746	2.00	0.80	0.30
1991 Bowman Tiffany #445	0.50	0.20	0.08
1991 Fleer Ultra #200	0.40	0.15	0.05
1991 Kenner Starting Lineup	15.00	4.50	2.00
1991 Leaf #139	0.60	0.25	0.10
1991 O-Pee-Chee #34	0.25	0.10	0.04
1991 Topps #194	1.75	0.75	0.30
1991 Topps Desert Storm #545	40.00	17.50	8.00
1991 Upper Deck #364	0.25	0.10	0.04
1992 Bowman #47	0.25	0.10	0.04

1992 Fleer Ultra #220	0.50	0.20	0.08
1992 Leaf #138	0.25	0.10	0.04
1992 Leaf Gold Inserts #138	0.75	0.30	0.12
1992 O-Pee-Chee Premier #163	0.30	0.12	0.05
1992 Score Pinnacle Team 2000 #22	0.60	0.25	0.10
1992 Topps Gold Inserts #515	2.00	0.80	0.25
1993 Fleer NL All-Stars #2	2.00	0.80	0.35
1993 Topps Gold Inserts #368	0.50	0.20	0.08
1993 Topps Black Gold Inserts #5	5.00	2.25	1.00
1993 Upper Deck Iooss Collection #10	2.50	1.00	0.40

Mike Devereaux

It took a while, but Mike Devereaux has at last lived up to expectations and blossomed into a top-flight major-league center fielder. He can go get the ball, run and hit, too — to all fields with a little power. He may not be a truly exceptional talent, the stuff that Hall of Famers are made of, but he is a very, very good baseball player. That counts for more on the field than it does in the cards, but that situation may not last for long. You should be able to make money on Mike Devereaux cards by buying cheap and selling in the short term.

	NM	EX	VG
1987 Team San Antonio (set)	7.50	3.50	1.50
1988 CMC Albuquerque (set)	8.50	3.75	1.75
1988 Score Glossy #637	2.50	1.00	0.40
1989 Classic Update #181	0.08	0.03	0.01
1990 Bowman Tiffany #260	0.30	0.12	0.05
1990 Score Rising Star #90	0.08	0.03	0.01
1990 Topps Big #178	0.08	0.03	0.01
1990 Toys 'R' Us Rookies #8	0.08	0.03	0.01

Doug Drabek

Former Cy Young Award winner Doug Drabek has taken his act to Houston, where fly balls go to die. With any luck at all Drabek could win 20 a couple more times, which would give some of his cards a needed boost. Right now they're priced fairly for the cards of a control pitcher who gets a lot of starts and wins more than he loses. They need an extra push from Drabek to get beyond that level. Drabek in Houston is capable of giving his cards that push. Whether he does it or not is another matter entirely.

	NM	EX	VG
1985 TCMA Albany-Colonie (set)	70.00	32.50	15.00
1986 Donruss Rookies #31	2.00	0.80	0.25

1986 Fleer Update #36	1.50	0.65	0.25
1987 Donruss #251	1.00	0.40	0.15
1987 Fleer #96	2.25	1.00	0.40
1987 Fleer Glossy Tin #96	2.50	1.00	0.40
1987 Topps #283	0.40	0.15	0.05
1988 Fleer Glossy Tin #327	0.65	0.25	0.15
1989 Bowman Tiffany #416	0.35	0.15	0.05
1989 Donruss Baseball's Best #17	0.05	0.02	0.01
1989 Fleer Glossy Tin #206	0.30	0.10	0.04
1989 Kenner Starting Lineup	8.00	3.50	1.50
1990 Leaf #296	0.40	0.15	0.05
1990 Topps Big #185	0.12	0.05	0.01
1991 Classic #82	0.10	0.04	0.01
1991 Donruss Elite #5	40.00	17.50	8.00
1991 Topps #202	0.50	0.20	0.08
1991 Topps Desert Storm #405	15.00	6.50	2.50
1991 Topps Desert Storm #685	15.00	6.50	2.50
1992 Leaf Gold Inserts #11	0.40	0.15	0.05
1992 Topps Gold Inserts #440	0.75	0.30	0.12
1993 Score Select Aces #16	3.00	1.25	0.50

Kirk Dressendorfer

It's hard to think of Kirk Dressendorfer and not think of Mike Lloynd. Lloynd was a big college winner who had trouble winning with his relatively slow stuff in the majors. Dressendorfer has better stuff but so far has produced about the same results. Injuries have also hampered Dressendorfer, part of the Zancan-peterpoppeldorfer quartet of pitchers — David Zancanaro, Don Peters, Todd Van Poppel, and Dressendorfer — drafted No. 1 by the A's in 1990 (and pictured on a Classic card that same year). Kirk can do a credible job if he's healthy. Now, will he ever get healthy?

	NM	EX	VG
1990 Best Southern Oregon (set)	20.00	8.50	3.50
1990 ProCards A and A Minor-League Stars #163	0.75	0.30	0.12
1990 ProCards Southern Oregon (set)	15.00	6.50	2.50
1991 Classic #77	1.45	0.60	0.20

Shawon Dunston

When the Cubs drafted Shawon Dunston they thought he was the shortstop equivalent of Darryl Strawberry — and he has been, right down to the irregular performance and the back problems. There was a time when it looked as though Dunston was going to make it big — several times, actually — but those times always came and went, and Dunston always settled back to a disappointing sort of modest productivity. Now, coming off of back surgery, Dunston will have to struggle to even make it back to that level. It's unfortunate — but it's baseball. His cards are fairly cheap, and rightly so.

	NM	EX	VG
1983 TCMA Quad Cities (set)	90.00	42.50	20.00
1985 Donruss #39	1.25	0.50	0.20
1985 Topps Tiffany #280	5.00	2.25	1.00
1986 Donruss #311	0.75	0.30	0.12
1986 Fleer #366	0.60	0.25	0.10
1986 Sportflics #155	0.50	0.20	0.08
1988 Donruss Cubs Team Book #146	0.35	0.15	0.05
1988 Kenner Starting Lineup	20.00	9.50	4.00
1988 Leaf #70	0.06	0.01	0.01
1988 Topps Big #225	0.08	0.03	0.01
1989 Marathon Cubs #12	0.50	0.20	0.08
1989 Topps Big #233	0.05	0.01	0.01
1990 Marathon Cubs #12	0.50	0.20	0.08
1990 Topps Big #62	0.10	0.04	0.01
1991 Marathon Cubs #12	0.35	0.15	0.05
1992 Topps Gold Inserts #370	0.75	0.30	0.12

Leo Durocher

Famous, firey, but is he Hall of Fame bound? That's the question and your feelings on it will determine whether you are in or out at today's prices.

	NM	EX	VG
1933 Goudey #147	250.00	100.00	35.00
1934 Batter-Up #156	325.00	125.00	50.00
1934 Goudey #7	225.00	85.00	25.00
1939 Play Ball #6	115.00	40.00	20.00
1941 Double Play #142	70.00	25.00	10.00
1950 Bowman #220	45.00	17.50	7.50
1951 Bowman #233	55.00	20.00	8.50
1952 Bowman #146	37.50	15.00	6.00
1952 Topps #315	265.00	100.00	35.00
1953 Bowman #55	65.00	25.00	10.00
1967 Topps #481	15.00	6.50	2.50
1968 Topps #321	3.00	1.00	0.25
1969 Topps #147	2.75	0.80	0.20

1970 Topps #291	2.00	0.85	0.15
1971 Topps #609	4.00	1.00	0.25
1972 Topps #576	1.50	0.50	0.20
1973 Topps #624	1.50	0.65	0.20

Lenny Dykstra

One of the game's better contact hitters but one who is his own worst enemy. Off the field problems have hurt his career to date, but maybe his solid 1993 season and super postseason will turn things around. His cards are inexpensive and only a few command any premium at all. Cards not listed are all priced as commons.

	NM	EX	VG
1986 Donruss #482	3.50	0.25	0.03
1984 Topps #53	1.50	0.10	0.02
1986 Topps #78	2.50	0.20	0.02

Dennis Eckersley

If Dennis Eckersley isn't a future Hall of Famer, he's darn close. And if he's not a Hall of Famer, it's because the Hall of Fame voters don't consider almost 200 wins and 200 saves grounds for enshrinement. And if they don't, shame on them. No one's ever had 200 wins and 200 saves before, and with the way relief pitchers accumulate saves but not wins, no one is likely to approach the marks again. That makes Dennis Eckersley special, in other words, the special sort that demands special prices for his cards. He has been the dominant relief pitcher in baseball for five consecutive years. He has been dominant in the extreme. While the end is probably near, there is no denying him his due or denying his cards their prices.

	NM	EX	VG
1976 O-Pee-Chee #98	2.50	1.10	0.45
1979 Kellogg's #9	1.50	0.65	0.20
1981 Topps Home Team Photos	0.50	0.20	0.08
1981 Topps Stickers #48	0.15	0.06	0.02
1982 Perma-Graphics Credit Card #1	1.00	0.45	0.15
1983 Topps Stickers #34	0.12	0.04	0.01
1984 Topps Tiffany #745	1.50	0.65	0.25
1987 Topps Tiffany Traded #31T	0.30	0.12	0.04
1988 Mother's Cookies A's #10	0.40	0.15	0.05
1990 Fleer League Leaders #11	0.10	0.04	0.01
1990 Mother's Cookies A's #7	0.60	0.25	0.10
1990 Topps Glossy All-Star (60) #53	0.20	0.08	0.03
1991 Score Superstar #73	0.15	0.06	0.02

Cal Eldred

Cal Eldred burst on the scene in 1992 with a sparkling second half of the season, going 11-2 and very nearly leading the Brewers to the A.L. East title. Back in the real world, Eldred is a fairly hard-throwing Iowa farm boy who mixes his pitches well and isn't afraid to come inside. Right now his cards are a little on the expensive side, but don't worry; they'll be coming down to earth right along with Cal.

	NM	EX	VG
1990 Bowman Glossy #387	3.50	1.50	0.70
1990 Score #669	1.60	0.75	0.30
1991 Bowman #56	0.25	0.12	0.05
1991 ProCards Tomorrow's Heroes #81	1.75	0.80	0.35
1992 Bowman #299	1.75	0.80	0.35
1992 Donruss #718	0.40	0.17	0.07
1992 Fleer Ultra #380	1.75	0.80	0.35
1992 Pinnacle #249	0.80	0.35	0.15
1992 Pinnacle Team 2000 #36	1.15	0.55	0.25
1992 Score Impact Player #9	0.75	0.35	0.15
1992 Stadium Club #327	0.50	0.65	0.30
1992 Topps Gold #433	0.75	0.30	0.10
1992 Upper Deck #477	0.45	0.20	0.08
1993 Score Select #296	0.35	0.15	0.06
1993 Upper Deck #375	0.30	0.12	0.05

Scott Erickson

As a sinker-slider pitcher who has the unenviable task of pitching half of his games in a hitter's paradise, Scott Erickson doesn't appear to meet the requirements for being one of the game's great pitchers. He is a pretty good pitcher, though, and he has the distinct advantage of having the Twins hitting for him. Erickson has never quite recovered from arm problems that struck him halfway through his great 1991 season, though he's arguably a better pitcher now than he was then. He's not nearly as good a card buy, however.

	NM	EX	VG
1990 Best Minor-League #106	10.00	4.50	2.00
1990 Star Co. Orlando #5	7.50	3.25	1.50
1990 Topps Tiffany Traded #29	3.50	1.25	0.50
1990 Topps Traded #29	0.75	0.30	0.12
1991 Bowman #335	0.20	0.08	0.03
1991 Donruss #767	0.20	0.08	0.03
1991 Fleer #608	0.30	0.12	0.05

	NM	EX	VG
1991 Leaf #527	1.00	0.45	0.20
1991 Score #812	0.20	0.08	0.03
1991 Studio #83	0.75	0.30	0.12
1991 Topps #234	0.15	0.05	0.01
1991 Upper Deck #522	0.25	0.10	0.04
1992 Donruss Diamond Kings #21	1.50	0.55	0.20
1992 Fleer All-Star #10	1.25	0.50	0.20
1992 Fleer Ultra #90	0.35	0.12	0.05
1992 Pinnacle Team 2000 #60	0.25	0.10	0.04
1992 Score Impact Player #13	0.20	0.08	0.03
1992 Topps Kids #110	0.15	0.04	0.01
1992 Topps Stadium Club #560	0.50	0.20	0.08
1993 Score Select #253	0.15	0.04	0.01
1993 Topps Gold #90	0.50	0.20	0.08

Alex Fernandez

It hasn't exactly gone as planned for Alex Fernandez since being drafted No. 1 by the White Sox in 1990. His climb to the majors was rapid. By the end of 1990 Fernandez was pitching in Chicago. But by 1992 Fernandez was back in the minors trying to get his stuff back together. Fernandez has more poise than raw speed. He has the stuff to be a consistent 15-to-17-game winner, but not a 20-game winner. His cards are priced on the low end of that scale, but it's not a scale where prices change quickly or hugely. Fernandez's cards will probably be worth more sooner rather than later, but the change just isn't likely to be significant.

	NM	EX	VG
1990 Best Minor League Baseball #321	1.25	0.50	0.20
1990 Classic Draft Picks #4	0.75	0.30	0.12
1990 Fleer Update #84	0.30	0.12	0.05
1990 Topps Major League Debut #48	0.30	0.12	0.05
1991 Classic Series II #7	0.15	0.05	0.01
1991 Donruss #31	0.70	0.30	0.12
1991 Donruss #59	0.20	0.08	0.03
1991 Fleer #117	0.15	0.05	0.01
1991 Fleer Ultra Update #14	0.40	0.15	0.05
1991 Leaf #296	0.25	0.10	0.04
1991 O-Pee-Chee #42	0.20	0.08	0.03
1991 Score #382	0.15	0.05	0.01
1991 Score Rising Star #66	0.40	0.15	0.05
1991 Topps #147	0.75	0.30	0.12
1991 Topps #278	0.15	0.05	0.01
1991 Upper Deck #645	0.20	0.08	0.03

1992 Donruss #191	0.15	0.05	0.01
1992 Fleer #78	0.15	0.05	0.01
1992 Fleer Ultra #335	0.25	0.10	0.04
1992 Leaf #85	0.30	0.08	0.03
1992 Leaf Gold Inserts #85	0.75	0.30	0.12
1992 Score Pinnacle #30	0.15	0.05	0.01
1992 Topps #467	0.25	0.10	0.04
1992 Topps Gold Inserts #755	2.00	0.80	0.30
1992 Upper Deck #551	0.15	0.05	0.01
1993 Topps Gold Inserts #41	0.25	0.10	0.04

Sid Fernandez

Sid Fernandez is all sorts of contradictions: a strikeout pitcher who doesn't throw that hard, a pitcher who strives constantly to take off weight but throws better when he's fat, and a New York Met who hasn't been shuttled off somewhere else, wasn't a big-money free-agent acquisition, and has basically filled the same role for the team since day one. Fernandez is another one of those stuff-heavy pitchers who doesn't win nearly as many games as he should, and likely never will. That does not mean good things for his cards, especially his overpriced '84 Donruss card, which fetches a 20-game-winner tariff. Sid's a good pitcher, and he pitches in New York, but nothing in his makeup suggests he'll move beyond his current level. A word of advice on El Sid: Leave him be.

	NM	EX	VG
1984 Donruss #44	4.00	1.50	0.65
1984 TCMA Tidewater Tides (set)	65.00	31.00	15.00
1985 Fleer #77	0.50	0.20	0.08
1985 Topps #649	0.60	0.25	0.12
1985 Topps Tiffany #649	3.00	1.25	0.50
1987 Leaf #93	0.08	0.03	0.01
1988 Fleer Glossy Tin #134	0.25	0.10	0.04
1988 Fleer Star Stickers #101	0.10	0.04	0.01
1988 Panini Stickers #336	0.06	0.01	0.01
1988 Score Glossy #615	0.65	0.25	0.10
1989 Topps Big #276	0.05	0.01	0.01
1992 Topps #382	0.75	0.30	0.12

Tony Fernandez

Tony Fernandez may have been shuttled about the last couple of seasons, and gotten lost in the shuttling, but he remains one of baseball's top shortstops, able to hit .300 with power, steal bases, and make all the plays from deep in the hole. You just often wish, as Rosalind Russell said of Cary Grant in the movie *His Girl Friday*, that he wasn't such a stinker. Oh, well, that's the sort of thing veterans' committees have a habit of overlooking. His disastrous half season with the Met's was resurrected by finishing off 93 with the champion Blue Jays. In the meantime, Fernandez's cards are cheap enough, and they stand good chance of appreciating over the very long term.

	NM	EX	VG
1984 Donruss #32	4.50	2.10	1.00
1984 Fleer #152	3.25	1.50	0.65
1985 Donruss #390	0.75	0.30	0.12
1985 Fleer #103	0.50	0.20	0.08
1985 Topps #48	0.75	0.30	0.12
1987 Fleer All-Stars #3	0.50	0.20	0.08
1991 Topps #515	0.25	0.10	0.04
1992 Leaf Gold Inserts #187	0.40	0.15	0.05
1992 Topps Gold Inserts #60	0.75	0.25	0.10

Cecil Fielder

Cecil Fielder couldn't cut it in a platoon situation with Fred McGriff, so he went off gladly to Japan. He learned to hit the breaking ball and came back a behemoth. No player has hit more homers in the last three seasons than Cecil, and his three consecutive RBI titles are the first trifecta of that sort since the days of Ruth and Gehrig. Fielder's pre-Japan cards have leaped up smartly in value, but three seasons do not a career make. Besides, there's that nasty downward trend to his numbers that ought to give you pause. If none of that bothers you and you still crave unrefined power, Cecil remains your guy. And he should for another couple of seasons.

	NM	EX	VG
1986 Blue Jays Police #23	2.25	1.00	0.40
1986 Blue Jays Police #23	2.25	1.00	0.40
1986 O-Pee-Chee #386	6.50	2.50	1.00
1986 Topps Tiffany #386	28.00	12.50	5.50
1987 Blue Jays Police #23	1.50	0.65	0.25
1987 Blue Jays Police #23	1.50	0.65	0.25
1987 O-Pee-Chee #178	1.50	0.65	0.25
1987 Topps Tiffany #618	2.50	1.00	0.45
1987 Topps Tiffany #618	2.50	1.00	0.45
1988 Blue Jays Police #23	1.00	0.40	0.15
1988 O-Pee-Chee #21	0.65	0.25	0.10
1988 Score Glossy #399	5.00	2.25	1.00
1988 Score Glossy #399	5.00	2.25	1.00
1989 Calbee Chips #107	65.00	30.00	12.50

	NM	EX	VG
1989 Calbee Chips #107 .... 65.00	30.00	12.50
1989 Calbee Chips #124 .... 65.00	30.00	12.50
1989 Calbee Chips #206 .... 65.00	30.00	12.50
1989 Calbee Chips #206 .... 65.00	30.00	12.50
1989 Calbee Chips #263 .... 60.00	27.50	13.00
1989 Calbee Chips #320 .... 85.00	40.00	17.50
1989 Calbee Chips #320 .... 85.00	40.00	17.50
1989 Calbee Chips #349 .... 85.00	40.00	17.50
1989 Lotte Gum #117 .... 85.00	40.00	17.50
1989 Lotte Gum #117 .... 85.00	40.00	17.50
1989 Takara Game 50.00	22.50	10.00
1990 Kroger/Coke Tigers 1.00	0.40	0.15
1990 Kroger/Coke Tigers 1.00	0.40	0.15
1990 Star Co. Nova (set of 9) 60.00	25.00	10.50
1991 Denny's Grand Slam Hologram #2 .... 4.00	1.75	0.75
1991 Denny's Grand Slam Hologram #2 .... 4.00	1.75	0.75
1991 Leaf preview #18 .... 5.00	2.25	1.00
1991 Topps Superstar Standups #13 .... 0.50	0.20	0.08
1991 Topps Superstar Standups #13 .... 0.50	0.20	0.08

Chuck Finley

Chuck Finley is a pretty good left-hander who used to be a real good left-hander, and if that sounds like damning with faint praise, well, so be it. Finley doesn't throw as hard as he used to or as well as he used to, and as a result his cards have been on a slight downward tack, which should probably continue for a little while before his cards level off.

	NM	EX	VG
1987 Fleer Glossy Tin #79 .... 0.75	0.35	0.15
1987 Topps Tiffany #446 .... 0.65	0.25	0.10
1988 Fleer Glossy Tin #489 .... 0.30	0.12	0.05
1990 Donruss A.L. Best #103 .... 0.10	0.04	0.01
1991 Classic #95 .... 0.10	0.04	0.01

Carlton Fisk

Fisk is without a doubt the best catcher of his time, a combination of power and dogged determination that could singlehandedly change the course of a game. Fisk is close to every record for catchers, including a number of all-time offensive records. His cards have not kept pace with his accomplishments. He has finally hung up the tools of ignorance, so Fisk and his cards will become more sought-after by collectors. Fisk's cards are a buy in the current market.

	NM	EX	VG
1972 Topps #79	145.00	70.00	32.50
1973 Kellogg's #23	1.50	0.70	0.30
1973 Topps #193	47.50	22.50	11.00
1974 Topps #105	22.50	11.00	5.00
1975 Topps #80	18.50	9.00	4.25
1975 Topps Mini #80	25.00	12.50	6.00
1976 Topps #365	12.00	5.75	2.75
1977 Topps #640	6.25	3.00	1.40
1978 Topps #270	5.00	2.50	1.10
1979 Topps #680	4.75	2.25	1.00
1980 Topps #40	4.75	2.25	1.00
1981 Donruss #350	2.00	1.00	0.45
1981 Fleer #224	2.00	1.00	0.45
1981 Topps #480	3.25	1.50	0.70
1981 Topps Stickers #46	0.15	0.07	0.01
1981 Topps Traded #762	7.50	3.60	1.50
1982 Donruss #495	1.75	0.75	0.35
1982 Fleer #343	1.75	0.75	0.35
1982 Topps #110	2.00	0.90	0.40
1982 Topps (in action) #111	1.50	0.75	0.30
1983 Donruss #104	1.25	0.60	0.25
1983 Fleer #235	1.00	0.45	0.20
1983 Topps #20	2.00	0.90	0.40
1983 Topps All-Star Glossy (40) #17	0.40	0.15	0.05
1984 Donruss #302	3.25	1.50	0.70
1984 Fleer #58	2.50	1.15	0.55
1984 Topps #560	1.00	0.45	0.20
1984 Topps Super #15	0.35	0.15	0.05
1984 Topps/Nestle #560	3.50	1.60	0.75
1985 Leaf-Donruss #155	0.15	0.07	0.01
1985 Topps Tiffany #770	4.50	2.00	0.75
1986 Donruss All-Stars #17	0.20	0.10	0.04
1986 Donruss Pop-Ups	0.35	0.15	0.05
1988 Coca-Cola White Sox	0.65	0.30	0.12
1989 Topps Big Baseball #24	0.10	0.05	0.01
1989 Upper Deck #609	0.70	0.30	0.12
1990 Leaf #384	0.30	0.12	0.05
1991 Topps Stadium Club #180	1.00	0.45	0.20
1992 Fleer Team Leaders #4	1.25	0.50	0.20

Dave Fleming

The top rookie pitcher of 1992, Dave Fleming is a carbon copy of Jimmy Key: left-hander, doesn't throw very hard. Sad to say, the prognosis on these guys isn't very good. Check out Bill James if you don't believe us. Fleming's cards are riding that initial wave of speculation and are very likely overpriced. Nothing personal, Dave; we really like your smarts out there on the mound. That's just the way it is in the card business.

	NM	EX	VG
1990 Best Minor League #57	2.25	1.00	0.45
1991 Classic-Best Minor League #284	1.50	0.65	0.25
1991 Line Drive AA #336	1.00	0.40	0.15
1991 ProCards Jacksonville (set)	9.00	4.25	2.00

Cliff Floyd

Cliff is more than just one more of the Expos' top rookie prospects. He is the top rookie prospect, a rare combination of size, power, and speed whose center-field play draws comparisons to Willie Mays and whose demeanor at the plate reminds people of Willie McCovey. Floyd was drafted out of high school, so his path to the majors is a little longer. Still, he should be playing for Montreal sometime in 1994 — and from then on, watch his cards jump in value. A solid buy.

	NM	EX	VG
1991 Classic Draft Picks #11	1.25	0.60	0.25
1992 Bowman #678	2.00	0.90	0.40
1992 Classic-Best Albany Polecats (set)	7.50	3.50	1.75
1992 Classic-Best Foil #380	1.00	0.45	0.20
1992 Fleer Excel #58	1.00	0.45	0.20
1992 Score #801	0.55	0.25	0.10
1992 Topps Stadium Club Dome #51	2.25	1.00	0.45

Julio Franco

The reports of Julio Franco's demise were greatly exaggerated. Franco is a pure hitter in search of a position. As a second baseman he makes a fine designated hitter, and about the same thing can be said of his play at short and in the outfield. But not to worry — Franco is a fine hitter, with a batting title under his belt. Bad knees have robbed him of most of his speed, but it's conceivable that if he were to stay healthy and play another five seasons — until he's 39 — he could wind up with 2,400 hits, 100 homers, 300 steals, and a batting average above .300. Not quite Hall of Fame numbers, but nothing to be ashamed of. His

cards are a little undervalued considering his accomplishments, but not undervalued considering his eventual disposition.

	NM	EX	VG
1981 TCMA Reading (set)	200.00	95.00	42.50
1982 TCMA Oklahoma City (set)	60.00	27.50	12.50
1983 Wheaties Indians	1.75	0.75	0.35
1984 Nestle #48	1.50	0.65	0.25
1984 Topps Tiffany #48	3.00	1.25	0.50
1984 Wheaties Indians #14	1.50	0.50	0.20
1985 Topps Stickers #245	0.10	0.04	0.01
1985 Topps Tiffany #237	2.00	0.80	0.35
1986 Fleer Baseball's Best #9	0.10	0.04	0.01
1986 Kay Bee #14	0.10	0.04	0.01
1986 Topps Stickers #211	0.10	0.04	0.01
1986 Topps Tiffany #391	1.25	0.50	0.20
1987 Donruss Opening Day #111	0.10	0.04	0.01
1987 Fleer Star Stickers #423	0.12	0.05	0.01
1987 Topps Stickers #210	0.10	0.04	0.01
1988 Fleer Baseball All-Stars #11	0.10	0.04	0.01
1988 Fleer Glossy Tin #609	0.50	0.20	0.08
1988 Fleer Star Stickers #19	0.12	0.05	0.01
1988 Score Glossy #60	0.65	0.25	0.10
1988 Topps Big Baseball #135	0.10	0.04	0.01
1989 Fleer Glossy Tin #404	0.45	0.20	0.08
1989 Mother's Cookies Rangers #3	0.70	0.30	0.12
1990 Topps All-Star Glossy (60) #35	0.15	0.05	0.01
1990 Topps Big #205	0.15	0.05	0.01

Travis Fryman

It's hard to call Travis Fryman the best young hitter on that team of slow-pitch
softball players called the Detroit Tigers, but he's pretty close. A shortstop or
third baseman with Cal Ripken Jr.'s power, Fryman is no longer the bargain he
was a year and a half ago, but he's still a solid card buy with just a little bit of
headroom left for appreciation. As usual, his first Bowman card is a good buy
and shouldn't be overlooked.

	NM	EX	VG
1988 ProCards Fayetteville (set)	25.00	11.50	5.00
1989 ProCards London (set)	15.00	5.50	2.25
1990 Bowman Tiffany #360	4.50	2.00	0.80
1990 Topps Major League Debut #49	1.00	0.40	0.15
1991 Classic #40	0.50	0.20	0.08

1991 Score Rising Star #68	0.50	0.20	0.08
1991 Topps Desert Storm #128	80.00	35.00	15.00
1991 Toys 'R' Us Rookies #8	0.50	0.20	0.08
1992 Bowman Gold #37	0.75	0.35	0.10

Charles "Chick" Gandil

Chick Gandil was not really a star. You could say that he was ethically chal-
lenged, or, more to the point, that he was the ringleader of the 1919 World
Series fix. That made him a baseball outcast and, you might add, infamous —
which translates into demand for his cards. There's no guarantee, though, that
people will continue to want the likes of Gandil in their collections.

	NM	EX	VG
1914 Cracker Jack #39	575.00	75.00	35.00
1915 Cracker Jack #39	175.00	65.00	30.00
E90-3 American Caramel	375.00	125.00	35.00
T206	165.00	50.00	25.00
T213 Type 2	125.00	40.00	20.00

Ron Gant

Ron Gant has known the bitter and the sweet of baseball. An out-of-nowhere
star as a second baseman in 1988, Gant fell all the way to Class-A ball the next
year before righting himself, heading to the outfield, and becoming one of
Atlanta's most consistently productive hitters. It doesn't seem likely that he'll
ever be a Hall of Famer, but he's a good, solid ballplayer firmly entrenched in
that second echelon of major-league stars. Card buyers haven't quite figured
that out yet, which is something of a problem.

	NM	EX	VG
1986 ProCards Durham Bulls (set)	55.00	26.50	12.00
1988 Donruss #654	2.50	1.10	0.50
1988 Donruss Rookies #47	3.25	1.50	0.65
1988 Fleer #538	6.25	3.00	1.35
1988 Fleer Glossy #538	15.00	7.00	3.00
1988 Score #647	2.00	0.85	0.40
1988 Topps Tiffany Traded #39	11.50	5.00	2.00
1988 Topps Traded #39	2.85	1.30	0.60
1989 Topps #296	0.45	0.20	0.08
1989 Topps American Baseball Glossy #29	0.30	0.12	0.04
1989 Toys 'R' Us Rookies #10	0.09	0.04	0.01
1989 Upper Deck #378	2.00	0.85	0.35
1990 Leaf #376	3.10	1.50	0.65

1990 Topps #567 .... 0.20	0.08	0.01
1990 Topps Tiffany #567 .... 1.00	0.45	0.20
1991 Leaf Studio #144 .... 0.30	0.12	0.05
1991 O-Pee-Chee Premier #49 .... 0.75	0.30	0.12
1991 Topps Stadium Club #454 .... 2.00	0.85	0.40
1992 Pinnacle #128 .... 0.25	0.10	0.04
1992 Pinnacle Slugfest #8 .... 1.10	0.50	0.20
1992 Topps Gold #25 .... 3.00	1.35	0.60
1992 Topps Gold All-Star #391 .... 2.00	0.85	0.35
1992 Upper Deck Home Run Heroes #7 .... 2.25	1.00	0.45

Steve Garvey

The golden image of Steve Garvey is not what it once was, but statistics don't change, and his chance for Cooperstown remains. His cards are currently quiet, but one phone call from Cooperstown could change all that.

	NM	EX	VG
1971 Topps #341 .... 90.00	30.00	10.00
1972 Topps #686 .... 75.00	25.00	7.50
1973 Topps #213 .... 14.00	5.00	1.50
1974 Topps #575 .... 11.00	3.50	1.00
1975 Topps #140 .... 7.50	2.00	0.75
1976 Topps #150 .... 5.75	1.25	0.35
1977 Topps #400 .... 4.50	1.00	0.25
1978 Topps #350 .... 3.75	0.85	0.20
1979 Topps #50 .... 1.50	0.35	0.10
1980 Topps #290 .... 1.75	0.85	0.20
1981 Topps #530 .... 1.50	0.35	0.10
1983 Topps Traded #37 .... 1.50	0.35	0.10
1984 Donruss #63 .... 1.25	0.25	0.50

Benji Gil

Once Andujar Cedeno, Jose Offerman, Wil Cordero, and Royce Clayton matriculate, if indeed they ever do, focus will shift to the Rangers' Benji Gil. Gil can do what those guys do, only not quite yet (though he did open the 1993 season as the Rangers' starting shortstop).

	NM	EX	VG
1992 Bowman Gold #339 .... 2.00	0.80	0.35
1992 Classic-Best Gastonia Rangers (set) 6.00	2.50	1.00

Bernard Gilkey

Baseball experts are talking about Bernard Gilkey as the next N.L. batting champ. Perhaps, but it would help if he would first win a starting job in the Cardinals' crowded outfield. Gilkey does have batting-title abilities, including the ability to beat out infield chops and slow rollers, and he's superb in the field, but his lack of power is a big drawback, both to his chances of landing and keeping a starting job and to his chances of turning his cards into something special. He's a solid ballplayer, though, and he just might make something of himself yet.

	NM	EX	VG
1988 Best Springfield (set)	18.50	9.00	4.25
1989 Grand Slam Arkansas (set)	10.00	4.50	2.00
1990 CMC Louisville (set)	25.00	11.50	5.50
1990 CMC Pre-Rookie #109	1.25	0.55	0.25

Tom Glavine

Arguably the game's best pitcher, Glavine may not have the best fastball in the world, but he more than makes up for it with his tenacity and competitiveness. Glavine is a former hockey goalie and an all-around athlete who has steadily improved his game to the point where he won the N.L. Cy Young Award in 1991. Glavine has a peculiar array of cards highlighted by a limited-edition series in the 1993 Fleer set. Glavine may be too far along in his career to qualify as a potential Hall of Famer, but he's a solid pitcher and a good short-term buy nonetheless.

	NM	EX	VG
1986 ProCards Greenville Braves (set)	32.00	15.00	7.00
1987 TCMA Richmond #5	15.00	6.50	3.00
1988 Donruss #644	3.50	1.50	0.60
1988 Fleer #539	9.50	4.50	1.75
1988 Fleer Glossy #539	18.50	9.00	4.25
1988 Score #638	3.25	1.50	0.65
1988 Score Glossy #638	20.00	9.50	4.50
1988 Topps #779	3.00	1.35	0.60
1988 Topps Tiffany #779	15.00	7.00	3.25
1989 Fleer #591	0.60	0.25	0.10
1989 Fleer Glossy #591	1.50	0.60	0.25
1989 Upper Deck #360	3.15	1.50	0.60
1990 Leaf #13	9.00	4.25	2.00
1991 Leaf #172	0.55	0.25	0.12
1991 Leaf Studio #145	0.50	0.20	0.08

1991 Topps Stadium Club #558 ...... 3.25	1.50	0.60
1992 Fleer All-Star #6 .... 2.25	1.00	0.50
1992 Fleer Ultra #162 .... 0.70	0.30	0.12
1992 Fleer Ultra All-Stars #20 .... 6.00	2.75	1.25
1992 Fleer Ultra Award Winners #7 ...... 6.50	3.00	1.25
1992 Kenner Starting Lineup 22.00	10.00	4.00
1993 Fleer Insert set #1–12 (first print) 20.00	8.50	4.00
1993 Fleer Insert set #1–12 (second print) 18.50	8.00	3.25
1993 Fleer N.L. All-Stars #11 .... 2.50	1.00	0.40
1993 Topps Black Gold #6 .... 5.50	2.50	1.00

Juan Gonzalez

Juan Gonzalez' nickname is "Igor," and opposing pitchers would tell you that's about right. Gonzalez is probably the best young pure power hitter in the game, a go-for-the-downs smasher who's not afraid to sacrifice batting average for a few more dingers. Batting .275 is about as good as it gets for Juan, yet considering his age and potential, 15 years of .275 batting averages and 40 homers a season is not out of the question — and certainly Hall of Fame stuff.

	NM	EX	VG
1987 ProCards #1764 .... 80.00	40.00	22.00
1988 Star Co. team #8 .... 25.00	12.00	8.00
1989 Topps Major League Debut #43 ...... 2.25	1.00	0.50
1990 Donruss (correct) #33 .... 2.00	0.90	0.40
1990 Donruss (Reversed negative) #33 ...... 6.25	3.00	1.25
1990 Fleer #297 .... 1.90	0.90	0.40
1990 Score #637 .... 2.75	1.30	0.60
1990 Upper Deck #72 .... 9.25	4.50	2.00
1991 Fleer Ultra Update #55 .... 9.50	4.50	2.00
1991 Leaf #119 .... 4.25	2.00	0.85
1991 Stadium Club #237 .... 14.50	7.25	3.50
1991 Studio #124 .... 3.25	1.50	0.75
1992 Pinnacle Team 2000 #26 .... 2.50	1.00	0.45
1992 Score Impact Players #27 .... 1.25	0.50	0.20
1992 Topps Gold #27 .... 4.00	1.75	0.75
1992 Topps Stadium Club #240 .... 2.75	1.25	0.55
1992 Upper Deck FanFest #9 .... 0.50	0.20	0.08
1992 Upper Deck Home Run Heroes #19 ...... 4.00	1.75	0.75
1992 Upper Deck Ted Williams' Best Hitters #14 .... 6.50	3.10	1.50
1993 Topps Gold #34 .... 2.25	1.10	0.50

Luis Gonzalez

Luis Gonzalez, when he first came into the league, had the look of a deer that had just leaped through the window of a suburban ranch home: a little terrified, a little dazed, a little beat-up. Gonzalez has since shaken that look, along with some of his initial promise, but he's not far enough along in his development to give up on, and his cards are cheap to boot. Cut him some slack, score a few of his cards, and wait for the fireworks.

	NM	EX	VG
1990 Best Columbus Mudcats (set)	12.00	5.00	2.00
1990 Best Minor-League Wax #95	4.00	1.75	0.75
1990 CMC Pre-Rookie #770	3.75	1.75	0.75
1990 ProCards Columbus (set)	12.00	5.00	2.00
1990 Star Co. Columbus Mudcats (set)	12.00	5.00	2.00
1991 Bowman Tiffany #550	1.25	0.50	0.20

Dwight Gooden

After an eye-popping start and a couple of seasons that went right off the Richter scale in terms of their impact on baseball and card collecting, Dwight Gooden's career has settled into a more or less mediocre groove, which is unfortunate. Even so, there are still some Dwight Gooden cards that are terrifically valuable, and there are a lot of Dwight Gooden cards, period. He may be the most popular figure on cards from 1985 to 1990, and if he's not, he doesn't trail Don Mattingly by much. Most of these cards are more moderately priced, but they're not undervalued or bargains. They're just the cards of a player who was going to be great but never got there.

	NM	EX	VG
1983 TCMA Lynchburg #10	85.00	40.00	17.50
1984 Fleer Update #43	80.00	37.50	15.50
1984 Topps Traded #42	20.00	9.00	3.75
1985 Donruss #190	6.50	3.00	1.25
1985 Donruss Action All-Stars #47	0.75	0.35	0.15
1985 Fleer #82	7.00	3.25	1.50
1985 Slurpee Coins #5	2.00	0.85	0.30
1985 Topps #620	3.00	1.25	0.50
1985 Topps All-Time Record Holders #16	0.60	0.25	0.10
1986 Donruss #75	1.50	0.65	0.25
1986 Fleer All-Stars #10	2.00	0.80	0.35
1986 Leaf #26	0.75	0.35	0.15
1986 O-Pee-Chee Box Panel #F	0.70	0.30	0.10
1986 Sportflics #100	2.00	0.85	0.40

1986 Sportflics #100 .... 1.25	0.40	0.15
1986 Topps #250 .... 0.75	0.30	0.12
1986 Topps 3-D #4 .... 1.00	0.45	0.20
1986 Topps Gallery of Champions Aluminum #4 .... 2.00	0.80	0.30
1986 Topps Gallery of Champions Bronze #4 .... 20.00	8.50	3.50
1986 Topps Gallery of Champions Silver #4 .... 100.00	45.00	20.00
1987 Classic #72 .... 1.25	0.55	0.25
1987 Fleer #9 .... 0.50	0.20	0.08
1987 Fleer Limited Edition #18 .... 0.40	0.15	0.05
1987 Kay Bee #13 .... 0.40	0.15	0.05
1987 Sportflics #100 .... 0.75	0.30	0.12
1987 Stickers #96 .... 0.30	0.10	0.04
1987 TCMA Tidewater #30 .... 8.00	3.50	1.50
1988 Donruss Mets Team Book #69 .... 0.80	0.35	0.15
1988 Fleer Star Stickers #102 .... 0.90	0.40	0.15
1988 Kenner Starting Lineup 12.00	5.00	2.00
1988 Nestle #21 .... 0.75	0.35	0.15
1988 Score Young Superstar II #3 .... 0.80	0.30	0.10
1988 Sportflics #200 .... 0.50	0.20	0.08
1988 Topps Big #11 .... 0.50	0.20	0.08
1989 K mart #31 .... 0.35	0.15	0.05
1989 Kahn's Mets #16 .... 1.75	0.75	0.35
1989 Scoremasters #26 .... 0.40	0.15	0.05
1989 Sportflics #140 .... 0.50	0.20	0.08
1990 Classic #58 .... 0.15	0.05	0.01
1990 Leaf #139 .... 0.50	0.20	0.08
1990 Post #29 .... 0.80	0.30	0.10
1991 Colla Dwight Gooden (set of 13) 8.00	3.50	1.50
1991 Donruss Elite #12 .... 60.00	27.50	12.50
1991 Fleer Pro Visions #7 .... 0.50	0.20	0.08
1992 Donruss Diamond Kings #15 .... 1.00	0.40	0.15
1992 Fleer Smoke'n Heat #8 .... 0.75	0.30	0.12
1992 Fleer Ultra #232 .... 1.25	0.50	0.20
1993 Score Select Aces #8 .... 3.00	1.25	0.50

Mark Grace

Mark Grace was one of those low-low-low-round draft choices who beat all the odds and made it to the big leagues, where he has sparkled in every respect except hitting for consistent power. The Cubs would rather he hit for that power, but in the meantime Grace has a nice little career and some nice little cards going for him.

	NM	EX	VG
1986 ProCards Peoria (set)	85.00	40.00	17.50
1987 ProCards Pittsfield (set)	65.00	31.00	14.50
1988 Donruss #40	1.00	0.40	0.15
1988 Donruss Rookies #1	2.00	0.80	0.30
1988 Donruss Cubs Team Book #45	1.75	0.75	0.35
1988 Fleer Update #77	2.25	1.00	0.40
1988 Fleer Glossy Tin #641	4.00	1.75	0.75
1988 Fleer Glossy Tin Update #77	3.00	1.25	0.55
1988 Fleer Mini #68	1.00	0.45	0.20
1988 Score Traded #80	12.00	5.50	2.50
1988 Score Glossy Traded #80	18.00	8.00	3.50
1988 Topps Traded #42	2.00	0.80	0.35
1988 Topps Tiffany Traded #42	10.00	4.50	2.00
1989 Fleer Baseball's Exciting Stars #17	0.30	0.12	0.05
1989 Marathon Oil Cubs #17	2.00	0.80	0.30
1989 Score #362	0.35	0.15	0.25
1989 Sportflics #15	0.75	0.30	0.12
1989 Topps Big Baseball #189	1.00	0.45	0.20
1989 Upper Deck #140	1.25	0.50	0.20
1990 Classic #8	0.30	0.10	0.04
1990 Leaf #137	1.75	0.75	0.35
1990 Marathon Cubs #17	1.50	0.65	0.30
1990 Sportflics #15	0.45	0.20	0.08
1990 Topps All-Star Glossy (60) #12	0.40	0.15	0.05
1990 Topps Big Baseball #19	0.20	0.08	0.03
1990 Upper Deck #128	0.35	0.15	0.05
1991 Donruss #157	0.30	0.12	0.04
1991 Marathon Cubs #17	0.75	0.35	0.15
1991 Topps #290	1.00	0.40	0.15
1992 Fleer Ultra #175	0.35	0.10	0.04
1992 Leaf Gold Inserts #26	1.00	0.40	0.15
1992 Topps #174	0.35	0.15	0.05
1992 Topps Gold Inserts #140	2.00	0.80	0.30
1993 Upper Deck Iooss Collection #8	2.00	0.80	0.30

Tyler Green

It's a race with Tyler Green as to what's going to happen first: major-league stardom or career-ending shoulder problems. Green throws a hard fastball and a fiendish knuckle-curve, a pitch that's as hard on the arm as it is to hit. He's come close to making the majors several times, but each time has been held back by arm problems. He may never make it — and if that's the case, what are you doing thinking about his cards? Stay away; you stand to lose a lot more than you could ever hope to gain with Tyler Green.

	NM	EX	VG
1991 Classic Draft Picks #7	0.50	0.20	0.08
1991 Classic Draft Picks #7	0.50	0.20	0.08
1991 Front Row Draft Picks #34	0.85	0.35	0.15
1992 Classic-Best Minor #230	0.50	0.20	0.08
1992 Donruss Phenoms #5	1.25	0.50	0.20
1992 Score #810	0.25	0.10	0.04
1992 Score Pinnacle #303	0.75	0.30	0.12
1992 Topps #764	0.30	0.12	0.04
1992 Topps Gold Inserts #764	10.00	4.50	2.00
1992 Upper Deck Minor League #167	0.35	0.12	0.05
1992 Upper Deck Minor League #68	0.20	0.08	0.03
1993 Fleer #85	0.50	0.20	0.08

Willie Greene

Willie Greene is now with his third organization, which would normally be a danger sign. However, in Greene's case, all three organizations wanted him, and two of the three gave him up for very good reasons. The Pirates drafted him and sent him along with Moises Alou to the Expos in the Zane Smith fleecing. The Expos then packaged him in a deal that also brought Dave Martinez to the Reds in exchange for John Wetteland. Good deals, and Greene is about ready to play, as he showed in a 1992 late-season call-up. His cards took a jump after that performance, but they've cooled a little as Greene cools his heels in the minors. With his talent, and with Chris Sabo declining fast at third base, Greene could be driving those prices back up again very soon. A nice little buy.

	NM	EX	VG
1990 Bowman #173	0.30	0.12	0.05
1990 Bowman Tiffany #173	3.00	1.25	0.55
1991 Bowman #448	0.10	0.04	0.01
1992 Bowman #429	0.50	0.20	0.08
1992 Bowman Gold #429	1.50	0.55	0.20
1992 Classic-Best Minor-League #48	0.10	0.04	0.01
1992 Fleer Update #81	0.20	0.08	0.03
1993 Fleer #34	0.20	0.08	0.03
1993 Score Select #348	0.15	0.05	0.01
1993 Upper Deck #4	0.25	0.10	0.04

Mike Greenwell

Greenwell's cards have taken a roller-coaster ride along with his career the last couple of years, but there are signs that it's coming to an end — the roller-coaster ride, not Greenwell's career. Greenwell is shaking out as a Bill Buckner or Al Oliver for the '90s — good average hitter, occasional power, but just a little bit short when it comes time for Cooperstown. His cards aren't all that expensive, but you're not getting all that much for your money. The one exception: the weird-beyond-words six-in-one Sportflics rookie card that features Greenwell and Jose Canseco among the Mark Funderburks and Steve Lombardozzis of the rookie world. That card remains a buy.

	NM	EX	VG
1986 Sportflics #178	15.00	7.00	3.00
1987 Donruss #585	1.50	0.65	0.30
1987 Donruss Rookies #4	0.70	0.30	0.12
1987 Fleer Update #37	0.70	0.30	0.12
1987 Topps #259	0.50	0.20	0.08
1987 Topps Tiffany #259	2.00	0.85	0.40
1988 Fleer #354	0.30	0.12	0.05
1988 Fleer Glossy #354	1.25	0.55	0.25
1988 O-Pee-Chee #288	0.65	0.30	0.12
1988 Toys 'R' Us #12	0.40	0.15	0.05
1989 Topps Mini League Leaders #48	0.50	0.20	0.08
1989 Upper Deck #432	0.50	0.20	0.08
1990 Leaf #143	0.75	0.35	0.15
1990 Topps Big #61	0.25	0.10	0.04
1991 Topps Stadium Club #253	0.50	0.20	0.08

Ken Griffey Jr.

Ken Griffey Jr. stands a great chance of having a Hall of Fame-type career. His showpiece card is his overproduced and overvalued 1989 Upper Deck card, but his Topps, Fleer, and Donruss cards from the same year represent better values. His cards continue to be accorded highest star status and should be among the first cards to profit from market expansion and the last to suffer from market contractions.

	NM	EX	VG
1989 Donruss #33	7.50	3.75	2.00
1989 Donruss Rookies #3	8.00	4.00	1.75
1989 Fleer #548	10.00	5.00	3.00
1989 Score Traded #100	6.25	3.00	1.50
1989 Topps Major League Debut #46	3.75	1.80	0.90

	NM	EX	VG
1989 Topps Traded #41	5.50	2.75	1.50
1989 Upper Deck #1	75.00	50.00	30.00
1990 Bowman #481	2.00	1.00	0.50
1990 Classic #20	2.00	0.75	0.25
1990 Leaf #245	25.00	17.00	10.00
1990 Topps All-Star Glossy (60) #20	1.50	0.75	0.35
1990 Topps Big #250	1.35	0.70	0.35
1990 Upper Deck #156	5.50	2.50	1.00
1991 Bowman #246	1.50	0.60	0.25
1991 Classic #3	1.00	0.45	0.20
1991 Classic III #120	1.25	0.60	0.25
1991 Donruss Studio #112	4.50	2.00	1.00
1991 Fleer Ultra #336	3.75	1.75	0.80
1991 Leaf #372	5.00	3.50	2.00
1991 O-Pee-Chee Premier #56	3.00	1.50	0.75
1991 Topps Desert Shield #790	650.00	325.00	180.00
1991 Topps Stadium Club #270	17.00	9.50	5.00
1991 Upper Deck #555	1.25	0.50	0.20
1992 Fleer Ultra #123	3.25	1.50	0.60
1992 Score Pinnacle #549	1.75	1.00	0.65
1992 Topps Stadium Club #400	3.75	1.75	0.75
1992 Topps Stadium Club #603 (Members Choice)	2.50	1.25	0.50

Marquis Grissom

The Expos thought they were getting another Andre Dawson when they drafted Marquis Grissom. They weren't, but they're not really complaining. Grissom came out higher on the speed chart and lower on the power chart, and that's translated into two stolen-base titles in the last two years. Grissom is still developing power, however, so there's nothing that says he won't turn into another Andre Dawson, all of which is good news to power-hungry card buyers. If Grissom does become another Dawson, his cards are awfully cheap. If he doesn't, you get about what you pay for.

	NM	EX	VG
1990 Bowman #115	0.40	0.50	0.05
1990 Bowman Tiffany #115	3.50	1.25	0.50
1990 Classic #65	0.70	0.30	0.10
1990 Donruss #36	0.50	0.20	0.08
1990 Donruss Rookies #45	0.50	0.20	0.08
1990 Fleer #347	0.50	0.20	0.08
1990 Leaf #107	6.75	3.00	1.25
1990 Score #591	0.50	0.20	0.08

1990 Score Rising Star #99	0.40	0.15	0.05
1990 Sportflics #134	0.50	0.20	0.08
1990 Topps Big #138	0.55	0.25	0.10
1990 Topps Major League Debut #48	0.40	0.15	0.05
1990 Upper Deck #9	2.00	0.80	0.35
1991 Bowman Tiffany #435	0.40	0.15	0.05
1991 Donruss #198	0.50	0.20	0.08
1991 Fleer Ultra #204	0.35	0.15	0.05
1991 Leaf #22	0.30	0.12	0.04
1991 Topps #8	2.00	0.80	0.30
1991 Topps Desert Storm #283	35.00	15.00	6.50
1991 Toys 'R' Us Rookies #9	0.40	0.15	0.05
1991 Upper Deck #477	0.25	0.10	0.04
1992 Bowman #14	0.25	0.10	0.04
1992 Bowman Gold #14	1.50	0.50	0.20
1992 Fleer Ultra #518	0.50	0.20	0.08
1992 Leaf #273	0.25	0.10	0.04
1992 Leaf Gold Inserts #273	0.25	0.10	0.04
1992 O-Pee-Chee Premier #176	0.35	0.15	0.05
1992 Score Impact Players #63	0.25	0.10	0.04
1992 Score Pinnacle #129	0.35	0.15	0.05
1992 Score Pinnacle Team 2000 #11	0.75	0.30	0.12
1992 Topps #120	0.40	0.15	0.05
1992 Topps Gold Inserts #647	2.00	0.80	0.35
1993 Topps Gold Inserts #15	0.50	0.20	0.08
1993 Topps Black Gold Inserts #7	4.00	1.50	0.50

Juan Guzman

Juan is another one of the Toronto Blue Jays' success stories. Spirited out of the Dodgers' organization for Mike Sharperson, Guzman found control with the Jays — and with control found incredible success. Guzman has the best winning percentage of any starting pitcher over the last two seasons, and he showed late last year he can overcome adversity with the best of them. Like the cards of any young pitcher, Guzman's cards are speculative at best. But compared to some of the other pitchers whose cards are doing well right now — and with his post season record — Guzman is a much more solid citizen and better card buy.

	NM	EX	VG
1990 Best Knoxville Blue Jays #9	8.00	3.50	1.60
1990 Best Minor-League Foil #79	7.50	3.50	1.60
1991 Fleer Ultra Update #60	5.25	2.50	1.10
1991 Impel Line Drive #504	3.25	1.50	0.65
1992 Donruss #534	0.80	0.35	0.15

	NM	EX	VG
1992 Fleer Rookie Sensations #13	8.25	4.00	1.75
1992 Fleer Ultra #132	2.25	1.00	0.45
1992 Leaf #35	0.65	0.30	0.12
1992 Pinnacle #183	0.75	0.35	0.15
1992 Pinnacle Team 2000 #27	4.25	2.00	0.80
1992 Score #424	0.50	0.20	0.08
1992 Studio #256	2.00	0.90	0.40
1992 Topps Stadium Club #402	3.75	1.75	0.80
1992 Upper Deck #625	1.25	0.60	0.25

Tony Gwynn

Ted Williams' measure of greatness in a hitter is: To prove that he's really good, have him do it five years in a row. Tony Gwynn has done that — double. Gwynn has never hit less than .300 in 11 major-league seasons. He's won four batting titles, stolen 56 bases one year, hit 14 homers another, and has acquitted himself quite well in the field. Gwynn will pass the 2,000-hit mark this year and needs only a few more good, consistent seasons of .300-or-better averages to assure himself of a place in Cooperstown. Because of that his cards cannot be considered overvalued at their present levels and are recommended buys.

	NM	EX	VG
1983 Donruss #598	22.00	10.00	4.50
1983 Fleer #360	20.00	8.50	3.75
1983 Topps #482	30.00	12.50	5.50
1984 Donruss #324	18.00	8.00	3.50
1984 Fleer #301	10.00	4.50	2.00
1984 Nestle #251	12.00	5.50	2.25
1984 Smokey Bear Padres #19	1.50	0.65	0.30
1984 Topps #251	4.50	2.00	0.80
1984 Topps Tiffany #251	35.00	15.75	7.25
1985 Donruss #63	6.00	2.50	1.00
1985 Donruss Action All-Stars #19	0.30	0.12	0.04
1985 Fleer #34	5.00	2.25	0.85
1985 Mother's Cookies Padres #2	3.00	1.25	0.50
1985 Topps #660	2.75	1.25	0.50
1986 Donruss #112	2.50	1.00	0.45
1986 Donruss Pop-Ups #4	0.50	0.20	0.08
1986 Fleer #323	2.75	1.25	0.50
1986 Sportflics #13	1.00	0.40	0.15
1986 Topps #10	1.00	0.40	0.15
1987 Bohemian Hearth Bread #19	12.00	5.50	2.25
1987 Classic #26	2.00	0.85	0.35
1987 Donruss #64	1.00	0.40	0.15

1987 Fleer #416	1.75	0.75	0.35
1987 Fleer Glossy Tin #416	1.25	0.55	0.20
1987 Fleer Star Stickers #52	0.40	0.15	0.05
1987 Leaf #235	0.25	0.10	0.04
1987 Sportflics #31	0.60	0.20	0.08
1987 Topps Gallery of Champions Aluminum	1.25	0.50	0.20
1987 Topps Gallery of Champions Bronze	12.00	5.00	2.00
1987 Topps Gallery of Champions Silver	50.00	22.50	10.50
1988 Bazooka #9	0.40	0.15	0.05
1988 Drake's Panel #6	2.75	1.25	0.50
1988 Fleer #585	0.50	0.20	0.08
1988 Fleer Star Stickers #123	0.40	0.15	0.04
1988 Panini Stickers #410	0.20	0.08	0.03
1988 Sportflics #16	0.50	0.20	0.08
1988 Topps Big #161	0.25	0.10	0.04
1989 Cap'n Crunch #5	0.60	0.25	0.10
1989 Donruss Baseball's Best #42	0.30	0.12	0.04
1989 Fleer Baseball MVP #17	0.20	0.08	0.03
1989 Scoremasters #37	0.40	0.15	0.05
1989 Sportflics #160	0.50	0.20	0.08
1989 Upper Deck #384	0.75	0.30	0.10
1990 Donruss Learning Series #48	4.00	1.75	0.75
1990 Leaf #154	3.00	1.25	0.50
1990 Post #5	0.50	0.20	0.08
1990 Sportflics #98	0.50	0.20	0.08
1990 Upper Deck #344	0.50	0.20	0.08
1991 Classic III #33	0.10	0.04	0.01
1991 Donruss #245	0.50	0.20	0.08
1991 Donruss Elite #14	75.00	35.00	16.50
1991 Topps #308	1.75	0.75	0.35
1992 Fleer Team Leaders #7	1.75	0.75	0.30
1992 Fleer Ultra #277	0.50	0.20	0.08
1992 Fleer Ultra Awards #12	5.00	2.25	1.00
1992 Fleer All-Stars #2	1.75	0.75	0.30
1992 Leaf Gold Inserts #206	2.50	1.00	0.40
1992 Topps #825	0.75	0.35	0.15
1992 Topps Gold Inserts #270	3.00	1.25	0.50
1992 Upper Deck Fan Fest #25	0.75	0.35	0.15
1992 Upper Deck Ted Williams' Best #6	2.25	1.00	0.40
1993 Score Select Rookies #8	4.50	2.00	0.80

1993 Topps Gold Inserts #5 .... 0.50	0.20	0.08
1993 Topps Black Gold Inserts #8 .... 4.00	1.50	0.60

Bob Hamelin

It was the small stuff that got Bob Hamelin. Bob Hamelin was supposed to be the power hitter that made everyone forget about Harmon Killebrew. As it turned out, everyone forgot about Bob Hamelin instead. Back problems were his downfall. One sidelight: We picked the Star Co. wax-series Bob Hamelin as one of the top 100 baseball cards of all time in our previous book, *The Top 100*. Oh, well, we can't call 'em all right.

	NM	EX	VG
1989 Best Memphis (set) 12.00	5.50	2.00
1989 ProCards Memphis (set) 13.00	6.00	2.50
1989 Star Memphis (set) 12.00	5.50	2.50
1989 Star Minor League Wax #42 .... 0.45	0.20	0.08
1990 Bowman Tiffany #379 .... 0.50	0.20	0.08

Rickey Henderson

Perhaps the best leadoff hitter in baseball history, and holder of the all-time stolen-base record, Rickey Henderson is headed into the Hall of Fame despite his sometimes contentious attitude. His speed and power are unmatched by anything this side of his ego. Henderson's cards have actually plateaued and declined some in value as his accomplishments have mounted and, not coincidentally, his braggadocio has increased. The man can play, and his card values will eventually reflect that. Right now they don't — and it might not be a bad idea to pick up some of his cards.

	NM	EX	VG
1979 TCMA Ogden A's (set) 250.00	115.00	55.00
1981 Granny Goose A's #35 .... 30.00	12.50	5.50
1981 O-Pee-Chee #261 .... 3.50	1.50	0.50
1982 Perma-Graphics All-Star Credit Cards #6 .... 2.00	0.80	0.35
1983 Fleer Stickers #192 .... 0.30	0.10	0.04
1983 Granny Goose A's #35 .... 10.00	4.50	2.00
1983 Topps Stickers (6) #197-202 .... 0.75	0.30	0.12
1983 Topps Stickers Boxes #8 .... 1.25	0.50	0.20
1984 Mother's Cookies A's #2 .... 3.00	1.25	0.50
1984 Topps All-Star Glossy (40) #6 .... 0.75	0.30	0.10
1985 Topps Super #14 .... 0.70	0.30	0.10
1986 Donruss All-Stars #6 .... 1.25	0.50	0.20

	NM	EX	VG
1986 Donruss Pop-Up 0.75		0.30	0.10
1986 Fleer Limited Edition #23 .... 0.50		0.20	0.08
1986 Fleer Star Stickers #53 .... 1.00		0.40	0.15
1986 Quaker Oats #26 .... 1.00		0.40	0.15
1987 Classic #12 .... 8.00		3.50	1.50
1987 Fleer Star Stickers #56 .... 1.00		0.40	0.15
1987 Topps All-Star Glossy (60) #21 .... 0.75		0.30	0.12
1988 Kenner 10.00		4.00	1.50
1988 Leaf-Donruss #208 .... 0.40		0.15	0.05
1989 Bazooka #14 .... 0.40		0.15	0.05
1989 Score Superstar #45 .... 0.25		0.10	0.04
1989 Topps Mini League Leaders #66 .... 0.25		0.10	0.04
1990 Ames All-Stars #13 .... 0.50		0.20	0.08
1990 Donruss Learning Series #7 .... 6.00		2.50	1.00
1990 Kenner 15.00		5.50	2.00
1990 Mother's Cookies A's #4 .... 1.50		0.50	0.20
1990 Post #25 .... 0.80		0.30	0.10
1990 Score McDonald's #5 .... 20.00		9.50	4.25

Tom Henke

The pitcher they call "The Terminator" has quietly — too quietly — become the American League's answer to Lee Smith; his 220 saves are second only to Dennis Eckersley among A.L. pitchers, and he shows no signs of slowing up. On the other hand, he shows no signs of accelerating, which in the current atmosphere of relief-pitcher backlash means his cards are going to stay about where they are for the long term.

	NM	EX	VG
1982 TCMA Tulsa Drillers (set) 100.00		45.00	20.00
1983 TCMA Oklahoma City (set) 20.00		9.50	4.50
1985 Police Blue Jays #50 .... 0.40		0.15	0.05
1986 Leaf #206 .... 0.10		0.04	0.01
1986 O-Pee-Chee #333 .... 0.06		0.01	0.01
1986 Police Blue Jays #50 .... 0.40		0.15	0.05
1987 Fleer Star Stickers #57 .... 0.10		0.04	0.01
1987 Leaf #73 .... 0.10		0.04	0.01
1988 Donruss Baseball's Best #104 .... 0.07		0.03	0.01
1988 Fleer Award Winners #18 .... 0.05		0.01	0.01
1988 Fleer Mini #62 .... 0.07		0.01	0.01
1988 Fleer Star Stickers #73 .... 0.10		0.04	0.01
1988 Panini Sticker #213 .... 0.04		0.01	0.01
1988 Police Blue Jays #50 .... 0.25		0.10	0.04
1990 Topps Big #101 .... 0.06		0.01	0.01

Orel Hershiser

The hero of the 1988 World Series hasn't been the same since his arm was ground to a stump through overwork, but he's still a competitive pitcher and a solid one. There's no reason outside of sentiment for his cards to be priced where they are, but sentiment does count for something in this business. If you're an investor, don't get sentimental; if you're a collector, enjoy.

	NM	EX	VG
1985 Topps Tiffany #493	7.50	3.50	1.50
1986 Diamond King Supers #18	0.70	0.30	0.10
1986 Leaf #18	0.65	0.25	0.10
1987 Donruss Opening Day #87	0.30	0.12	0.05
1987 Mother's Cookies Dodgers #6	1.00	0.40	0.12
1988 Fleer Award Winners #17	0.20	0.08	0.03
1988 Fleer Star Stickers #$92	0.35	0.15	0.05
1988 Topps Big Baseball #98	0.25	0.10	0.04
1989 Fleer Baseball MVP #19	0.25	0.10	0.04
1989 Kenner Starting Lineup	10.00	4.00	1.50
1989 Scoremasters #21	0.50	0.20	0.08
1990 Mother's Cookies Dodgers #12	0.50	0.20	0.04

Phil Hiatt

One of the real up-and-comers in the game, at least as far as the Royals are concerned, Hiatt will forever be remembered by someone, somewhere, as the player who made Sean Berry expendable. Hiatt is a power-hitting third baseman in the Dann Howitt/Stan Royer mold. What sort of mold is that? Imagine Dean Palmer with two-thirds the power and you're on the right track. Hiatt's cards aren't much, and they shouldn't be. But they are worth a sidelong glance every now and then.

	NM	EX	VG
1991 ProCards Baseball City Royals #1403	4.50	2.00	0.85
1991 ProCards Tomorrow's Heroes #76	0.40	0.15	0.05

Ken Hill

An undisciplined pitcher as a St. Louis Cardinal, Hill was dispatched to the Expos for Andres Galarraga and blossomed, becoming one of the league's top hurlers. There's no reason why Hill shouldn't be among the game's elite: He's a hard thrower with excellent breaking stuff and (now) fine control. His cards are cheap — none of the garden-variety stuff is more than $1 — and should continue to go up in value over the short term.

	NM	EX	VG
1987 ProCards Arkansas (set) 12.00		5.50	2.50
1989 Donruss Rookies #31 .... 0.20		0.08	0.03
1989 Fleer Update #119 .... 0.20		0.08	0.03
1989 Score Traded #98 .... 0.20		0.08	0.03
1989 Team Louisville (set) 15.00		6.50	3.00
1989 Topps Traded #50 .... 0.25		0.10	0.04
1990 Score Rising Star #34 .... 0.10		0.04	0.01
1990 Topps #233 .... 0.15		0.05	0.01
1990 Upper Deck #336 .... 0.15		0.05	0.01
1991 Bowman Tiffany 0.25		0.10	0.04
1991 Topps #435 .... 0.25		0.10	0.04
1991 Topps Desert Storm #591 .... 3.00		1.25	0.50
1992 Bowman Gold #507 .... 0.50		0.20	0.08
1992 Fleer Ultra #520 .... 0.15		0.05	0.01
1992 Leaf Gold Inserts #468 .... 0.40		0.15	0.05
1992 Topps #138 .... 0.15		0.05	0.01
1992 Topps #735 .... 0.15		0.05	0.01
1992 Topps Gold Inserts #664 .... 0.75		0.30	0.10
1993 Score Select Aces #14 .... 3.00		0.25	0.50

Tyrone Hill

Comparisons are made between Tyrone Hill and Steve Carlton, but they can't be completely serious. Though there are some similarities — both are left-handed and throw hard fastballs and sliders with a deceptively easy motion — Hill has volumes and volumes to learn about pitching, and was even shut down toward the end of '92 with a sore shoulder. Still, Hill is one of the top two or three pitching prospects in the minor leagues, and that accounts for something. In Hill's case, it accounts for about 75 cents.

	NM	EX	VG
1991 Classic Draft Picks #12 .... 0.25		0.10	0.04
1991 Topps Stadium Club Dome #84 .... 1.50		0.65	0.25
1992 Classic-Best Beloit (set) 6.00		2.75	1.25
1992 Classic-Best Minor League #364 .... 0.75		0.30	0.10
1992 Score #807 .... 0.25		0.10	0.04
1992 Score Pinnacle #301 .... 0.65		0.30	0.10
1992 Topps #444 .... 0.35		0.15	0.05
1992 Topps Gold #444 .... 5.00		2.25	1.00
1992 Upper Deck Minor League #135 .... 0.75		0.30	0.10

Chris Hoiles

Hard to believe, but if not for Doyle Alexander the Tigers would have John Smoltz, and if not for Fred Lynn they'd still have Chris Hoiles. The fact that the Tigers were willing to trade the only things in their farm system that weren't Scott Aldred or Steve Searcy for those two broken-down warhorses speaks volumes about the Tigers' attitude toward rookies and the nearsightedness of their front office. Not that Hoiles minds. The catcher has been more than happy to do his bashing in Camden Yards. Hoiles is a good one. His cards are a little undervalued but he still has an awful lot to prove. Two more solid, consistent years, though, and Hoiles' cards will pass Ivan Rodriguez's and Hoiles, not Rodriguez, will be touted as the catcher of the future. Or maybe it'll be Carlos Delgado.

	NM	EX	VG
1987 ProCards Glens Falls (set)	25.00	12.00	5.50
1989 ProCards Rochester (set)	7.50	3.50	1.50
1990 CMC Pre-Rookie #313	1.50	0.65	0.25
1990 CMC Rochester (set)	30.00	12.50	5.50
1990 ProCards AAA #461	1.75	0.75	0.35

Dave Hollins

If he's a top young infielder, he must be a former Padre. Sad but true. Dave Hollins was drafted out of the Padres' farm system by the Phillies, who basically sat him on the bench for a year so they could retain the rights to him. Good move. Hollins has blossomed into a superb offensive third baseman, as adept at drawing walks as he is at slamming the ball out of the yard. He's youngish and he has another two or three years of improvement ahead of him, all of which makes his cards nice short-term, turnaround-style buys.

	NM	EX	VG
1989 Rock's Dugout Wichita (set)	13.00	6.00	2.50
1989 Rock's Dugout Wichita Highlight (set)	13.00	6.00	2.50
1989 Rock's Dugout Wichita Stadium (set)	13.00	6.00	2.50
1990 Bowman #161	0.35	0.15	0.05
1990 Bowman Tiffany #161	2.00	0.85	0.35
1990 Donruss Rookies #47	0.40	0.15	0.06
1990 Fleer Update #43	0.50	0.20	0.08
1990 Score Traded #75	0.75	0.30	0.12
1990 Topps Traded #41	0.55	0.20	0.08
1990 Topps Major League Debut #69	0.30	0.12	0.05
1990 Upper Deck #785	1.25	0.50	0.20
1991 Score #61	0.15	0.05	0.01

	NM	EX	VG
1991 Score Rising Star #96	0.15	0.06	0.01
1991 Topps #264	0.15	0.05	0.01
1991 Topps Desert Storm #264	35.00	16.50	7.50
1991 Upper Deck #518	0.20	0.08	0.03
1992 Bowman #6	0.20	0.08	0.03
1992 Bowman Gold #6	1.00	0.45	0.20
1992 Fleer Ultra #244	0.40	0.15	0.05
1992 Leaf #278	0.20	0.08	0.03
1992 Leaf Gold Inserts #278	1.25	0.50	0.20
1992 Score Pinnacle #67	0.30	0.12	0.04
1992 Score Pinnacle Team 2000 #16	0.50	0.20	0.08
1992 Topps #246	0.25	0.10	0.04
1992 Topps Gold Inserts #383	0.75	0.30	0.12
1993 Topps Gold Inserts #17	0.25	0.10	0.04

Steve Hosey

Steve Hosey might turn out to be the perfect power-hitting complement to Barry Bonds, but he's not quite there yet. His cards are relatively affordable, but there's a reason for that.

	NM	EX	VG
1990 Bowman #242	0.35	0.15	0.05
1990 Score #666	0.50	0.20	0.08
1991 Bowman #629	0.10	0.04	0.01
1992 Bowman #544	0.45	0.20	0.08
1992 Bowman Gold #544	1.00	0.45	0.20
1992 Donruss Rookies #54	0.40	0.15	0.05
1992 Fleer Update #127	0.45	0.20	0.08
1992 Leaf Gold #23	4.00	1.75	0.75
1992 Leaf Gold #23	4.00	1.75	0.75
1992 Upper Deck #62	0.30	0.12	0.05
1993 Fleer Major League Prospects #11	0.75	0.30	0.12
1993 Upper Deck #15	0.20	0.08	0.03

Kent Hrbek

Say what you want to about his size and shape, call him "Shamu" if you want, but the fact remains that Kent Hrbek has been one of the A.L.'s best hitters for more than 10 years. Hrbek has excellent power to all fields and is an underrated defensive first baseman. He's not a Hall of Famer unless he does something beyond the statistical realm of possibility, like string together five .300-plus seasons in a row. Still, you'd think there'd be a little more activity in some of his cards. His Donruss rookie card is priced on a par with Dave Stewart's but five bucks below George Bell's.

	NM	EX	VG
1982 Donruss #557	2.35	1.25	0.60
1982 Topps Traded #44T	6.25	3.00	1.35
1983 Fleer #616	0.70	0.30	0.12
1983 Minnesota Twins Team Issue #9	0.75	0.35	0.15
1983 Topps #690	0.45	0.20	0.08
1984 Donruss #70	0.55	0.25	0.10
1984 Fleer #567	0.55	0.25	0.10
1985 Minnesota Twins Team Issue #10	0.55	0.25	0.12
1988 Master Bread Twins #10	1.75	0.75	0.30
1988 Minnesota Twins Team Issue #8	15.50	7.50	3.75
1991 Topps Stadium Club #248	0.30	0.12	0.05
1992 Topps Gold #347	0.75	0.35	0.15

Bo Jackson

So far the lesson of the 1993 season has been: You can play baseball with an artificial hip — if you're Bo Jackson. Jackson's comeback makes for great headlines but doesn't do much for his cards one way or another. Jackson's values have pretty much been set, and nothing is going to have too much of an impact on them. When you buy Bo Jackson cards you're not buying cards of Bo Jackson the baseball player or Bo Jackson the former football player. You're buying cards of Bo Jackson, cultural icon. Beware — counterfeits exist of his Time Out Sports minor-league cards.

	NM	EX	VG
1986 Time Out Sports Memphis Chicks Gold #28	40.00	18.50	8.50
1986 Time Out Sports Memphis Chicks Silver #28	40.00	18.50	8.50
1987 Donruss Rookies #14	1.45	0.65	0.25
1988 Donruss #220	0.25	0.10	0.04
1988 Fleer #260	0.75	0.30	0.12
1988 Score #180	0.25	0.10	0.03
1988 Topps #750	0.20	0.08	0.02
1989 Topps Big #238	0.50	0.20	0.08
1989 Upper Deck #221	0.50	0.20	0.08
1990 Donruss All-Star (error version) #650	0.30	0.12	0.04
1990 Donruss Diamond King Supers #1	0.25	0.10	0.04
1990 Donruss Grand Slammers #12	0.60	0.20	0.08
1990 Score #697	1.50	0.65	0.25
1990 Score Dream Team #687	0.25	0.10	0.04

	NM	EX	VG
1990 Upper Deck #105 .... 0.25	0.10	0.04
1990 Upper Deck #75 .... 0.30	0.12	0.05
1991 Donruss Highlights #10 .... 0.15	0.05	0.01
1991 Fleer Pro Visions #5 .... 0.30	0.12	0.04
1991 Fleer Ultra #149 .... 0.20	0.08	0.03
1991 Score Traded/Update #1 .... 0.20	0.08	0.03
1991 Topps Stadium Club #224 .... 1.00	0.45	0.20
1991 Topps Traded #58 .... 0.20	0.08	0.02
1992 Score Impact Players #53 .... 0.25	0.10	0.04
1992 Topps Stadium Club #654 .... 0.45	0.20	0.08

Joseph Jefferson "Shoeless Joe" Jackson

Banished from the game for his alleged involvement in the fixing of the 1919
World Series, Joe Jackson may well be more popular today than at any time in
his career. His cards are certainly more popular. In fact, he ranks right up there
with Cobb and Ruth and has far fewer cards. The market may be leveling off a
bit simply because his cards are out of the price range of most collectors. Books
and movies about Joe Jackson just keep coming. The interesting question is,
Would his cards go up if he was placed in the Hall of Fame?

	NM	EX	VG
1914 Cracker Jack #103 .... 15000.00	5000.00	2250.00
1915 Cracker Jack #103 .... 8500.00	3750.00	1500.00
1940 Play Ball #225 .... 2250.00	1000.00	650.00
E224 Texas Tommy 5000.00	2000.00	1200.00
E90-1 American Caramel 9500.00	4000.00	1850.00

John Jaha

The Brewers regard John Jaha with the ghost of Billy Jo Robidoux held firmly in
mind. Robidoux was a batting-average champ all up and down the minor
leagues when the Brewers brought him up. In five or six major-league seasons
Robidoux managed to spend as much time on the disabled list as off, and when
he was healthy he had trouble mustering up anything stronger than a dump
single to left field. Jaha has won the same string of batting titles and has some
of Robidoux's opposite-field tendencies, but he has more genuine power and
has shown a better-than-Billy-Jo bat so far in his major-league career. Jaha isn't
terribly young (26), but his pairing with Ryan Klesko on a '92 Topps four-in-one
rookie card (#126) is nothing if not intriguing.

	NM	EX	VG
1991 Classic-Best #291 .... 1.00	0.45	0.20
1991 Line Drive AA #188 .... 0.50	0.20	0.08

1991 ProCards El Paso #2756 .... 1.75	0.80	0.35
1991 ProCards Yesterday's Heroes #84 .... 0.40	0.15	0.07
1992 Bowman #399 .... 0.50	0.20	0.08
1992 Bowman #542 .... 0.50	0.20	0.08
1992 Donruss #398 .... 0.20	0.08	0.01
1992 Fleer Update #35 .... 0.40	0.15	0.07
1992 Topps #126 .... 0.90	0.40	0.15
1992 Topps Gold #126 .... 9.00	4.35	2.10
1993 Fleer #252 .... 0.10	0.04	0.01
1993 Score Select #308 .... 0.10	0.04	0.01
1993 Upper Deck #177 .... 0.15	0.07	0.01

Gregg Jefferies

He was the player voted Most Likely to Resemble Pete Rose, a switch-hitter who swung in a half-lit room at a baseball that was half-painted and took batting practice underwater. Everyone figured that he was the can't-miss player of all time. And, naturally, he missed. He didn't miss badly, but he didn't live up to the hype that attaches itself to every vaunted New York rookie. A trade to Kansas City helped, and a trade to St. Louis appears to have really helped. Gregg Jefferies may never break any of Pete Rose's records, but he's a wonderful hitter with the potential to win a couple of titles of one sort or another. His cards have plummeted. They're now affordable if you're interested, which you probably ought to be.

	NM	EX	VG
1986 ProCards Columbia Mets (set) 85.00	40.00	17.50
1987 Team Jackson Mets (set) 15.00	6.50	3.00
1988 CMC Tidewater (set) 24.00	11.50	5.50
1989 Kahn's Mets #9 .... 1.00	0.45	0.20
1989 Kenner Starting Lineup 20.00	8.50	3.50

Howard Johnson

He may never be the do-it-all, play-anywhere player New York assumed he was or would be, but Howard Johnson does all right, thank you. He's a home-run threat, a stolen-base threat, and an asset just about everywhere he plays, though he'll never win a Gold Glove anywhere. What you've seen with Howard Johnson is about all you're going to get — no Cooperstown, nothing for people to remember from his career but some pretty happy memories. Nothing in all this really justifies the prices of his cards, which means if you're looking for any cards that stand the remotest chance of going up in value you'd best look elsewhere.

	NM	EX	VG
1981 TCMA Birmingham (set)	195.00	90.00	42.50
1983 Donruss #328	5.00	2.25	1.00
1983 Fleer #332	5.00	2.25	1.00
1985 Donruss #247	1.75	0.75	0.35
1985 Fleer #12	1.25	0.50	0.20
1985 Fleer Update #62	1.75	0.75	0.35
1985 Topps #192	2.00	0.80	0.35
1985 Topps Traded #64	1.75	0.75	0.35
1986 Donruss #312	0.75	0.35	0.15
1986 Fleer #85	0.75	0.35	0.15
1986 New York Mets Super Fan Club #6	0.70	0.30	0.12
1987 Fleer #13	0.50	0.20	0.08
1988 Donruss Mets Team Book #569.............	0.20	0.08	0.03
1988 Farmland Dairies Mets #20	0.70	0.30	0.10
1988 Fleer Star Stickers #108	0.15	0.05	0.01
1988 Kenner Starting Lineup	14.00	6.50	3.00
1990 Fleer All-Stars #4	4.25	2.00	0.85
1990 Fleer Award Winners #21	0.15	0.05	0.01
1990 Leaf #272	0.50	0.20	0.08
1991 Donruss Elite #15	40.00	17.50	8.00
1992 Fleer Team Leaders #2	1.00	0.40	0.20
1992 Fleer Ultra #235	1.00	0.40	0.20
1992 Topps #430	0.50	0.20	0.08
1992 Topps Gold Inserts #590	2.00	0.80	0.30
1992 Upper Deck Home Run Heroes #3	0.50	0.20	0.08
1993 Upper Deck Iooss Collection #14	1.50	0.65	0.25

Randy Johnson

Every pitch is an adventure for Randy Johnson — as it ought to be, when you're 6-foot-10 and breaking new ground with every pitch. Just ask John Kruk about his at-bat in the 93 All Star game. Johnson has maybe the best stuff in all of baseball — a left-hander's fastball, hard curveball, change-of-pace — when he can get it over the plate, which is about half the time. There's the hope with Johnson that he will rein in his stuff and become a dominant major-league pitcher. In the meantime his cards are in sort of a holding pattern waiting for that big breakthrough season. If you're the sort who believes that season will come soon, jump on Johnson's cards now while you can.

	NM	EX	VG
1986 ProCards West Palm Beach (set)	14.00	6.50	3.00
1987 ProCards Jacksonville (set)	15.00	6.50	3.00
1988 ProCards Indianapolis (set)	8.00	3.50	1.50

1989 Classic #95 .... 0.40	0.15	0.05
1989 Donruss #42 .... 0.30	0.12	0.05
1989 Donruss Baseball's Best #80 .... 0.25	0.10	0.04
1989 Fleer #381 .... 0.40	0.15	0.05
1990 Leaf #483 .... 0.85	0.35	0.15
1990 Mother's Cookies Mariners #13 .... 0.50	0.20	0.08
1990 Score Rising Stars #52 .... 0.10	0.04	0.01
1991 Topps #409 .... 0.50	0.20	0.08
1991 Topps Desert Storm #409 .... 50.00	22.50	10.00
1992 Donruss Diamond Kings #22 .... 1.00	0.40	0.15
1992 Fleer Smoke'n Heat #11 .... 0.75	0.30	0.12
1992 Leaf Gold Inserts #302 .... 0.40	0.12	0.05
1992 Topps Gold Inserts #525 .... 0.75	0.30	0.12

Chipper Jones

When the Atlanta Braves passed over an unsignable (or so they thought) Todd Van Poppel in favor of high-school shortstop Chipper Jones, the peanut gallery howled at the knuckleheaded Braves. What were they thinking of? As it turns out, the knuckleheaded Braves were thinking of a perfect shortstop to complement their fine young pitchers, and they nabbed a prospect in young Chipper. As he's matured, he's added power to his repertoire, giving him potentially the best total shortstop package south of Cal Ripken. Collectors and other card-buying members of the peanut gallery caught onto his cards early and haven't yet let go. There aren't many out-and-out bargains to be found. But Chipper's good enough to make those buys look considerably less than knuckleheaded.

	NM	EX	VG
1990 Classic Draft Picks #1 .... 1.00	0.45	0.20
1991 Bowman #569 .... 0.35	0.15	0.05
1991 Bowman Tiffany #569 .... 1.50	0.65	0.30
1991 Score #671 .... 0.60	0.25	0.10
1991 Topps #333 .... 0.50	0.20	0.08
1991 Topps Tiffany #333 .... 2.25	1.00	0.45
1991 Upper Deck #55 .... 1.00	0.45	0.20
1992 Bowman #28 .... 0.75	0.30	0.12
1992 Classic Baseball #93 .... 0.60	0.25	0.10
1992 Topps Stadium Club #1 Draft Pick #SP1 .... 7.50	3.50	1.50
1992 Upper Deck Minor-League #165 .... 0.45	0.20	0.08
1992 Upper Deck Minor-League #5 .... 0.65	0.30	0.12
1992 Upper Deck Minor-League #66 .... 0.45	0.20	0.08

Brian Jordan

Upper Deck saves card No. 3 in its regular set for the player it deems most likely to go nowhere. In its 1992 set that player was Brian Jordan. That's a little harsh. Jordan falls somewhere between Deion Sanders and Bo Jackson on the football-player-turned-baseball-player continuum. He has Bo's power and Deion's speed, Bo's tendency to strike out and Deion's tendency to bounce up and down from the bigs to the minors. Jordan is a wonderful prospect, and if he learns some discipline at the plate before he turns 30 he could have a superb career — not the stuff of Cooperstown, but maybe the stuff of legend.

	NM	EX	VG
1992 Bowman #464	0.15	0.05	0.01
1992 Bowman Gold #464	0.75	0.30	0.10
1992 Donruss Power Hitters #14	0.85	0.30	0.10
1992 Leaf #337	0.45	0.20	0.08
1992 Leaf Gold #337	3.50	1.50	0.65
1992 Pinnacle #555	0.45	0.20	0.08
1992 Pinnacle Team 2000 #39	0.70	0.30	0.10
1992 Score Traded/Update #83	0.25	0.10	0.04
1992 Studio #93	0.45	0.20	0.08
1992 Topps Traded #58	0.20	0.08	0.03
1992 Upper Deck #3	0.35	0.15	0.05
1992 Upper Deck Scouting Report #11	1.25	0.50	0.20
1993 Score Select #280	0.20	0.08	0.03

Felix Jose

When you talk to baseball experts who aren't plugged into the system, they'll tell you what a great talent Felix Jose is and how fortunate any club is to have him. You talk to the scouts and front-office people from the A's or the Cardinals, though, and they'll tell you that Jose is a disrupting influence, a bad baserunner, an indifferent fielder, and the antithesis of a team player. Okay, but can he hit? Yes, as a matter of fact he can. So what's the big deal? Just this: If all an organziation wants to do with a player once they get him is to ship him off to some other organization, the best that player's going to be is another Alex Johnson or Richie Allen. And have you priced any Alex Johnson cards lately? Jose's a talent, no doubt, but he's going to have to show he's more of a team player to justify the prices on his cards.

	NM	EX	VG
1987 Team Huntsville Stars (set)	10.00	4.50	2.00
1989 Fleer Glossy Tin #15	2.00	0.85	0.35
1989 Mother's Cookies A's #22	0.45	0.20	0.08

1990 Bowman Tiffany #455 .... 0.85	0.40	0.15
1990 Mother's Cookies A's #17 .... 0.55	0.25	0.10

Wally Joyner

You almost feel sorry for Wally Joyner, having to be a member of the same class that produced Ruben Sierra, Will Clark, Barry Larkin, and the rest, because he's just not in their class. He's a solid all-around hitter in the mold of a Cecil Cooper, only taken down a notch. He'll have a solid but forgettable career, he'll never win a batting title, he'll never win a home-run crown, so what's the fuss? Actually, there is less of a fuss made over Joyner and his cards with each passing day.

	NM	EX	VG
1985 Cramer Edmonton Trappers (set)	25.00	11.50	5.00
1986 Sportflics Rookies #7	2.00	0.85	0.35
1987 Drake's #2	1.00	0.45	0.20
1987 Fleer Star Stickers #68	0.50	0.20	0.08
1987 Fleer's Baseball's Best #22	0.50	0.20	0.08
1987 Leaf #252	2.50	1.10	0.50
1987 Topps All-Star Glossy (22) #13	0.70	0.30	0.12
1988 King-B #9	1.50	0.60	0.20
1988 Score Young Superstar #27	0.50	0.20	0.08
1988 Upper Deck Prototype (most common type) #700	75.00	35.00	15.00
1989 Donruss MVP #29	0.30	0.12	0.04

Dave Justice

When Dave Justice first came up, his quick, clean left-handed swing was compared to that of Ted Williams. You don't hear the comparisons to Teddy Ballgame anymore, though Justice remains a fearsome hitter. Does it matter that the prices for his cards are out of line with his accomplishments? No. The same thing could be said about Darryl Strawberry, Eric Davis or a host of other players. Baseball cards are a funny business. When you're charmed you're charmed. At this point in his career, Justice is proof of that.

	NM	EX	VG
1986 ProCards Sumter Braves (set)	65.00	30.00	12.50
1988 Bob's Photo Richmond Braves #13	27.50	12.50	5.50
1988 CMC Richmond Braves #17	12.50	5.50	2.25
1988 Team Richmond Braves #18	12.50	5.50	2.25
1989 CMC Richmond Braves #15	12.50	5.50	2.25
1989 ProCards Richmond Braves #838	12.50	5.50	2.25

1989 Topps Major League Debut #65	2.25	1.00	0.45
1990 Donruss #704	1.15	0.50	0.20
1990 Donruss Rookies #14	1.15	0.50	0.20
1990 Leaf #297	22.50	10.50	5.00
1990 Score #650	1.25	0.55	0.25
1990 Topps Traded #48	0.90	0.40	0.15
1990 Upper Deck #711	5.75	2.75	1.25
1991 Classic Collectors' Edition #193	1.75	0.75	0.30
1991 Fleer Ultra #7	1.30	0.55	0.25
1991 Fleer Ultra Elite Performer #394	0.35	0.15	0.06
1991 Kenner Starting Lineup	22.50	10.00	4.50
1991 Leaf #77	2.25	1.00	0.40
1991 Score Rising Star #45	0.95	0.40	0.15
1991 Stadium Club Dome #97	0.85	0.35	0.15
1991 Star Co. Dave Justice set (11)	15.00	6.50	2.50
1991 Studio #146	2.00	0.85	0.35
1991 Topps Stadium Club #26	8.50	4.00	1.75
1991 Toys 'R' Us Rookies #14	0.45	0.20	0.08
1992 Fleer Ultra #164	1.25	0.55	0.25
1992 Pinnacle #100	0.45	0.20	0.08
1992 Pinnacle Slugfest #5	1.75	0.75	0.30
1992 Pinnacle Team 2000 #9	1.00	0.45	0.20
1992 Score Impact Players #44	0.60	0.25	0.10
1992 Team Pinnacle (w/Ruben Sierra) #10	40.00	17.50	7.50
1992 Topps Stadium Club #182	1.00	0.40	0.15
1992 Topps Stadium Club Members Choice #592	1.00	0.40	0.15
1993 Score Select #39	0.20	0.08	0.01

Jim Kaat

Sooner or later the speculation on Cooperstown will catch up with the prices on Jim Kaat cards. Carlton Fisk cards went that way until a few years ago, then they went up about tenfold in one year. Expect good things from Kaat cards fairly soon.

	NM	EX	VG
1960 Topps #136	35.00	10.00	3.50
1961 Topps #63	9.00	2.50	1.00
1962 Topps #21	6.50	1.50	0.50
1963 Fleer #22	9.50	2.50	1.00
1963 Topps #165	7.50	2.00	0.75
1964 Topps #567	12.50	3.50	1.25

1965 Topps #62	4.50	1.50	0.50
1966 Topps #445	7.00	2.25	0.85
1967 Topps #300	5.00	1.50	0.50
1968 Topps #450	5.50	1.50	0.50
1969 Topps #290	6.00	1.75	0.50
1970 Topps #75	4.00	1.00	0.25
1971 Topps #245	4.00	1.00	0.25
1972 Topps #709	11.00	3.50	1.00
1972 Topps #710	5.50	1.50	0.50
1973 Topps #530	5.00	1.50	0.50
1974 Topps #440	1.50	0.50	0.15
1975 Topps #243	1.50	0.50	0.15
1976 Topps #80	1.00	0.25	0.10

Eric Karros

With the ascendance of Eric Karros, the Dodgers have what they haven't had since the days of Steve Garvey: a homegrown, immobile first baseman who can hit in the middle of the order with power and drive in runs. Karros fits the bill in every respect. Karros should have a long, productive career in Los Angeles, which should keep his cards perking right along. Right now they're a little more expensive than they should be because of his recent rookie of the year performance, but in another year or two they might approach recommended-buy levels. For the time being, just watch Karros and his cards. But watch carefully.

	NM	EX	VG
1990 Grand Slam San Antonio Missions (set)	8.00	3.50	1.50
1991 Bowman Tiffany #604	5.25	2.50	1.00
1991 Impel Line Drive AAA #12	1.00	0.45	0.20
1991 ProCards Albuquerque Dukes (set)	7.00	3.25	1.50
1991 ProCards Tomorrow's Heroes #240	1.50	0.65	0.25
1992 Bowman Gold #288	5.50	2.50	1.10

Roberto Kelly

Kelly never achieved his potential in New York, which isn't that unusual. In Cincinnati he'll have every opportunity to become a full-blown superstar, and he may need them all. It's not that Kelly is lacking in the tools department. He has excellent power, good speed, a very good throwing arm, and a consistent bat. He's just always seemed to have been missing that little something extra all the great players have. Whether or not he'll find it in Cincinnati is a good question. Tell you what, though: his cards could use the boost.

	NM	EX	VG
1988 Donruss #635	1.25	0.55	0.20
1988 Fleer #212	2.50	1.00	0.45
1988 Fleer Tin Glossy #212	3.25	1.25	0.50
1988 Score #634	1.00	0.45	0.20
1988 Score Glossy #634	15.00	6.50	2.75
1988 Topps Tiffany Traded #57	3.50	1.50	0.65
1988 Topps Traded #57	0.85	0.40	0.15
1989 Score Yankees #18	0.50	0.20	0.08
1989 Upper Deck #590	0.80	0.35	0.15
1990 Leaf #17	1.00	0.45	0.20
1991 Leaf Studio #94	0.20	0.08	0.03
1991 Topps Stadium Club #319	0.70	0.30	0.10
1992 Fleer Ultra All-Star #7	3.00	1.35	0.55
1992 Topps Gold #266	2.00	0.85	0.30

Jimmy Key

A solid pitcher but pitchers are by definition a risk when it comes to collecting their cards. Key is no exception.

	NM	EX	VG
1984 Fleer Update #61	27.50	4.00	0.25
1984 Topps Traded #62	10.00	2.00	0.25
1985 Donruss #559	4.25	0.75	0.10

Ryan Klesko

Drafted as a sore-armed pitcher and hyped as a hitter since his first minor-league at-bat, Ryan Klesko could make people forget about the same transformation made by Stan Musial five decades earlier. Klesko is a superb prospect despite the hype and is just about ready to take over as Atlanta's starting first baseman. The only drawback to Klesko as a card buy is a big one: the guy's absolutely no secret. Everyone who thinks he's an expert on rookies has picked up on Klesko, and as a result, there are few bargains to be had. Console yourself in the knowledge that you didn't buy the hype and start looking at Ray McDavid cards.

	NM	EX	VG
1990 Best Minor League Baseball #236	18.50	9.00	4.25
1991 Bowman #590	0.60	0.25	0.10
1991 Bowman Tiffany #590	3.75	1.75	0.75
1991 Classic II #53	0.85	0.35	0.15
1991 Gold Leaf Rookies #21	7.75	3.75	1.75

1991 Impel Line Drive AA #209 .... 3.75	1.75	0.75
1991 ProCards Greenville Braves #3011 .... 4.50	2.10	1.00
1991 ProCards Tomorrow's Heroes #181 ..... 4.25	2.00	0.85
1991 Upper Deck Final Edition #8 .... 1.25	0.55	0.25
1992 Bowman #549 .... 0.95	0.40	0.15
1992 Bowman #623 .... 0.70	0.30	0.12
1992 Donruss #13 .... 0.50	0.20	0.08
1992 Donruss Rookie Phenoms #15 .... 5.25	2.50	1.10
1993 Fleer #6 .... 0.20	0.08	0.01
1993 Upper Deck #376 .... 0.50	0.20	0.08

Chuck Knoblauch

Scrappy second basemen normally aren't the stuff of baseball-card greatness — priced any good Jim Gantner cards lately? — but Knoblauch offers a good chance for appreciation. He's got a better-than-average bat and he hits in the Metrodome, where everything makes the baggies. Five years from now collectors may be wondering what all the fuss was about, but for now Knoblauch supplies the right answers. Note: In 1992 Score bought a bunch of Score Knoblauch rookies from Knoblauch's agent, had Knoblauch autograph and number them, and inserted the autographed cards at random into '92 Score packs. Those cards are not listed here.

	NM	EX	VG
1990 Best Minor-League #146 .... 10.00	4.50	2.00
1990 Best Orlando #3 .... 12.00	5.50	2.50
1990 Bowman #415 .... 1.00	0.45	0.20
1990 ProCards Orlando #1090 .... 8.00	3.50	1.50
1990 Score #672 .... 1.75	0.75	0.35
1990 Star Co. Orlando #8 .... 8.00	3.50	1.50
1991 Bowman #330 .... 0.35	0.15	0.06
1991 Donruss #39 .... 0.55	0.25	0.12
1991 Fleer Ultra #382 .... 2.00	0.85	0.40
1991 Fleer Ultra Update #37 .... 2.00	0.85	0.40
1991 Leaf #396 .... 2.00	0.85	0.40
1991 Topps Stadium Club #548 .... 5.50	2.50	1.10
1991 Topps Traded #69 .... 0.65	0.30	0.12
1991 Upper Deck #40 .... 1.25	0.55	0.25
1992 Bowman #24 .... 0.35	0.15	0.06
1992 Fleer Rookie Sensations #10 .... 11.50	5.50	2.50
1992 Fleer Ultra #93 .... 1.00	0.45	0.20
1992 Fleer Ultra Award Winners #2 .... 7.50	3.50	1.50
1992 O-Pee-Chee Premier #35 .... 0.25	0.10	0.04
1992 Pinnacle Team 2000 #6 .... 1.00	0.45	0.20

1992 Score Impact Players #1	1.00	0.45	0.20
1992 Topps Kids #112	0.15	0.05	0.01
1992 Topps Stadium Club #601 (Members Choice)	1.00	0.45	0.20
1993 Score Select #36	0.25	0.10	0.04
1993 Upper Deck #254	0.20	0.08	0.01

John Kruk

The latest in a long line of big hitters that runs from Babe Ruth and Hack Wilson through Ted Kluszewski and Greg Luzinski, Kruk is not gorgeous or graceful. He's just a tough out. In 1992 he almost won a batting title, which finally got a few heads to turn his way. If they would have turned earlier they would have discovered four .300-plus seasons and a couple in the .290s. Kruk can hit the ball, but as an outfielder he makes a better first baseman and as a first baseman he won't make anyone forget Cecil Cooper. His cards continue to edge upward, as they should. His 1993 World Series performance should land him quite a bit of media exposure and that attention can't hurt prices. All things considered, his cards might even be a little undervalued.

	NM	EX	VG
1985 Cramer Las Vegas Stars (set)	15.00	6.50	2.75
1986 Donruss Rookies #42	2.25	1.00	0.40
1986 Fleer Update #61	1.75	0.75	0.35
1986 Topps Traded #56	1.25	0.50	0.20
1986 Topps Tiffany Traded #56	6.50	2.50	1.00
1987 Bohemian Hearth Bread #8	4.00	1.50	0.65
1987 Donruss #328	1.00	0.40	0.15
1987 Fleer #420	2.25	1.00	0.40
1987 Fleer Glossy Tin #420	2.75	1.25	0.50
1987 Topps #123	0.60	0.25	0.10
1988 Classic Travel (red) #162	0.25	0.10	0.04
1988 Fleer #589	0.35	0.15	0.05
1988 Fleer Glossy Tin #589	0.50	0.20	0.08
1988 Kenner Starting Lineup	13.50	6.00	2.50
1988 Leaf #176	0.25	0.10	0.04
1988 O-Pee-Chee #32	0.10	0.04	0.01
1989 Fleer Glossy Tin #565	0.40	0.15	0.05
1990 Leaf #284	0.60	0.25	0.10
1990 Topps Big #214	0.06	0.02	0.01
1991 Topps #227	0.40	0.15	0.05
1992 Donruss Diamond Kings #12	1.00	0.40	0.15
1992 Leaf Gold Inserts #313	0.40	0.15	0.05
1992 Topps Gold Inserts #30	0.75	0.30	0.12
1992 Upper Deck Home Run Heroes #23	0.50	0.20	0.05

Mark Langston

The quintessential great-stuff/lousy-record guy, Langston seems to finally have figured out the winning part of the game in 1992. Even after 10 years in the bigs Langston throws as hard as any left-hander, but he mixes in a little more savvy these days. While he's won 19 games twice, lots of pro types will tell you he should have won 20 twice as many times with the stuff he has. Well, he hasn't. And he probably won't make the Hall of Fame, either. But if you figure that maybe, just maybe, Langston has a couple 20-win seasons in him yet, $12 for that '84 Fleer Update card looks awfully reasonable.

	NM	EX	VG
1984 Fleer Update #70	12.00	6.00	2.00
1984 Mother's Cookies Mariners #13	1.75	0.75	0.35
1984 Topps Tiffany Traded #70	25.00	12.00	5.00
1985 Mother's Cookies Mariners #3	1.25	0.50	0.20
1985 Topps Tiffany #625	3.00	1.25	0.50
1986 Mother's Cookies Mariners #6	1.00	0.45	0.20
1986 O-Pee-Chee #198	0.15	0.05	0.01
1986 Topps Tiffany #495	1.25	0.50	0.20
1987 Donruss Opening Day #116	0.25	0.10	0.04
1987 Fleer Baseball's Hottest Stars #26	0.08	0.03	0.01
1987 Fleer Mini #62	0.10	0.04	0.01
1987 Fleer Star Stickers #70	0.15	0.05	0.01
1988 Classic Travel Blue #250	0.50	0.20	0.08
1988 Fleer Baseball's Best #23	0.10	0.04	0.01
1988 Fleer Glossy Tin #377	0.50	0.20	0.08
1988 Fleer Star Stickers #60	0.15	0.05	0.01
1988 Kenner Starting Lineup	13.00	6.00	2.50
1988 Leaf #123	0.10	0.04	0.01
1988 Panini Stickers #181	0.08	0.03	0.01
1988 Score Baseball Promo #30	15.00	7.00	2.50
1988 Score Glossy #30	0.65	0.25	0.10
1988 Topps American Baseball Glossy #42	0.50	0.20	0.08
1988 Topps Big #176	0.08	0.03	0.01
1988 Topps Coins #18	0.15	0.05	0.01
1988 Topps Gallery of Champions Aluminum	0.75	0.35	0.15
1988 Topps Gallery of Champions Bronze	7.50	3.50	1.50
1988 Topps Gallery of Champions Silver	20.00	8.50	3.50
1989 Donruss Baseball's Best #136	0.10	0.04	0.01
1989 Fleer Superstars #27	0.15	0.05	0.01
1989 Scoremasters #13	0.30	0.12	0.05

Ray Lankford

Not too many young players are described — seriously — with terms like "future MVP" or "Triple Crown contender." Ray Lankford is one of the few young players who deserves the descriptions. He may not have the sort of power that wins home-run titles, but he has 20-homer power. He also has a batting-title bat, 40-steal speed, and the sort of range and arm in center field that Cardinal fans haven't seen since the glory days of Curt Flood. All this performance comes at a price, of course, though the price is considerably less than some players of lesser talent who didn't have the misfortune to debut during the baseball-card nadir year of 1991. Lankford's a superb ballplayer. His card values don't reflect his talent. Now's the time to buy if you're buying.

	NM	EX	VG
1989 Grand Slam Arkansas (set) 11.50	5.50	2.50
1990 CMC Louisville (set).............................. 25.00	11.50	5.00
1990 CMC Pre-Rookie #114 .... 4.00	1.75	0.75
1990 Impel AAA #530 .... 2.75	1.25	0.55
1990 ProCards Louisville (set) 8.25	4.00	1.75
1990 Team Louisville (set) 16.00	7.50	3.50

Barry Larkin

Barry Larkin gets a little lost in the shuffle of all the great rookies who made their first appearances in the 1987 sets, and the reason might be that he's just too complete a player. Sorry, all you Cal Ripken Jr. fans, but Larkin is the premier shortstop in the game; he hits for average and power, drives in runs, runs the bases, and is superb in the field. For all this you pay about as much as you would for the first card of Bobby Bonilla or Bo Jackson, a couple of mere sluggers compared to an all-arounder — and a solid candidate for Cooperstown.

	NM	EX	VG
1987 Donruss #492 .... 3.25	1.50	0.65
1987 Fleer #204 .... 7.25	3.50	1.50
1987 Kahn's Reds #15.. 2.00	0.85	0.40
1987 Topps #648 .... 1.25	0.55	0.25
1987 Topps Tiffany #648.................................... 3.75	1.75	0.75
1988 Fleer #239 .... 0.40	0.15	0.05
1988 Score #72 .... 0.25	0.10	0.04
1988 Score Glossy #72 .... 1.25	0.55	0.25
1988 Score Promo 15.00	6.50	3.00
1988 Topps #102 .... 0.25	0.10	0.04
1988 Topps Stickercards #140 .... 0.05	0.01	0.01
1989 Kenner Starting Lineup 9.00	4.00	1.50

1989 Topps Mini League Leaders #11	0.15	0.05	0.01
1989 Upper Deck #270	0.55	0.25	0.12
1990 Kahn's Reds #15	0.80	0.30	0.12
1990 Leaf #18	1.65	0.75	0.30
1991 Fleer All-Star #2	1.50	0.65	0.30
1991 Score Cooperstown Collection #899	0.75	0.30	0.12
1991 Topps Stadium Club #92	1.00	0.45	0.20
1991 Upper Deck Silver Slugger #18	2.00	0.85	0.40
1992 Fleer All-Star #16	1.75	0.75	0.35
1992 Fleer Ultra All Stars #13	4.50	2.00	0.85
1992 Leaf Gold #73	1.00	0.45	0.20
1992 Topps Gold #465	2.00	0.85	0.35
1992 Topps Stadium Club Members Choice #596	1.00	0.45	0.15

Pat Listach

Pat Listach is a very quick middle infielder who came out of nowhere, thrived under Brewer manager Phil Garner's system, and won the A.L. Rookie of the Year Award in 1992. Listach's virtues are limited. He's not a great fielder and he has zero power. Think of him as Kenny Lofton with a lower ceiling. Yet he's an exciting player to watch, even if his cards come off as being something less than exciting.

	NM	EX	VG
1990 Best Cards Stockton Ports #5	2.75	1.25	0.60
1991 Impel AA #191	0.75	0.30	0.12
1992 Bowman #526	2.50	1.20	0.55
1992 Fleer Ultra #385	4.25	2.00	0.85
1992 Leaf #370	1.75	0.80	0.35
1992 Leaf Gold #370	10.00	0.45	2.00
1992 Pinnacle #562	1.75	0.80	0.35
1992 Score Rookie/Traded #80	1.00	0.45	0.20
1992 Topps Stadium Club #757	2.75	1.30	0.60
1992 Upper Deck #775	1.75	0.80	0.35
1992 Upper Deck Scouting Report #134	6.25	3.00	1.40
1993 Pinnacle #33	0.25	0.12	0.05
1993 Score Select #273	0.70	0.30	0.12

Kenny Lofton

Maybe Ed Taubensee will turn out all right for the Houston Astros, but right now the 'Stros look like stupes for dealing Kenny Lofton to the Indians for

Taubensee. Lofton is an ideal center fielder. He can range far into the gaps and snag practically anything, he can hit line drives and get on base, and once he's on base he can really run. He was edged out by Milwaukee's Pat Listach for the 1992 A.L. Rookie of the Year Award, but take our word for it, Lofton, the former University of Arizona point guard, will be the better player by far over time. His cards run the gamut pricewise. Some of them, like his base-brand 1992 rookie cards, are good buys.

	NM	EX	VG
1991 Bowman #565	0.65	0.30	0.12
1991 Bowman Tiffany #565	3.50	1.50	0.65
1991 Impel Line Drive AAA #614	1.25	0.50	0.20
1991 ProCards Tomorrow's Heroes #223	2.25	1.00	0.45
1991 Upper Deck Final Edition #24	1.75	0.75	0.35
1992 Bowman #110	1.00	0.45	0.20
1992 Donruss #5	0.45	0.20	0.08
1992 Fleer #655	0.35	0.15	0.05
1992 Fleer Ultra All-Rookie Team #7	7.50	3.50	1.50
1992 Leaf Gold Rookies #4	5.75	2.50	1.10
1992 O-Pee-Chee Premier #72	0.50	0.20	0.08
1992 Score Impact Player #32	0.75	0.30	0.12
1992 Score Pinnacle#582 #585	1.00	0.45	0.20
1992 Score Pinnacle Rookie Idols #7	35.00	0.15	6.50
1992 Score Pinnacle Team 2000 #35	2.25	1.00	0.45
1992 Studio #168	1.00	0.45	0.20
1992 Topps #69	0.50	0.20	0.08
1992 Topps Gold #69	4.00	1.75	0.75
1992 Topps Stadium Club #695	2.25	1.00	0.45
1992 Topps Traded #66	0.40	0.15	0.05
1992 Upper Deck #25	0.60	0.25	0.12
1992 Upper Deck Scouting Report #15	4.25	2.00	0.75
1993 Upper Deck #262	0.30	0.10	0.04

Shane Mack

Now here's a guy with a checkered career — both on and off cards. Shane Mack was a contemporary of Mark McGwire on the 1984 U.S. Olympic Team, signed with the Padres, rattled around Beaumont and Las Vegas for a while, simply could not cut it in the eyes of the Padres' brass, was drafted by the Twins out of the Padres' minor-league system, made the Twins' starting lineup in a flash, and has been one of the league's best hitters ever since. The stuff of Cooperstown? No, but definitely the stuff good short-term card buys are made of. Hey, is Mark McGwire's first card in the '85 Topps set worth $29 more than this guy's first card? Not to our way of thinking. What we have here is your basic value shortfall.

	NM	EX	VG
1985 Topps #398 .... 4.75		2.25	1.10
1986 ProCards Beaumont (set) 33.00		15.50	7.50
1987 Donruss Rookies #42 .... 1.50		0.65	0.30
1987 ProCards Las Vegas #123 .... 7.00		3.25	1.50
1987 Topps Tiffany Traded #69T 3.00		1.25	0.50
1987 Topps Traded #69T 0.75		0.30	0.12
1988 Donruss #411 .... 0.20		0.08	0.03
1988 Fleer Glossy #590 .... 1.75		0.85	0.35
1988 Score #414 .... 0.25		0.12	0.05
1988 Score Glossy #414 .... 2.50		1.25	0.55
1988 Topps #548 .... 0.20		0.08	0.03
1988 Topps Tiffany #548 .... 0.60		0.25	0.10
1989 Upper Deck #182 .... 0.15		0.05	0.01
1990 Leaf #136 .... 0.75		0.30	0.12
1991 Topps Desert Storm #672 .... 5.25		2.50	1.25
1991 Topps Stadium Club #259 .... 0.85		0.40	0.15
1992 Fleer Ultra #95 .... 0.15		0.06	0.01
1992 Topps Gold #164 .... 0.75		0.30	0.12
1993 Topps Gold #282 .... 0.50		0.20	0.08
1993 Upper Deck #236 .... 0.10		0.04	0.01

Greg Maddux

Despite what might seem like a lateral move from one "superstation" team to another, Greg Maddux took a major leap up in visibility when he left the Chicago Cubs for the Atlanta Braves after the 1992 season. The previous season Maddux had been the practically perfect pitcher, going 20-11 with a sparkling 2.18 earned-run average. Maddux is a control pitcher with a little pop and the guts of a burglar. He's also a top-notch fielder and not a bad hitter. His cards took a quick jump after he joined the Braves but have leveled off since. Expect them to keep rising if he does anything more than post a winning record with the Braves. Too bad the Phillies ended his 1993 season before the World Series. Note: He's young enough that a Hall of Fame caliber career isn't out of the question.

	NM	EX	VG
1986 ProCards Pittsfield 28.00		13.50	6.50
1987 Donruss #36 .... 7.25		3.50	1.50
1987 Donruss Rookies #52 .... 4.25		2.00	0.85
1987 Fleer Update #68U 4.25		2.00	0.85
1987 Topps Tiffany Traded #70T 12.50		6.00	2.75
1987 Topps Traded #70T 2.75		1.25	0.60
1988 David Berg Hot Dogs Cubs #40 .... 0.85		0.40	0.15

1988 Donruss #539	0.45	0.20	0.08
1988 Donruss Baseball's Best #82	0.15	0.06	0.01
1988 Donruss Team Book #539	0.60	0.25	0.10
1988 Fleer #423	1.60	0.75	0.35
1988 Fleer Glossy #423	3.00	1.35	0.60
1988 Topps #361	0.60	0.25	0.12
1989 Score Superstar #48	0.25	0.12	0.05
1989 Topps Tiffany #240	1.25	0.60	0.25
1989 Upper Deck #241	0.85	0.40	0.15
1990 Leaf #25	3.25	1.50	0.70
1991 Topps Stadium Club #126	1.40	0.60	0.25
1992 Topps Gold #580	0.80	0.30	0.12
1993 Fleer N.L. All-Stars #10	2.25	1.00	0.40
1993 Topps Black Gold #12	4.25	2.00	0.85

Pat Mahomes

Pat Mahomes is a hard-throwing right-hander with control and what appears to be all the stuff great careers are made of. At this point it's hard to say too much more about him than that. Some of his cards have attracted speculation, which is misguided at this point but understandable.

	NM	EX	VG
1990 Cal League Visalia Oaks #60	2.50	1.10	0.50
1991 Impel Line Drive AA #485	0.80	0.35	0.15
1991 ProCards Tomorrow's Heroes #93	0.80	0.35	0.15
1992 Bowman # 131	0.40	0.15	0.07
1992 Donruss #403	0.25	0.12	0.05
1992 Fleer Ultra #398	0.75	0.35	0.15
1992 Fleer Ultra All-Rookie Team # 9	2.75	1.25	0.55
1992 Fleer Update #40	0.35	0.15	0.05
1992 Leaf Gold Rookies #17	3.25	1.50	0.65
1992 Score Pinnacle #472	0.35	0.15	0.05
1992 Score Pinnacle Team 2000 #80	0.65	0.30	0.12
1992 Score Rookie/Traded #102	0.25	0.10	0.04
1992 Studio #208	0.45	0.20	0.08
1992 Upper Deck # 776	0.30	0.12	0.05
1992 Upper Deck Scouting Report #16	1.25	0.60	0.25
1993 Score Select #324	0.20	0.08	0.03
1993 Upper Deck #337	0.15	0.05	0.01

Dennis Martinez

Dennis Martinez is one for the ages. Before the age of 30 Martinez won 108 games for the Orioles and was an alcoholic. After the age of 30 Martinez has won 84 games, mostly with the Expos, kept his ERA under 2.50 for the most part, and has stayed clean and sober. It's a heck of a story, and Martinez is a heck of a pitcher. His cards ought to be worth more, but it's hard to see how they could be. It's an odd situation, but somehow not inappropriate for Martinez, who at least for now can make time stand still.

	NM	EX	VG
1977 Topps #491	6.00	2.75	1.25
1978 Topps 119 #2	0.80	0.35	0.01
1979 Topps #211	1.00	0.40	0.15
1980 Topps #10	0.60	0.25	0.10
1981 Donruss #533	0.20	0.08	0.03
1981 Fleer #180	0.25	0.10	0.04
1981 Topps #367	0.60	0.25	0.10
1982 Donruss #79	0.20	0.08	0.03
1982 Fleer #170	0.20	0.08	0.03
1982 Topps #712	0.25	0.10	0.04
1983 Fleer Stickers #199	0.04	0.01	0.01
1984 Donruss #633	0.15	0.05	0.01
1984 Topps Tiffany #631	0.50	0.20	0.08
1985 Topps Tiffany #199	0.35	0.15	0.05
1986 Topps Tiffany #416	0.25	0.10	0.04
1987 Topps Tiffany #252	0.15	0.05	0.01
1988 Fleer Glossy Tin #188	0.25	0.10	0.04
1988 Leaf #262	0.20	0.08	0.03
1988 Topps Tiffany #76	0.20	0.08	0.03
1989 Fleer Glossy Tin #385	0.15	0.05	0.01
1989 Topps Tiffany #313	0.20	0.08	0.01
1990 Leaf #54	0.20	0.08	0.03
1991 Topps #273	0.50	0.20	0.08
1992 Donruss Diamond Kings #24	1.00	0.40	0.15
1992 Fleer Ultra #223	0.75	0.30	0.12
1992 Leaf Gold Inserts #190	0.40	0.15	0.05
1992 Topps #860	0.15	0.05	0.01
1992 Topps Gold Inserts #15	0.75	0.30	0.12
1993 Score Select Aces #6	3.00	1.25	0.50

Edgar Martinez

While Ken Griffey Jr. gets all the headlines in Seattle and Robin Ventura gets the reputation as the next great hitting machine, Edgar Martinez goes about the business of winning batting titles. Martinez won his first major-league title in 1992 after topping the Pacific Coast League in 1988. Hitting out of a classic straight-up stance, Martinez generates surprising power. All the fantasy baseballers love him, and card collectors are starting to warm up to him, too. Martinez isn't going to get into the Hall of Fame; he's too old and spent too many years shuttling between Seattle and Calgary to pull that off. But he's a solid major-league hitter, who, like Julio Franco, stands an outside chance of developing into something even better.

	NM	EX	VG
1986 ProCards Chattanooga (set)	18.00	8.00	3.50
1987 ProCards Calgary (set)	9.00	3.50	1.50
1988 CMC Calgary (set)	10.00	4.50	0.20
1988 Donruss Rookies #36	2.25	1.00	0.40
1988 Fleer #378	3.75	1.75	0.75
1989 Bowman #216	0.25	0.10	0.04
1989 Donruss #645	0.60	0.25	0.10
1989 Donruss Rookies #15	0.75	0.30	0.12
1989 Fleer #552	0.25	0.10	0.04
1989 Mother's Cookies Mariners #11	0.60	0.25	0.10
1989 Score #637	0.60	0.25	0.10
1989 Upper Deck #768	2.00	0.80	0.35
1990 CMC Pre-Rookie #439	2.25	1.00	0.45
1990 Fleer #520	0.25	0.10	0.04
1990 Leaf #299	3.00	1.25	0.50
1990 Mother's Cookies Mariners #10	0.60	0.25	0.10
1990 Score #324	0.25	0.10	0.04
1990 Topps #148	0.30	0.12	0.05
1990 Upper Deck #532	0.50	0.20	0.08
1991 Donruss #117	0.25	0.10	0.04
1991 Donruss Elite #27	50.00	23.50	11.00
1991 Fleer Ultra #340	0.20	0.08	0.03
1991 Leaf #477	0.15	0.05	0.01
1991 Topps #47	1.25	0.50	0.20
1992 Bowman #33	0.15	0.05	0.01
1992 Fleer Ultra #126	0.15	0.05	0.01
1992 Leaf #197	0.20	0.08	0.03
1992 Leaf Gold Inserts #197	0.40	0.15	0.05
1992 Topps #267	0.15	0.05	0.01
1992 Topps Gold Inserts #553	2.00	0.80	0.35

1993 Score Select Rookies #16	3.00	1.25	0.50
1993 Topps Gold Inserts #315	0.25	0.10	0.04

Ramon Martinez

Ramon Martinez has the stringiest hair in the major leagues, which stands to reason: He's the stringiest pitcher in the major leagues. His lean physique helps him get extra whip on his extra-hard fastball. Martinez mixes that with a changeup, and that's basically all there is to his repertoire. There are some questions about the health of Martinez's arm — there are always questions about the health of a pitcher's arm when Tommy Lasorda's the manager — and those should also cause some questions about Martinez's cards, which right now carry some premium-for-pitchers price tags. Not recommended.

	NM	EX	VG
1987 Pro Cards Vero Beach (set)	37.50	16.50	7.50
1988 Best San Antonio (set)	17.50	7.50	3.25
1989 Donruss #464	0.25	0.10	0.04
1989 Donruss Rookies #45	0.35	0.15	0.05
1989 Fleer #67	0.35	0.15	0.05
1989 Fleer Glossy Tin #67	2.25	1.00	0.40
1989 Score #635	0.30	0.12	0.04
1989 Score Young Superstar I #40	1.00	0.45	0.20
1989 Topps #225	0.30	0.12	0.04
1990 Bowman #88	0.15	0.05	0.01
1990 Bowman Tiffany #88	1.75	0.75	0.35
1990 Donruss #685	0.15	0.05	0.01
1990 Fleer #402	0.40	0.15	0.05
1990 Leaf #147	1.25	0.50	0.20
1990 Mother's Cookies Dodgers #17	0.75	0.35	0.15
1990 Score #461	0.15	0.05	0.01
1990 Score McDonald's #13	5.00	2.25	1.00
1990 Score Rising Star #59	0.50	0.20	0.08
1990 Sportflics #68	0.60	0.25	0.10
1990 Sportflics #68	0.50	0.15	0.05
1990 Topps #62	0.15	0.05	0.01
1990 Upper Deck #675	0.35	0.12	0.05
1991 Donruss #184	0.30	0.10	0.04
1991 Donruss #557	0.20	0.08	0.03
1991 Fleer Ultra #164	0.15	0.05	0.01
1991 Fleer Ultra Gold #7	0.25	0.10	0.04
1991 Kenner Starting Lineup	17.50	6.50	2.50
1991 Leaf #61	0.20	0.08	0.03
1991 Score #408	0.15	0.05	0.01

1991 Score #419	0.20	0.08	0.03
1991 Score Super Star #16	0.20	0.08	0.03
1991 Topps #516	0.50	0.20	0.08
1992 Fleer Ultra #213	0.25	0.10	0.04
1992 Fleer All-Stars #7	1.00	0.40	0.15
1992 Fleer Citgo 7-11 #21	0.15	0.05	0.01
1992 Leaf #297	0.15	0.05	0.01
1992 Leaf Gold Inserts #297	0.75	0.30	0.12
1992 Score Pinnacle Team 2000 #49	0.15	0.05	0.01
1992 Topps #207	0.40	0.15	0.05
1992 Topps Gold Inserts #730	2.00	0.80	0.35
1993 Topps Gold Inserts #120	0.25	0.10	0.04

Tino Martinez

Like Edgar Martinez, Tino Martinez is taking his own sweet time about getting good. Unlike Edgar, Tino was supposed to be good from the get-go. A former Olympian and star of one of the many University of Miami powerhouses of the late '80s, Martinez has torn up opposing pitching at every level except the major-league level, and the jury's still out as to whether he can rip with the big kids at this height. There's certainly no physical reason why he can't; the tools are all in place. The only thing that's missing is the consistent discipline it takes to be a great major-league hitter. Card collectors must believe it'll come for Tino; his cards are priced way out of line with his performance to date. They're buying into expectations, and in the case of Tino Martinez, those expectations may not be fulfilled.

	NM	EX	VG
1988 Topps Tiffany Traded #66	6.00	2.50	1.00
1989 Bowman #211	0.30	0.12	0.04
1989 Topps Big Baseball #93	0.70	0.30	0.10
1990 CMC Calgary (set)	25.00	12.00	5.00
1990 Fleer Update #119	0.25	0.10	0.04
1990 ProCards Calgary (set)	8.00	3.50	1.50
1990 ProCards Future Stars #124	1.75	0.75	0.35
1990 Score #596	0.30	0.12	0.04
1990 Topps Major League Debut #99	0.25	0.10	0.04
1990 Upper Deck #37	0.50	0.20	0.08
1991 Bowman Tiffany #257	0.50	0.20	0.08
1991 Classic Collector's Edition #150	0.50	0.20	0.08
1991 Donruss #118	0.50	0.20	0.08
1991 Fleer #341	0.15	0.05	0.01
1991 Fleer #458	0.35	0.15	0.05
1991 Impel AAA #66	0.75	0.35	0.10

1991 Score Rookies #38 .... 0.20	0.08	0.03
1991 Topps #179 .... 0.85	0.35	0.15
1991 Topps #482 .... 0.15	0.05	0.01
1991 Upper Deck #553 .... 0.15	0.05	0.01
1992 Bowman #626 .... 0.20	0.08	0.03
1992 Fleer Ultra #127 .... 0.15	0.05	0.01
1992 Leaf #329 .... 0.15	0.05	0.01
1992 Leaf Gold Inserts #329 .... 0.75	0.30	0.12
1992 Score Pinnacle Team 2000 #62 .... 0.15	0.05	0.01
1992 Topps Gold Inserts #481 .... 0.75	0.30	0.12
1992 Upper Deck #554 .... 0.15	0.05	0.01
1993 Topps Gold Inserts #232 .... 0.25	0.10	0.04

Don Mattingly

At one time the best player in the game, Don Mattingly had his string of wonderful seasons halted by back problems that robbed him of his power. The line-drive stroke is back now, but the rest of Mattingly's game has suffered, to the extent that it will probably keep him out of Cooperstown. It's hard to say, though; he has around 2,000 hits, and with any sort of good health at all he could post some superb career numbers. His cards, which did so much toward fueling the initial surge in the baseball-card market, have really fallen off from those heights and are even affordable. Sure, there's a little bit of a risk involved with Mattingly, but his cards are reasonably priced and have a good long-term outlook. Give them a try.

	NM	EX	VG
1981 Arby's Nashville Sounds (set) 27.50	13.00	5.50
1982 Columbus Clippers Police (set) 50.00	22.50	10.00
1982 TCMA Columbus Clippers (set) 400.00	185.00	85.00
1984 Nestle's #8 .... 125.00	55.00	25.00
1984 O-Pee-Chee #8 .... 22.50	10.00	4.50
1984 Topps Stickers #325 .... 0.50	0.20	0.08
1984 Topps Tiffany #8 .... 85.00	40.00	17.50
1985 Donruss Highlights #36 .... 2.50	1.10	0.50
1985 Donruss Highlights #44 .... 2.50	1.10	0.50
1985 Donruss Highlights #45 .... 2.50	1.10	0.50
1985 Fleer Sticker #4 .... 0.90	0.40	0.15
1985 Topps Sticker #171 .... 0.30	0.10	0.04
1985 Topps Sticker #171 .... 0.30	0.10	0.04
1986 Dorman's Panel #7 .... 4.00	1.50	0.50
1986 Dorman's Panel #7 .... 4.00	1.50	0.50
1986 Meadow Gold Bubble Gum Cooler Panel #3 .... 8.00	3.50	1.50

1986 Star Co. (set of 24)	15.00	6.50	2.50
1986 Topps 3-D #15	1.50	0.50	0.20
1986 Topps 3-D #15	1.50	0.50	0.20
1987 Classic Travel Edition #104	1.75	0.75	0.35
1987 Classic Travel Edition #104	1.75	0.75	0.35
1987 Educational Insights Sports Reading Card Series #21	2.50	1.10	0.50
1987 Kraft Home Plate Heroes #29	1.50	0.50	0.20
1987 Star Co. "Yankee Hitman" (set of 11)	15.00	5.50	2.50
1987 Star Co. "Yankee Hitman" (set of 11)	15.00	5.50	2.50
1987 Topps American Sticker #294	1.25	0.50	0.20
1988 Donruss Team Collection Card Sheet	15.00	5.50	2.50
1988 Donruss Team Collection Card Sheet	15.00	5.50	2.50
1988 Hi-Pro sample card	85.00	35.00	15.00
1988 Hi-Pro sample card	85.00	35.00	15.00
1988 Topps Big #229	0.75	0.35	0.15
1989 Kenner Starting Lineup	13.00	6.00	2.50
1989 Kenner Starting Lineup	13.00	6.00	2.50
1989 LJN Talking Baseball Card #82	1.25	0.50	0.20
1989 Topps Doubleheaders	1.25	0.50	0.20
1989 Topps Heads-Up #19	0.50	0.20	0.08
1989 Topps Heads-Up #19	0.50	0.20	0.08
1990 Colla card set (12)	10.00	4.00	1.50
1991 Donruss Learning Series #12	6.00	2.50	1.10
1991 Donruss Learning Series #12	6.00	2.50	1.10

Carl Mays

For years no one cared very much about Carl Mays except to remember that it was his pitch that killed Ray Chapman. A little publicity, a little rumored Hall of Fame attention, and Mays is now one of the hotter old stars.

	NM	EX	VG
Yuengling's Ice Cream	25.00	10.00	5.00
E120 American Caramel	55.00	25.00	10.00
E121 American Caramel Set of 120	55.00	25.00	10.00
E121 American Caramel Set of 80	65.00	25.00	10.00
E210 York Caramel	45.00	20.00	10.00

David McCarty

Dave McCarty is one of the top hitting prospects in baseball. A 1991 first-round pick of the Minnesota Twins and possessor of a sweet home-run stroke, McCarty is slated to take over either at first base or in the outfield for the Twins as early as the end of 1993. His cards are high-priced and worth investing in only if he reaches the upper bounds of his potential.

	NM	EX	VG
1991 Classic Draft Picks #3	2.25	1.10	0.50
1992 Classic-Best foil #350	2.25	1.10	0.50
1992 Classic-Best Orlando (set)	8.00	4.00	1.75
1992 Upper Deck #75	1.60	0.75	0.35

Jack McDowell

Just your basic guitar-toting, rock-singing staff ace, Jack McDowell has continued to improve from his first major-league game, which was very nearly his first pro game. A power pitcher with the best stuff this side of Roger Clemens, McDowell is up with Jack Morris and Clemens as one of the A.L.'s winningest pitchers of the last couple of years, but his card prices don't come anywhere near those of Clemens and Morris — yet. Given a chance, McDowell's cards should move right up there and stick. He's that good.

	NM	EX	VG
1988 Coca-Cola White Sox (14)	0.50	0.20	0.08
1988 Donruss #47	1.00	0.40	0.15
1988 Donruss Rookies #40	2.75	1.25	0.50
1988 Fleer #407	4.00	1.75	0.75
1988 Score Traded #85	12.00	5.50	2.50
1988 Score Glossy Traded/Update #85	45.00	20.00	8.50
1988 Topps Traded #68	2.75	1.25	0.50
1988 Topps Tiffany Traded #68	10.00	4.50	2.00
1989 Bowman #61	0.30	0.12	0.04
1989 Bowman Tiffany #61	1.50	0.65	0.20
1989 Fleer #504	0.30	0.12	0.04
1989 Score #2899	0.40	0.15	0.05
1989 Topps #486	0.30	0.12	0.04
1989 Toys 'R' Us Rookies #20	0.15	0.05	0.01
1989 Upper Deck #530	1.25	0.50	0.20
1990 Bowman Tiffany #305	0.75	0.30	0.12
1990 Coca-Cola White Sox #29	0.35	0.15	0.05
1990 Upper Deck #625	0.45	0.20	0.08
1991 Classic III #66	0.10	0.04	0.01

1991 Donruss #36	0.40	0.15	0.05
1991 Leaf #340	0.30	0.12	0.04
1991 Topps #87	1.50	0.65	0.25
1992 Bowman #605	0.50	0.20	0.08
1992 Bowman Gold #371	1.25	0.50	0.20
1992 Fleer Smoke'n Heat #2	0.75	0.30	0.12
1992 Fleer Ultra All-Stars #10	3.25	1.50	0.65
1992 Leaf Gold Inserts #422	1.00	0.40	0.15
1992 Topps #52	0.30	0.12	0.05
1992 Topps Gold Inserts #11	3.00	1.25	0.50
1993 Score Select Aces #3	3.00	1.25	0.50

Fred McGriff

The "Crime Dog" isn't quite enough to make the Roberto Alomar/Joe Carter for McGriff/Tony Fernandez trade palatable, but he's close. He hs led the N.L. in homers and dispelled any notion that he couldn't hit in the clutch. Truth is, McGriff can hit just about anywhere at any time. He's more than a mere power hitter, as his batting averages of the last couple of years bear out. In Atlanta's line-up he may have even better stats. He's a decent first baseman, too. McGriff's cards are up there; only a few of his cards, such as his Blue Jay police cards, are interesting and affordable enough to be recommended.

	NM	EX	VG
1985 TCMA Syracuse (set)	75.00	36.50	17.50
1986 Leaf #28	20.00	9.00	3.50
1986 Pro Cards Syracuse (set)	32.00	15.00	6.50
1987 Donruss #621	3.75	1.75	0.75
1987 Donruss Rookies #31	3.75	1.75	0.75
1987 Fleer Update #75	3.75	1.75	0.75
1987 Police Blue Jays #19	2.00	0.85	0.35
1987 Sportflics Rookies #12	1.50	0.60	0.25
1987 Topps Traded #74	2.50	1.10	0.45
1988 Fleer #118	1.25	0.50	0.20
1988 Police Blue Jays #19	1.00	0.45	0.20
1988 Score Glossy #107	2.50	1.00	0.45
1988 Score Young Superstar II #28	0.40	0.15	0.05
1988 Topps #463	0.50	0.20	0.08
1989 Sportflics #14	0.50	0.20	0.08
1989 Upper Deck #572	1.00	0.40	0.15
1990 Donruss A.L. Best #56	0.25	0.10	0.09
1990 Donruss Grand Slammers #9	0.25	0.10	0.04
1990 Fleer Award Winners #23	0.25	0.10	0.04
1990 Leaf #132	2.25	1.00	0.40

	NM	EX	VG
1990 Topps Big Baseball #134 .... 0.20	0.08	0.03
1991 Donruss #247 .... 0.60	0.25	0.10
1991 Donruss Elite #20 .... 75.00	35.00	16.50
1991 Topps #357 .... 1.25	0.50	0.20
1992 Donruss Diamond Kings #26 .... 2.00	0.80	0.30
1992 Kenner Starting Lineup 18.00	8.50	3.50
1992 Leaf Gold Inserts #264 .... 1.00	0.40	0.15
1992 Topps #580 .... 0.60	0.25	0.10
1992 Topps Gold Inserts #660 .... 2.00	0.80	0.30
1992 Upper Deck Home Run Heroes #10 ..... 1.00	0.40	0.15
1992 Upper Deck Ted Williams' Best #8 .... 2.75	1.25	0.50
1993 Donruss Long Ball Leaders #2 .... 2.50	1.10	0.40
1993 Fleer NL All-Stars #1 .... 2.50	1.10	0.40
1993 Score Select Rookies #1 .... 5.00	2.25	1.00
1993 Topps Gold Inserts #30 .... 0.50	0.20	0.08
1993 Topps Black Gold Inserts #13 .... 6.00	2.50	1.00
1993 Upper Deck Iooss Collection #16 .... 3.00	1.25	0.50
1993 Upper Deck Traded #5 .... 6.00	2.50	1.10

Mark McGwire

Win 27 games, as the A's Bob Welch did in 1990, and three years later no one remembers. But hit 49 homers, as the A's Mark McGwire did in 1987, and no one forgets — especially card collectors. It's a fact of card life that homers are more exciting than wins, and Mark McGwire is one of the most exciting players of all. From a purist's point of view, he's a mere basher rather than a great hitter, but he does bash well and often. He's hit more home runs than anyone his age (though Juan Gonzalez is likely to pass him as soon as he's old enough), and he stands an outside chance of keeping it up long enough to reach Cooperstown. For the time being we say no, though, and cast our doubts about the merits of his cards.

	NM	EX	VG
1987 Leaf #46 .... 4.50	2.00	0.80
1988 Donruss All-Stars #19 .... 0.65	0.25	0.10
1988 Donruss Oakland Team Book #256 ...... 0.60	0.25	0.10
1988 Fleer Star Stickers #56 .... 0.60	0.25	0.10
1988 Fleer's Baseball's Best #27 .... 0.80	0.35	0.15
1988 Kay Bee #18 .... 0.60	0.25	0.10
1988 Mother's Cookies Mark McGwire (set of 4) 12.00	5.50	2.50
1988 Topps All-Star Glossy (60) #39 .... 0.80	0.35	0.15
1988 Topps Gallery of Champions Aluminum 3.00	1.25	0.50
1988 Topps Gallery of Champions Bronze .. 25.00	11.50	5.50

1988 Topps Gallery of Champions Silver ...	125.00	55.00	25.00
1989 Fleer Glossy Tin #17	1.25	0.50	0.20
1989 Fleer Superstars #31	0.80	0.35	0.15
1989 Fleer Superstars #31	0.80	0.35	0.15
1989 Mother's Cookies Mark McGwire (set of 4)	12.00	5.50	2.50
1989 Mother's Cookies Rookies of the Year #2	3.00	1.25	0.50
1990 K mart #32	0.20	0.08	0.03
1990 Mother's Cookies Mark McGwire (set of 4)	13.00	6.00	2.50
1991 Donruss Grand Slammers #11	0.20	0.08	0.01

Jeff McNeely

Jeff McNeely is not the quintessential Boston Red Sox outfielder, which means one of two things: he will be traded, or he will change. For the time being, and with a horrendous 1992 minor-league season forgotten, Jeff McNeely is a package of a type Bostonians are not used to seeing: speed on the basepaths, defense in the outfield, and a bat that produces more base hits than whiffs. He has occasional long-ball power, too. He's not a Red Sox style of outfielder, yet his arrival in Boston is keenly anticipated by fans in the know and card companies, which have been clamoring to put him in their sets. His future might be cloudy, but there are sunny skies for McNeely in at least a couple of quarters.

	NM	EX	VG
1991 Bowman #113	0.15	0.05	0.01
1991 Bowman Tiffany #113	1.00	0.45	0.20
1991 Classic-Best #169	1.75	0.75	0.30
1991 ProCards Lynchburg Red Sox #22	3.25	1.50	0.60
1991 ProCards Tomorrow's Heroes #20	1.25	0.55	0.25
1991 Upper Deck Final Edition #20	0.40	0.15	0.05
1992 Classic-Best Minor Leagues #198	0.50	0.20	0.08
1992 Donruss Rookies #75	0.30	0.10	0.04
1992 Topps #618	0.60	0.25	0.10
1992 Topps Gold #618	3.00	1.25	0.50
1992 Upper Deck Minor-League #258	0.40	0.15	0.05

Brian McRae

Brian McRae has had an extremely difficult time emerging from his father's shadow, and the fact that his father's the manager has not made things any easier for him. McRae has a wide range of talents, starting with speed on the basepaths and in the outfield and a fine line-drive bat, but he has been unable to put it all together. This could be a case of Dave Sisler-itis: the son is not the equal of the father. In any event, stay away from McRae's cards; they're valued far too much on expectation and far too little on reality.

	NM	EX	VG
1990 Best Memphis (set)	6.00	2.75	1.25
1990 Best Minor League #276	6.00	2.75	1.25
1990 CMC Pre-Rookie #829	4.25	2.00	0.85
1990 ProCards Minor League Stars #50	2.00	0.85	0.35
1990 Star Minor-League Wax #68	2.00	0.85	0.35
1991 Bowman Tiffany #292	1.00	0.45	0.20

Kevin Mitchell

The quintessential misunderstood power hitter, theoretically all Kevin Mitchell wants is all Greta Garbo wanted — to be left alone. But leave him alone and his weight balloons and his bat slows down and he becomes even more useless in the field. It didn't used to be that way. If you can remember back to the Mets' world championship season of 1986 Mitchell was Mr. Play Everywhere, filling in at all the infield and outfield positions, and even catching an inning or two. He's on his fifth organization, having worn out his welcome in places where welcomes are not easily worn out, like San Francisco and Seattle. Right now his cards are down. But all it would take to turn them around is 40 measly homers.

	NM	EX	VG
1986 Donruss Rookies #17	3.25	1.50	0.65
1986 Fleer Update #76	2.00	0.85	0.40
1986 Topps Tiffany #74	1.50	0.65	0.25
1986 Topps Tiffany Traded #74	6.50	3.00	1.25
1987 Fleer #17	3.25	1.50	0.65
1987 Fleer Update #82	0.85	0.40	0.15
1987 Topps #653	0.80	0.35	0.15
1988 Donruss #66	0.45	0.20	0.08
1988 Fleer #92	0.60	0.25	0.10
1988 Fleer Glossy Tin #92	1.25	0.55	0.25
1988 Leaf #87	0.06	0.02	0.01
1988 Mother's Cookies Giants #3	1.50	0.65	0.30
1990 Fleer All-Star #6	0.75	0.30	0.12
1990 Fleer Baseball All Stars #27	0.35	0.15	0.05
1990 Fleer World Series #2	0.30	0.12	0.05
1990 Mother's Cookies Giants #5	0.50	0.20	0.08
1990 Topps Glossy All Star (60) #21	0.30	0.12	0.05
1992 Topps Gold #180	2.00	0.85	0.35

Paul Molitor

It's fair to say that the only thing that has been able to stop Paul Molitor has been injuries. Molitor has missed parts of five seasons with severe injuries, yet has still managed to amass more than 2,300 hits and fashion a .303 lifetime batting average. Molitor is a truly complete ballplayer, fast enough and adept enough at reaching base to be a perfect leadoff hitter, yet with enough sock in his bat to hit third, fourth, or fifth. Molitor has hit better than .300 nine times in his 16-year career and must be viewed as a legitimate Cooperstown possibility. His 1993 playoff performance and World Series MVP can only help. His rookie card, which he shares with Alan Trammell, is a most interesting buy because of the paths of these players' careers; other Molitor cards are very affordable.

	NM	EX	VG
1978 Topps #707 (w/Trammell)	62.00	30.00	14.00
1979 O-Pee-Chee #8	4.50	2.00	1.00
1979 Topps #24	11.00	5.00	2.25
1980 Topps #406	5.25	2.50	1.15
1981 Donruss #203	1.75	0.75	0.30
1981 Fleer #515	1.25	0.60	0.25
1981 Topps #300	2.50	1.15	0.50
1982 Brewers Police #4	1.00	0.45	0.20
1982 Donruss #78	1.00	0.45	0.20
1982 Fleer #148	1.00	0.45	0.20
1982 Topps #195	1.75	0.75	0.30
1983 Fleer Stickers #19	0.20	0.08	0.01
1983 Gardner's Brewers #4	4.25	2.00	0.80
1983 Topps #630	1.30	0.60	0.25
1984 Donruss #107	2.00	1.00	0.45
1984 Donruss Action All-Stars #35	0.20	0.08	0.01
1984 Topps Tiffany #60	7.00	3.25	1.50
1984 Topps/Nestle #60	4.25	2.00	0.95
1985 Fleer #588	0.85	0.40	0.15
1986 Brewers Police #4	0.75	0.35	0.15
1986 Fleer Star Stickers #76	0.25	0.10	0.04
1986 Sportflics #39	0.20	0.08	0.01
1987 Classic #45	0.30	0.12	0.05
1987 Fleer Glossy #350	0.50	0.20	0.08
1988 Kay Bee #19	0.15	0.05	0.01
1988 Kenner Starting Lineup	12.00	5.50	2.00
1988 Score Glossy #340	4.50	2.20	1.00
1989 Upper Deck #525	0.20	0.08	0.01
1990 Bowman Glossy #140	1.50	0.65	0.30

1990 Leaf #242 .... 0.40	0.18	0.06
1991 Topps Stadium Club #245 .... 0.35	0.15	0.06
1992 Donruss Diamond Kings #1 .... 2.50	1.20	0.50

Hal Morris

When Hal Morris was traded from the Yanks to the Reds everyone figured the Reds had stolen themselves another hitting machine along the lines of George Brett — which they did, when Morris is healthy. In 1992 he spent several weeks on the DL after straining his hamstring in the on-deck circle; in 1993 he landed on the 60-day DL after charging Jose Mesa in spring training and separating his shoulder. Morris is a wonderful hitter who leads a double life as an accident waiting to happen. Because of that, he's too much of a gamble for us to recommend his cards.

	NM	EX	VG
1987 ProCards Albany-Colonie Yanks (set) 33.50	16.00	7.50
1988 ProCards Columbus Clippers (set) 10.00	4.50	2.00
1990 Leaf #321 .... 1.50	0.65	0.25
1990 Upper Deck #31 .... 0.75	0.30	0.10
1991 Donruss #168 .... 0.40	0.15	0.05
1991 Score Rising Star #98 .... 0.20	0.08	0.02
1991 Topps #339 .... 0.50	0.20	0.08
1991 Topps Desert Storm #642 .... 30.00	12.50	5.50
1992 Donruss Diamond Kings #19 .... 1.00	0.40	0.15
1992 Fleer Ultra #192 .... 1.00	0.40	0.15
1992 Leaf Gold Inserts #205 .... 0.40	0.15	0.05
1992 Topps Gold Inserts #773 .... 2.00	0.80	0.35

Jack Morris

Jack Morris has been a very good pitcher on good teams, which suggests two things: that he is either an extraordinary pitcher capable of pushing the teams he plays on to new heights, or that he is exceptionally lucky. Morris has been the beneficiary of some fortuitous circumstances. No pitcher goes 21-6 with a 4.04 ERA, as Morris did in 1992, without amazing support from his teammates. But in the seventh game of the 1991 World Series, Morris showed that he can shut the door. Suffice it to say that Morris is a pitcher who pitches well enough to win and shows no sign of deviating from that pattern anytime soon. He is emerging as the top Hall of Fame pitching prospect to come out of the '80s, though his cards are not yet priced accordingly. Whether or not you like the way Morris pitches, you have to seriously consider his cards as solid bargains.

	NM	EX	VG
1978 Burger King Tigers #8	16.50	8.00	3.75
1978 Topps #703	20.00	9.50	4.50
1979 Topps #251	7.25	3.50	1.50
1980 Topps #371	5.50	2.65	1.25
1981 Coca-Cola #6	0.40	0.15	0.07
1981 Donruss #127	2.25	1.00	0.45
1981 Fleer #475	1.25	0.55	0.25
1981 Topps #572	3.25	1.50	0.65
1982 Donruss #107	1.50	0.65	0.30
1982 Fleer #274	1.50	0.75	0.35
1982 Topps #450	2.25	1.00	0.45
1983 Donruss #107	1.25	0.55	0.25
1983 Fleer #336	1.00	0.45	0.20
1983 Topps #65	1.50	0.65	0.30
1984 Donruss #415	4.00	1.75	0.75
1984 Fleer #87	1.75	0.75	0.35
1984 Topps #195	1.00	0.45	0.20
1984 Topps Tiffany #195	7.50	3.50	1.65
1985 Topps #610	0.45	0.20	0.08
1986 Cain's Chips Tigers #11	3.50	1.50	0.65
1986 Fleer #232	0.45	0.20	0.08
1986 General Mills Booklets #1	3.75	1.75	0.75
1987 Donruss Opening Day #212	0.15	0.06	0.01
1987 Fleer #158	0.60	0.25	0.12
1987 Kay Bee #20	0.15	0.06	0.01
1988 Classic #174	0.10	0.04	0.01
1988 Fleer Award Winners #26	0.12	0.05	0.01
1988 Score #545	0.25	0.12	0.05
1988 Score Glossy #545	3.25	1.50	0.65
1989 Upper Deck #352	0.45	0.20	0.08
1990 Leaf #482	0.40	0.15	0.06
1991 Topps Stadium Club #447	0.30	0.12	0.05
1992 Fleer Ultra Award Winners #1	4.25	2.00	0.85
1992 Topps Gold #235	2.00	0.85	0.40

Pedro Munoz

Pedro Munoz is yet another outfielder allowed to escape from the Toronto Blue
Jays. Unlike Sil Campusano, Rob Ducey, and Geronimo Berroa, this one can hit
and isn't a head case. Munoz isn't big but he hits the ball hard. He fits in
perfectly with the bash-happy Twins and finally earned a starting spot in the
Twins' outfield in 1993. Munoz is young enough and his cards are cheap

enough, yet there's still this nagging suspicion that maybe the Blue Jays knew what they were doing when they let Pedro walk.

	NM	EX	VG
1988 Star Co. Dunedin #13	11.50	5.50	2.25
1989 ProCards Knoxville #1126	4.50	2.00	0.85
1990 ProCards Syracuse #585	2.20	1.00	0.45
1991 Bowman #336	0.30	0.12	0.04
1991 Bowman Tiffany #336	2.50	1.15	0.55
1991 Donruss Rookies #21	0.25	0.12	0.04
1991 Fleer #620	0.20	0.08	0.03
1991 Fleer Ultra #192	0.80	0.35	0.15
1991 Topps Stadium Club #318	1.50	0.65	0.24
1991 Upper Deck #432	0.60	0.25	0.10
1992 Fleer Ultra #399	0.45	0.20	0.08
1992 Leaf Gold #53	1.50	0.65	0.25
1992 Pinnacle Team 2000 #61	0.40	0.15	0.06
1992 Topps Stadium Club #541	0.45	0.20	0.08

Dale Murphy

Dale Murphy has ended with a whimper and not a bang, and it's a shame. For a time there Murphy was everyone's favorite kid-next-door Hall of Famer. At the end of the 1987 season he was on a pace to break the 600-home-run barrier. Then it all fell apart. Murphy will end his career with more than 400 homers and a decent batting average. But Murphy had a great career, even if it isn't Cooperstown-caliber. His cards have plateaued, which is what they should be doing.

	NM	EX	VG
1979 Hostess Panel #41	14.00	6.50	3.00
1979 Hostess Panel #41	14.00	6.50	3.00
1979 Topps #39	7.75	3.75	1.75
1980 O-Pee-Chee #183	4.50	2.00	0.80
1981 Donruss #437	0.90	0.40	0.15
1981 Fleer #243	0.50	0.20	0.08
1981 Fleer Star Stickers #119	1.00	0.40	0.15
1981 O-Pee-Chee #118	2.25	1.00	0.45
1981 Topps #504	1.75	0.75	0.35
1982 Donruss #299	0.60	0.25	0.10
1982 Fleer #443	0.75	0.30	0.12
1982 O-Pee-Chee #391	1.75	0.75	0.35
1982 Topps #668	1.50	0.65	0.25
1983 Donruss #47	0.75	0.30	0.12

1983 Donruss Action All-Stars #43	0.25	0.10	0.04
1983 Fleer #142	0.60	0.25	0.10
1983 Fleer Star Stickers #90	0.30	0.12	0.05
1983 Kellogg's #53	0.75	0.20	0.08
1983 O-Pee-Chee #23	1.25	0.50	0.20
1983 Topps #760	1.00	0.45	0.20
1984 Donruss #66	2.50	1.10	0.50
1984 Fleer #186	1.00	0.45	0.20
1984 O-Pee-Chee #150	1.25	0.50	0.20
1984 Topps #150	0.75	0.30	0.12
1984 Topps Glossy All-Star (22) #19	0.80	0.35	0.15
1984 Topps Stickers #27	0.25	0.10	0.05
1984 Topps Super #2	0.90	0.50	0.15
1985 Donruss #66	0.75	0.30	0.12
1985 Fleer #335	0.80	0.35	0.15
1985 Fleer Limited Edition #22	0.30	0.10	0.04
1985 Hostess Braves #16	2.00	0.80	0.30
1985 Hostess Braves #16	2.00	0.80	0.30
1985 Leaf-Donruss #222	0.40	0.15	0.05
1985 Topps #320	0.60	0.25	0.10
1985 Topps 3-D #3	0.90	0.35	0.15
1985 Topps Gallery of Champions			
Aluminum	1.50	0.65	0.20
1985 Topps Gallery of Champions Bronze	15.00	6.50	2.75
1985 Topps Gallery of Champions Silver	80.00	35.00	15.00
1986 Donruss #66	0.70	0.30	0.12
1986 Drake's Panel 6	2.50	1.00	0.40
1986 Fleer Star Stickers #80	0.40	0.15	0.05
1986 Sportflics #5	0.50	0.20	0.08
1986 Sportflics #5	1.00	0.40	0.15
1986 Topps Stickers #145	0.15	0.05	0.01
1987 Classic #37	0.50	0.20	0.08
1987 Donruss Box Panel A	4.00	1.50	0.45
1987 Sportflics #3	0.50	0.20	0.08
1988 Baseball Superstars Discs Panel 8	1.00	0.40	0.15
1988 Kenner Starting Lineup	10.00	4.50	2.00
1988 Topps Big #14	0.30	0.10	0.04
1988 Topps Stickercards #18	0.10	0.04	0.01
1989 Topps #274	4.50	2.00	0.80
1991 Topps #243	0.65	0.25	0.10
1992 Fleer Ultra #249	0.50	0.20	0.08
1992 Topps Gold Inserts #680	2.00	0.80	0.35

Eddie Murray

In the last several years, card buyers have come around to accept what baseball insiders have known for a lot longer: Eddie Murray is going into the Hall of Fame. That burst of recognition has sent Murray's cards up in value, though many of them are very affordable and will go up in value in the next couple of years. With Murray's enshrinement practically a done deal, the only question that remains is, "Which ones do I buy?" As always, the regionals, stickers, and peripheral sets provide the greatest opportunities.

	NM	EX	VG
1978 O-Pee-Chee #154	30.00	12.50	5.50
1979 Hostess Panel #39	17.50	7.50	3.25
1979 O-Pee-Chee #338	4.25	2.00	0.80
1980 Kellogg's #24	2.50	1.15	0.50
1981 Drake's #6	0.60	0.20	0.08
1981 Fleer Star Stickers #117	0.50	0.20	0.08
1981 O-Pee-Chee #39	1.25	0.50	0.20
1983 Donruss Action All-Stars #1	0.30	0.12	0.05
1983 Topps Stickers #29	0.20	0.08	0.03
1984 Fleer Stickers #38	0.25	0.10	0.04
1985 Topps Stickers #196	0.20	0.08	0.03
1986 Burger King Panel	1.25	0.50	0.20
1986 Quaker Oats #27	0.30	0.10	0.04
1987 Boardwalk and Baseball #2	0.35	0.15	0.05
1987 French/Bray #33	1.50	0.50	0.20

Mike Mussina

Another gutty pitcher with a great arm besides — that's Mike Mussina in a nutshell. Mussina practically walked from the Stanford campus right into the Orioles' starting rotation. He would have been a 22-game winner in 1992 if the bullpen hadn't squandered leads in four games, and that's not a fluke. He has the stuff to pitch that way for years. Some of his cards are pricey, particularly his Gold Leaf rookie, but other Mussina cards are better buys. No Mussina card is a bad buy.

	NM	EX	VG
1991 Bowman Tiffany #97	5.00	2.25	1.00
1991 Impel Line Drive AAA #462	3.25	1.50	0.50
1991 ProCards Rochester (set)	12.00	5.00	2.00
1991 ProCards Tomorrow's Heroes #1	4.00	1.50	0.50
1991 Topps Major League Debut #130	0.30	0.12	0.05
1992 Bowman Gold #612	10.00	4.50	2.00

Charles Nagy

The ace of the Cleveland Indians' pitching staff had his career abruptly ended when he was killed in a boating accident during spring training prior to the 1993 season. His stats to that point were decent, and what effect his death will have on his cards over the long term remains to be seen.

	NM	EX	VG
1989 Bowman #73	0.75	0.30	0.12
1989 Bowman Tiffany #73	4.00	1.75	0.75
1990 Best Minor-League #244	1.50	0.65	0.30
1990 ProCards Wax #9	1.50	0.65	0.30
1990 Score #611	0.60	0.25	0.10
1991 Bowman #65	0.20	0.08	0.03
1991 Donruss #592	0.35	0.15	0.05
1991 Donruss Rookies #18	0.30	0.12	0.04
1991 Fleer Ultra Update #20	1.75	0.75	0.35
1991 Fleer Update #20	0.45	0.20	0.08
1991 Topps Desert Storm #466	85.00	40.00	18.50
1991 Upper Deck #19	1.00	0.45	0.20
1992 Fleer Ultra #351	0.75	0.30	0.12
1992 Leaf Gold #115	1.00	0.45	0.20
1992 O-Pee-Chee Premier #138	0.05	0.01	0.01
1992 Score Pinnacle #383	0.30	0.12	0.05
1992 Score Pinnacle Team 2000 #19	0.45	0.20	0.08
1992 Topps Gold #299	0.75	0.30	0.12
1992 Topps Stadium Club #389	0.50	0.20	0.08
1993 Upper Deck #243	0.30	0.12	0.04

Jaime Navarro

The son of former major leaguer Julio Navarro, Jaime is carving a niche for himself as an effective power pitcher with more than the usual complement of pitching smarts. He's underrated as a pitcher and unusually underrated as a card buy.

	NM	EX	VG
1990 Bowman #388	0.25	0.10	0.04
1990 Donruss #640	0.30	0.12	0.05
1990 Fleer #331	0.20	0.08	0.01
1990 Leaf #85	2.25	1.10	0.50
1990 Score #569	0.25	0.10	0.04
1990 Upper Deck #646	0.75	0.35	0.15

	NM	EX	VG
1991 Fleer Update #31 .... 0.50		0.20	0.08
1991 Topps Stadium Club #436 .... 1.00		0.45	0.20
1991 Topps Tiffany #436 .... 1.50		0.65	0.30
1992 Leaf Gold #195 .... 0.50		0.20	0.08
1992 Pinnacle #212 .... 0.20		0.08	0.01
1992 Topps Gold #222 .... 0.75		0.35	0.15
1993 Topps Gold #222 .... 0.75		0.30	0.12

Phil Nevin

Phil Nevin is supposed to be an above-average third baseman with above-average power and good contact, which means he is a most unusual prospect. He ought to be: he was the first player taken in the 1992 baseball draft. He should be up with the Astros by 1994 and ought to have a very nice, long, productive career after that. Considering all those factors, his cards are reasonably priced.

	NM	EX	VG
1992 Bowman Gold #670	18.50	8.50	3.75
1992 Topps Stadium Club Insert Set (3)	10.00	4.50	2.00

David Nied

The hero for the three months prior to the '93 baseball season was David Nied, the untested No. 1 starter for the expansion Colorado Rockies. It's sort of silly any way you slice it, going crazy over a pitcher who's bound to spend his first couple of seasons getting bombed and posting 6-14 records. Still, Nied has quite a bit of potential, even if his cards are overvalued right this minute, and promise to be for a little while. He'll be fun to watch, even if you're not buying.

	NM	EX	VG
1990 SportsPrint Durham Bulls #17	6.50	3.00	1.25
1991 ProCards Tomorrow's Heroes #188	1.50	0.65	0.30
1992 Bowman #504	3.75	1.75	0.75
1992 Donruss Rookies #86	2.75	1.35	0.60
1992 Fleer Update #68	4.25	2.00	0.85
1992 Gold Leaf Rookies #10	8.75	4.25	2.00
1993 Fleer #9	0.85	0.40	0.15
1993 Upper Deck #27	1.25	0.55	0.25

Melvin Nieves

A teammate of Chipper Jones, Mike Kelly, and Javy Lopez on the 1992 Greenville Braves, arguably one of the best minor-league teams ever, Melvin Nieves is a solid outfield package: pretty good stick, pretty good power, decent speed, okay arm. Right now buying his cards would be a reach. If he's going to play in the majors soon, it probably won't be for the Braves. Still, because he has a number of major-league cards to choose from, he's one of those players who makes life interesting for card collectors.

	NM	EX	VG
1991 ProCards Durham Bulls #156	0.75	0.30	0.12
1992 Bowman #143	0.60	0.25	0.10
1992 Bowman Gold #143	1.25	0.55	0.20
1992 Classic-Best Greenville Braves (set)	7.00	3.25	1.25
1993 Donruss #320	0.20	0.08	0.01
1993 Fleer Major League Prospects #1	2.75	1.25	0.55
1993 Upper Deck #21	0.55	0.25	0.10

Dave Nilsson

Dave is an interesting player for a number of reasons, only a few of which have to do with baseball. First, he's Australian, and is the best major leaguer ever to hail from Australia (having passed Craig Shipley for that honor sometime after his first at-bat). Second, he's a left-handed-hitting catcher, and there aren't too many of them around. And third, he could be one of the very few catchers capable of winning a batting title. All these attributes have intrigued card buyers and driven up the prices of Nilsson's cards, making him a little too expensive in the short term but more than all right for the long.

	NM	EX	VG
1990 Best Stockton Ports #2	3.00	1.30	0.60
1990 Cal League Stockton #187	3.00	1.30	0.60
1990 ProCards Stars #151	1.80	0.80	0.35
1991 Classic-Best #227	1.25	0.60	0.25
1991 ProCards El Paso #2751	4.50	2.20	0.10
1992 Donruss #4	0.30	0.12	0.05
1992 Line Drive AA #194	1.50	0.70	0.30

John Olerud

A brain aneurysm nearly cost John Olerud his career — and his life — before it began. But the lanky lefty out of Washington State, a former collegiate player of the year, persevered and found stardom with the Jays. There are signs that Olerud may be one of the most productive hitters in the game — league batting titles help — by the time he finally hangs 'em up. His cards, especially his rookie and second-year cards, still reflect some of the early hype, though their prices have stabilized and they're not really bad buys if you consider his 1993 season. And suppose he does it again in 1994?

	NM	EX	VG
1990 Bowman #510	0.45	0.20	0.08
1990 Classic #35	1.25	0.60	0.25
1990 Donruss #711	0.60	0.25	0.12
1990 Donruss Rookies #12	0.50	0.20	0.08
1990 Leaf #237	5.25	2.50	1.10
1990 Score #589	0.65	0.30	0.12
1990 Topps Traded #83	0.40	0.15	0.07
1990 Upper Deck #56	1.20	0.55	0.25
1991 O-Pee-Chee Premier #92	0.55	0.25	0.10
1991 Topps Stadium Club #482	2.25	1.10	0.50
1992 Score Impact Players #41	0.25	0.12	0.05

Gregg Olson

A former first-round pick of the Orioles and widely regarded as the possessor of the best curveball in baseball, Olson has nonetheless struggled recently as the O's closer, making his cards quite a bit less than swell, even at slightly reduced levels. Still, Olson is a pitcher; there's nothing that says he can't come back from his recent setbacks and be dominant once more.

	NM	EX	VG
1989 Bowman Tiffany #6	1.00	0.40	0.15
1990 Classic #3	0.30	0.10	0.04
1990 Donruss A.L. Best #43	0.10	0.04	0.01
1990 Fleer Award Winners #25	0.15	0.05	0.01
1990 Score Rising Stars #342	0.20	0.08	0.03
1990 Topps Big #241	0.15	0.05	0.01
1991 Topps DesertStorm #10	16.00	6.50	2.50

Donovan Osborne

A former No. 1 pick out of the University of Nevada-Las Vegas, Osborne made a quick, big name for himself in 1992 by pitching sparkling baseball in his first dozen starts before unraveling almost completely the second half of the season. Osborne doesn't throw hard, which is not the best thing you can say about a pitcher, though he is smart. His cards aren't likely to do much over time, although, like Osborne, they should be around for a while.

	NM	EX	VG
1991 ProCards Tomorrow's Heroes #317	1.75	0.75	0.35

Rafael Palmeiro

Another of the Latino cogs in the Rangers' machine, Palmeiro alternates between being a pretty good power hitter and a very good hitter period. The Rangers have enough bashers; they could stand for Palmeiro to focus on his average and soft-pedal the power, but recently that's just made Palmeiro into an okay power hitter with an okay average — definitely not the ideal compromise.

	NM	EX	VG
1987 Topps Tiffany #634	2.00	0.80	0.30
1988 Donruss Cubs Team Book #324	0.75	0.30	0.10
1988 Fleer Glossy Tin #429	1.00	0.40	0.15
1988 O-Pee-Chee #186	0.40	0.15	0.05
1988 Score Glossy #186	2.50	1.10	0.45
1989 Bowman Tiffany #237	0.75	0.30	0.10
1989 Fleer Glossy Tin #434	0.25	0.10	0.04
1989 Topps American Baseball #59	0.08	0.03	0.01
1990 Donruss A.L. Best #41	0.10	0.04	0.01
1990 Mother's Cookies Rangers #9	0.60	0.20	0.08
1990 Topps Big Baseball #127	0.12	0.05	0.01

Dean Palmer

Dean Palmer is the classic all-or-nothing power hitter who has card buyers drooling over what he can do — hit baseballs out of sight, basically — and totally overlooking what he can't — make consistent contact. Palmer's young enough to learn plate discipline; without it, he's just another Dave Hostetler. With it, he could just make the prices his cards are currently fetching seem reasonable.

	NM	EX	VG
1989 Star Co. Florida State League All-Stars (set)	13.00	6.00	2.50
1989 Topps Major League Debut #95	0.25	0.10	0.04
1990 Classic II #39	0.60	0.25	0.10
1990 ProCards AAA #675	5.25	2.50	1.00
1990 ProCards Tulsa Drillers (set)	9.00	3.50	1.50
1990 Score Rising Stars #38	0.10	0.04	0.01
1991 Bowman Tiffany #288	1.00	0.40	0.15

1991 Impel AAA #314	2.25	1.00	0.40
1991 ProCards Oklahoma City (set)	9.00	3.50	1.50
1992 Bowman Gold #107	2.00	0.80	0.30

Terry Pendleton

Now the heart and soul of the Atlanta Braves, Terry Pendleton has a card history that includes one of Donruss' two notorious error cards in the 1986 set (the other being the Floyd Bannister card that pictures Tom Seaver). His cards have increased significantly in value over the last two years but still are fairly priced for a player who is a longshot for making the Hall of Fame.

	NM	EX	VG
1983 TCMA Arkansas #15	125.00	60.00	27.50
1984 Riley's Louisville Redbirds #15	26.00	12.50	6.00
1985 Donruss #534 (Jeff)	10.50	5.00	2.35
1985 Donruss #534 (Terry)	24.50	12.00	5.75
1985 Fleer #236	10.50	5.00	2.35
1985 Topps #346	3.25	1.50	0.70
1985 Topps Tiffany #346	25.00	12.00	5.50
1986 Donruss #205	1.50	0.70	0.30
1986 Fleer #44	1.75	0.75	0.30
1986 Topps #528	1.00	0.45	0.20
1987 Fleer #306	0.90	0.40	0.15
1987 Leaf #124	0.30	0.12	0.05
1988 Smokey Bear Cardinals #17	0.40	0.15	0.05
1989 Fleer Glossy #461	1.00	0.45	0.20
1989 Upper Deck #131	0.40	0.15	0.05
1990 Leaf #260	1.00	0.45	0.20
1991 Donruss Elite #16	65.00	30.00	14.50
1991 Topps Desert Storm #485	12.00	6.00	3.00
1991 Topps Stadium Club #327	1.00	0.45	0.20
1992 Fleer All-Star #15	1.50	0.70	0.30
1992 Topps Gold #115	2.00	0.85	0.40

Phil Plantier

Phil Plantier has exceptional power and has even shown flashes that he can hit to all fields for good average. His awkward stance that makes him look like Stan Musial doing deep knee bends has "batting slump" written all over it. His recent trade from Boston to San Diego didn't do wonders for his cards, which were overpriced to start with. They're still too expensive by about 10 percent. Major curiosity about Plantier: With his ugly-as-a-board-fence swing, how'd he ever wind up in Upper Deck's Ted Williams' Best Hitters set? Could it be that the Uppers were looking to pad the set for investors? Nah.

	NM	EX	VG
1988 Star Co. Winter Haven (set)	30.00	14.50	7.00
1989 Star Co. Lynchburg (set)	21.50	10.50	5.00
1989 Star Minor League Wax II #170	10.50	5.00	2.25
1990 CMC Pre-Rookie #272	11.50	5.50	2.50
1991 Bowman #117	0.40	0.15	0.05
1991 Donruss #41	0.30	0.12	0.05
1991 Fleer #107	0.45	0.20	0.08
1991 Fleer Ultra #38	1.00	0.45	0.20
1991 Score #348	0.40	0.12	0.05
1991 Studio #18	2.00	0.75	0.30
1991 Topps #474	0.45	0.20	0.08
1991 Topps Stadium Club #459	5.25	2.50	1.10
1991 Upper Deck #2	1.00	0.45	0.20
1992 Bowman Gold #1	0.45	0.20	0.04
1992 Fleer Rookie Sensations #19	9.50	4.50	2.10
1992 Fleer Ultra #318	0.85	0.40	0.15
1992 Leaf #50	0.30	0.12	0.05
1992 Leaf Gold #50	2.50	1.15	0.50
1992 Pinnacle Team 2000 #2	0.85	0.40	0.15
1992 Score Impact Player #20	0.60	0.25	0.10
1992 Studio #136	0.20	0.08	0.03
1992 Topps Gold #782	4.00	1.75	0.75
1992 Upper Deck Ted Williams' Best Hitters #18	2.50	1.10	0.50
1993 Score #242	0.10	0.04	0.01

Kirby Puckett

Kirby Puckett's first major-league card, in the 1984 Fleer Update set, is so valuable it makes your teeth hurt. But shortly thereafter the values for Puckett's cards fall off and stay relatively affordable. Puckett is a fan favorite who'll likely top the 2,000-hit mark sometime in 1994. He deserves to be mentioned in the same breath as Ryne Sandberg as a likely Hall of Famer, even if his cards don't quite keep pace up and down the line.

	NM	EX	VG
1984 Fleer Update #93	375.00	175.00	85.00
1985 Donruss #438	55.00	25.00	12.00
1985 Fleer #286	55.00	27.00	13.00
1985 Minnesota Twins Team Issue #24	0.85	0.40	0.15

1985 Topps #536	23.50	11.50	5.50
1985 Topps Tiffany #536	125.00	60.00	27.50
1986 Donruss #72	11.00	5.00	2.25
1986 Fleer #401	11.50	5.50	2.50
1986 Topps #329	3.75	1.75	0.75
1987 Classic #112	2.00	0.85	0.40
1987 Donruss #149	2.00	0.85	0.40
1987 Fleer #549	3.75	1.75	0.75
1987 Fleer All-Star #5	3.00	1.45	0.65
1987 Fleer Glossy Tin #549	4.00	1.85	0.85
1987 General Mills Booklets #3	3.75	1.75	0.75
1987 Minnesota Twins Team Issue #21	0.80	0.35	0.12
1987 Sportflics #7	0.85	0.40	0.15
1987 Topps #450	0.85	0.40	0.15
1988 Donruss #368	0.40	0.15	0.06
1988 Leaf #144	0.60	0.25	0.12
1988 Master Bread Twins #8	4.00	1.85	0.85
1988 Minnesota Twins Team Issue #23	25.00	12.00	5.50
1988 Score #24	0.40	0.15	0.06
1989 Bowman Tiffany #162	1.50	0.65	0.30
1989 Fleer Baseball MVP #32	0.35	0.15	0.06
1989 Upper Deck #376	2.00	0.85	0.40
1990 Hills Hit Men #27	0.70	0.30	0.12
1990 Leaf #123	3.25	1.50	0.65
1990 Upper Deck #236	0.70	0.25	0.12
1991 Mootown Snackers #2	0.35	0.15	0.07
1991 Score Superstar #7	0.12	0.05	0.01
1991 Topps Stadium Club #110	3.00	1.35	0.60
1991 Topps Tiffany #300	1.00	0.45	0.20
1992 Donruss Elite #17	150.00	72.50	35.00
1992 Fleer All-Star #22	2.50	1.15	0.55
1992 Fleer Ultra #97	1.25	0.55	0.25
1992 Fleer Ultra All-Star #8	7.50	3.50	1.50
1992 Fleer Ultra Award Winner #23	7.50	3.50	1.50
1992 Leaf Gold #98	4.00	1.85	0.85
1992 Pinnacle Slugfest #13	4.00	1.75	0.65
1992 Topps Gold #575	3.00	1.35	0.65
1992 Upper Deck Ted Williams' #575	3.00	1.35	0.65

Manny Ramirez

Manny Ramirez is the Indians' best hitting prospect, and arguably one of the two or three best hitting prospects in baseball. He's young and has a way to go yet through the minors, but every single one of the necessary skills are there in more than ample supply. His cards aren't cheap right now, but they're not likely to get any cheaper.

	NM	EX	VG
1991 Classic Draft Picks #10	1.00	0.45	0.20
1991 Front Row #47	1.00	0.45	0.20
1991 Topps Stadium Club Dome #146	3.25	1.50	0.65
1992 Bowman #532	1.00	0.45	0.20
1992 Bowman #676	3.00	1.45	0.65
1992 Bowman Gold #532	5.00	2.25	1.00
1992 Classic-Best Minor-League #155	0.75	0.30	0.12
1992 Donruss Rookies #98	0.45	0.20	0.08
1992 Pinnacle #295	1.00	0.45	0.20
1992 Score #800	0.50	0.20	0.08
1992 Topps Gold #156	12.00	5.00	2.25
1992 Upper Deck #63	0.80	0.35	0.15
1992 Upper Deck Minor League #146	0.75	0.30	0.12
1992 Upper Deck Minor League #55	0.75	0.30	0.12

Jeff Reardon

Now that Jeff Reardon's been shorn of his sole claim to fame — being the free world's all-time save leader — will his cards tumble in the process? Will he be booted off the "A" list for Cooperstown? Will he hang on as a clean-shaven setup man with the Reds? Yes, Yes, and Does it really matter? Reardon is a serviceable relief pitcher whose greatest asset has been his longevity. The Hall of Fame hasn't seen fit to take the catcher's version of Jeff Reardon — Bob Boone — seriously, and there's no reason to believe they'll do any favors for Reardon. Reardon has some awfully pricey cards for just another relief pitcher.

	NM	EX	VG
1979 TCMA Tidewater Tides #5	22.50	10.00	4.50
1981 Donruss #156	4.75	2.25	1.00
1981 Fleer #335	4.75	2.25	1.00
1981 Topps #456	8.00	3.50	1.50
1982 Donruss #547	1.75	0.75	0.35
1982 Fleer #204	2.00	0.85	0.35
1982 Topps #667	2.25	1.00	0.45
1983 Donruss #194	0.75	0.35	0.15
1983 Fleer #293	0.75	0.35	0.15
1983 Topps #290	1.25	0.55	0.25
1984 Donruss #279	1.50	0.65	0.30
1984 Fleer #283	1.50	0.65	0.30
1984 Topps #595	0.50	0.20	0.08

1985 Donruss #331 .... 0.60	0.25	0.10
1985 Fleer #407 .... 0.40	0.15	0.05
1985 Topps Tiffany #375 .... 3.75	1.75	0.75
1986 Donruss #209 .... 0.35	0.15	0.05
1986 Fleer #257 .... 0.50	0.20	0.08
1986 Fleer Baseball's Best #26 .... 0.10	0.04	0.01
1986 Fleer Star Stickers #94 .... 0.10	0.04	0.01
1987 Fleer #329 .... 0.35	0.15	0.05
1987 Fleer Limited Edition #34 .... 0.10	0.04	0.01
1988 Score Glossy #91 .... 0.55	0.25	0.12
1990 Leaf #276 .... 0.50	0.20	0.08
1992 Leaf Gold #151 .... 0.40	0.15	0.05
1992 Topps Gold #182 .... 0.75	0.30	0.10
1992 Topps Gold Record Breaker #3 .... 0.75	0.30	0.12

Cal Ripken Jr.

Baseball's soon-to-be Iron Man, Ripken has all but guaranteed himself a spot in Cooperstown on the basis of his incredible streak of consecutive games played, though you can't overlook his two MVP awards and his position as the best power-hitting shortstop since Ernie Banks. Ripken's card prices have been reflecting his feats right along, but as the magic day nears his cards are sure to go even higher.

	NM	EX	VG
1980 WBTV Charlotte O's #16 .... 900.00	425.00	210.00
1981 TCMA Rochester Red Wings #15 .... 250.00	120.00	55.00
1981 WTF Co. Rochester Red Wings #1 ..... 225.00	110.00	50.00
1982 Donruss #405 .... 55.00	25.00	12.00
1982 Fleer #176 .... 55.00	25.00	12.00
1982 Topps #21 (with Bob Bonner and Jeff Schneider) 80.00	37.50	17.50
1982 Topps Traded #98T 265.00	125.00	55.00
1983 Donruss #279 .... 20.00	9.50	4.75
1983 Fleer #70 .... 18.00	9.00	4.25
1983 Fleer Stickers #198 .... 0.30	0.12	0.05
1983 Topps #163 .... 21.00	10.00	5.00
1984 Donruss #106 .... 27.50	13.00	6.50
1984 Fleer #17 .... 20.00	10.00	4.50
1984 Topps #470 .... 8.00	3.75	1.75
1984 Topps Stickers #204 .... 0.50	0.20	0.05
1984 Topps Super #1 .... 0.75	0.35	0.12
1984 Topps Tiffany #470 .... 65.00	30.00	12.50
1985 Fleer #187 .... 9.50	4.75	2.25

1985 Topps #30 .... 4.25	2.00	0.95
1985 Topps Tiffany #704 (AS) 7.50	3.50	1.50
1986 Donruss #210 .... 5.00	2.25	1.00
1986 Fleer #284 .... 6.00	2.80	1.35
1986 Jiffy Pop Disc #9 .... 2.75	1.35	0.65
1986 Topps Tiffany #340 .... 12.00	5.75	2.75
1987 Donruss #89 .... 1.80	0.80	0.35
1987 Fleer #478 .... 3.75	1.75	0.80
1987 Fleer Tin Glossy #478 .... 4.00	1.75	0.80
1987 French/Bray Orioles #8 .... 3.25	1.50	0.65
1987 Leaf #98 .... 2.25	1.00	0.50
1987 Topps Tiffany #784 .... 6.00	2.75	1.25
1988 Fleer Star Stickers #3 .... 0.75	0.30	0.10
1988 Score Glossy #550 .... 6.00	2.75	1.25
1988 Topps America Baseball #61 .... 0.30	0.12	0.05
1988 Topps Big #62 .... 0.30	0.12	0.05
1988 Topps Stickercards #44 .... 0.10	0.04	0.01
1989 Classic #56 .... 1.00	0.45	0.20
1989 Fleer Tin Glossy #617 .... 5.00	2.25	1.10
1989 Scoremasters #3 .... 0.85	0.40	0.15
1989 Upper Deck #467 .... 2.75	1.30	0.60
1990 Sportflics #100 .... 0.20	0.08	0.01
1990 Topps All Star Glossy Set (60) #51 .... 0.60	0.25	0.10
1991 O-Pee-Chee Premier #100 .... 2.50	1.20	0.50
1991 Topps Stadium Club #430 .... 2.50	1.20	0.50
1992 Donruss Elite Signature card 350.00	180.00	100.00
1992 Fleer Ultra #11 .... 2.50	1.20	0.50
1992 Fleer Ultra Award Winners #5 .... 10.00	4.50	2.00

Frank Rodriguez

Frankie Rodriguez is either one heck of a pitcher playing shortstop or the world's greatest shortstop on the mound. He was drafted as both and has played a little of both in the minors, though pitching seems to be his ultimate destination. Rodriguez can bring it at 95-plus mph and get it over the plate to boot. Rodriguez was supposed to be in the 1992 Upper Deck minor-league set but wasn't, due to some machinations involving Classic and Front Row. If you want a draft-pick card of him, you have to go with Front Row. It's a slight reason to buy the set, but it's a reason.

	NM	EX	VG
1991 Front Row #1	0.85	0.35	0.15
1991 Front Row gold promo	8.00	3.25	1.50

1991 Front Row silver promo	5.00	2.25	1.00
1991 Upper Deck Final Edition #21	1.50	0.65	0.25
1992 Bowman #45	1.00	0.45	0.20
1992 Classic-Best Minor League #391	1.25	0.55	0.25
1992 Front Row autographed promo	20.00	8.00	3.00
1992 Upper Deck Minor League #266	0.85	0.35	0.15
1992 Upper Deck Minor League #54	0.85	0.35	0.15
1993 Topps #656	0.35	0.12	0.05
1993 Topps Gold #656	1.50	0.65	0.25

Ivan Rodriguez

They call him "Pudge," after Carlton "Pudge" Fisk, and Rodriguez stands the best chance of any catcher to come along in many a moon to take over as the dominant catcher in baseball for a lot of years — at least, that's what the card-geek types believe. They've jumped on Rodriguez and driven his cards up to outrageous levels. His cards aren't worth what you have to pay for them, though they may be over time — a long time. Pudge Rodriguez is the IRA of baseball cards; don't expect to take anything out of him until you retire.

	NM	EX	VG
1990 Star Charlotte Rangers (set)	12.50	5.50	2.25
1991 Bowman Tiffany #272	4.50	2.00	0.80
1991 Classic II #82	1.00	0.40	0.15
1991 Classic-Best Minor League #136	5.50	2.50	1.00
1991 Impel Line Drive AA #592	4.50	2.00	0.80
1991 ProCards Tomorrow's Heroes #153	4.00	1.50	0.50
1991 ProCards Tulsa (set)	12.00	5.00	2.00
1991 Topps Major League Debut #150	1.50	0.55	0.25
1992 Bowman Gold #1	5.00	2.25	1.00

Pete Rose

The Pete Rose market is unique. There's no price trend for a modern player with more hits than anyone else in history. He may or may not make the Hall of Fame, depending upon whatever rules baseball is functioning under at the time. Rose's troubles have hurt his card prices, but whether or not they are resolved may not matter, as seen in the case of Joe Jackson. In all probability the trend for Rose cards will remain up except for the most recent ones, which were heavily produced. (Pete Rose cards not listed are priced under $1.00 in Near Mint condition.)

	NM	EX	VG
1963 Topps #537	675.00	225.00	100.00
1964 Topps #125	185.00	55.00	25.00
1965 Topps #207	175.00	50.00	20.00
1966 Topps #30	50.00	15.00	5.00
1967 Topps #430	85.00	25.00	10.00
1968 Topps #230	55.00	15.00	5.00
1969 Topps #120	50.00	12.00	4.00
1970 Topps #458	12.50	4.00	1.00
1970 Topps #580	85.00	25.00	10.00
1971 Topps #100	55.00	10.00	3.50
1972 Topps #559	47.50	15.00	2.50
1972 Topps #560	24.00	3.50	1.00
1973 Topps #130	22.00	7.50	2.00
1974 Topps #300	16.00	3.50	1.00
1975 Topps #320	20.00	3.50	1.00
1976 Topps #240	15.00	3.00	0.75
1977 Topps #450	10.00	1.50	0.50
1978 Topps #20	4.50	1.00	0.25
1979 Topps #204	1.75	0.35	0.10
1979 Topps #650	5.50	1.25	0.25
1980 Topps #540	4.25	1.00	0.25
1981 Donruss #131	1.50	0.25	0.10
1981 Donruss #251	1.25	0.20	0.50
1981 Donruss #271	1.25	0.20	0.50
1981 Fleer #1	2.00	0.40	0.10
1981 Topps #180	2.75	1.00	0.25
1982 Donruss #1	1.25	0.20	0.50
1982 Donruss #168	1.65	0.35	0.10
1982 Fleer #256	1.25	0.20	0.50
1982 Topps #781	1.25	0.20	0.50
1983 Donruss #42	1.25	0.20	0.50
1983 Fleer #171	1.25	0.20	0.50
1983 Topps #100	2.25	0.60	0.20
1984 Donruss #61	3.50	0.75	0.25
1984 Fleer #46	2.25	0.60	0.20
1984 Fleer Update #102	17.00	3.00	1.00
1984 Topps Traded #103	8.50	1.75	0.50
1985 Donruss #254	1.50	0.20	0.50
1985 Donruss #641	1.50	0.20	0.50
1985 Fleer #550	1.25	0.20	0.50

Nolan Ryan

Statistically, the most dominant strikeout pitcher ever. Realistically, neither the best nor the most remarkable. But realism plays a very small part in regarding the cards or the career of Lynn Nolan Ryan. You either believe — and many, many collectors do — or you don't. Enough collectors believe to make Ryan's cards, except for his first couple, very good buys that will continue to go up in value in anticipation of his enshrinement at Cooperstown. Few players have had more cards, so you have plenty to choose from. Pick comparatively inexpensive cards from tough sets.

	NM	EX	VG
1968 O-Pee-Chee #177	1500.00	675.00	325.00
1968 Venezuelean Topps #177	2500.00	1100.00	500.00
1970 O-Pee-Chee #1 (Mets team)	3.50	1.50	0.50
1971 O-Pee-Chee #513	200.00	85.00	35.00
1973 Kellogg's #16	15.00	6.50	3.00
1973 O-Pee-Chee #220	18.50	8.50	3.50
1973 Topps Candy Lids	18.00	8.25	3.50
1973 Topps Comics #18	60.00	25.00	10.50
1974 Kellogg's #8	10.00	4.25	2.00
1974 O-Pee-Chee #20	50.00	22.50	10.00
1974 Topps Stamps	15.00	6.50	2.50
1975 Hostess Panel #20	15.00	6.50	2.50
1975 Hostess Twinkie #58	12.00	5.50	2.25
1975 Kellogg's #26	20.00	8.50	3.50
1975 O-Pee-Chee #500	6.00	3.50	1.50
1975 SSPC #10	6.50	3.00	1.25
1975 Topps Mini #500	60.00	27.50	12.50
1976 O-Pee-Chee #330	12.50	5.50	2.50
1977 O-Pee-Chee #65	15.00	6.50	3.00
1977 Topps Cloth Stickers #40	40.00	17.50	6.50
1977 Venezuelean Sticker #158	4.00	1.50	0.45
1978 Hostess Panel #28	11.00	5.00	2.25
1978 Kellogg's #51	8.00	3.50	1.50
1978 O-Pee-Chee #105	9.00	4.00	1.50
1979 O-Pee-Chee #51	7.50	3.25	1.50
1980 Burger King Pitch, Hit and Run #9	2.50	1.10	0.45
1980 O-Pee-Chee #303	4.50	2.00	0.80
1981 Fleer Star Sticker #108	1.50	0.65	0.20
1981 O-Pee-Chee #303	4.50	2.00	0.80
1981 Topps Home Team Photo #240	3.00	1.25	0.50
1981 Topps Thirst Break #10	2.00	0.80	0.35
1982 O-Pee-Chee #90	2.00	0.80	0.30

1982 Topps Team Leader Sheet	4.00	1.75	0.75
1983 Donruss Action All-Star #23	1.00	0.40	0.15
1983 Fleer Sticker #207	0.25	0.10	0.04
1983 O-Pee-Chee #360	1.50	0.50	0.20
1983 Sticker #235	0.50	0.20	0.06
1984 Donruss Champion #39	0.75	0.30	0.10
1984 Mother's Cookies Astros #1	2.50	1.10	0.50
1984 Nestle #4	2.00	0.80	0.30
1984 Nestle #470	12.00	5.50	2.50
1984 Nestle #66	1.25	0.50	0.20
1984 Nestle #707	2.00	0.80	0.35
1984 O-Pee-Chee #66	1.50	0.50	0.10
1984 Tiffany Active Strikeout Leaders #707	2.50	1.00	0.40
1984 Topps Tiffany #470	50.00	22.00	10.00
1984 Topps Tiffany Highlight #4	2.50	1.00	0.40
1984 Topps Tiffany Team Leader #66	2.00	0.80	0.30
1985 Fleer Limited Edition #30	1.25	0.50	0.20
1985 Leaf-Donruss #216	0.45	0.20	0.08
1985 Mother's Cookies Astros #2	3.00	1.25	0.50
1985 Rubdown #26	0.25	0.10	0.04
1986 Drake's Panel	4.50	1.50	0.65
1986 Fleer Future Hall of Famers #5	2.00	0.80	0.30
1986 Fleer Sticker #102	0.25	0.10	0.04
1986 Mini #43	0.30	0.12	0.05
1986 Mother's Cookies Astros #23	1.50	0.50	0.20
1986 O-Pee-Chee Stickers #9	0.30	0.10	0.01
1986 Sportflics Decade Greats #63	0.50	0.20	0.08
1986 Tatoo #24	0.50	0.20	0.08
1986 Topps Tiffany #100	12.00	5.25	2.00
1987 Classic #82	12.00	5.50	2.50
1987 Mother's Cookies Astros #8	3.00	1.25	0.50
1987 Ralston Purina #1	2.00	0.80	0.30
1987 Topps Italian Sticker #27	0.40	0.15	0.05
1987 Topps U.S. Sticker #27	0.90	0.40	0.10
1988 Classic #179	5.00	2.00	0.80
1988 Donruss Baseball's Best #232	0.65	0.25	0.10
1988 Mini #79	0.60	0.20	0.08
1988 Mother's Cookies Astros #8	2.00	0.80	0.30
1988 Score Glossy #575	7.50	3.50	1.50
1988 Shaeffer Eaton folder	3.00	1.25	0.50
1988 Topps Big #29	0.80	0.30	0.10
1988 Topps Sticker #7	0.20	0.08	0.03
1989 Mother's Cookies Rangers #2	1.50	0.50	0.20

1989 Sportflics Great Moments #23 .... 0.60	0.20	0.08
1989 Topps Mini #15 .... 0.60	0.25	0.10
1990 Donruss Preview #7 .... 2.50	1.10	0.45
1990 Mother's Cookies Nolan Ryan (set) 1–4 .... 20.00	8.50	3.50
1990 Mother's Cookies Rangers #2 .... 3.00	1.25	0.50
1990 Topps Kings of Baseball #28 .... 0.30	0.10	0.04
1992 Highland Mint Topps Mint-Card (Silver) #1 .... 250.00	115.00	50.00
1993 Pacific Nolan Ryan set............................ 15.00	6.50	2.50

Bret Saberhagen

Once a victim of an on-year, off-year cycle, Saberhagen has been on a down cycle for the last two years through a combination of arm trouble and bad luck, and he doesn't seem to be making his way out of it with the Mets. Saberhagen won a lot early in his career, when he was very young. Now there's the sense that some of those early victories may be catching up with him. Whatever the reason for his decline, his cards are no longer the hot stuff they used to be. Saberhagen is still young enough to fashion a decent career out of this roller-coaster beginning, but it's probably too late for his cards.

	NM	EX	VG
1985 O-Pee-Chee #23 .... 2.75	1.00	0.45
1986 Donruss Diamond King Supers #11 ..... 0.70	0.30	0.10
1986 Glossy All-Star (60) #27 .... 0.30	0.10	0.04
1987 Classic Baseball Travel #116 .... 0.30	0.10	0.04
1987 Fleer Baseball's Best #36 .... 0.15	0.05	0.01
1988 Donruss Pop-Ups 0.35	0.15	0.05
1988 Fleer Star Stickers #32 .... 0.10	0.04	0.01
1988 Kenner Starting Lineup 10.00	4.00	1.50
1988 Nestle #11 .... 0.35	0.15	0.05
1988 Topps Stickers #260 .... 0.12	0.05	0.01
1989 Topps Big #6 .... 0.12	0.05	0.01

Tim Salmon

Tim Salmon nearly won the Triple Crown in the Pacific Coast League in 1992. His progress toward that honor was only interrupted by his call-up to California. Salmon is big and strong and can hit for average and power. The '92 Bowman costs a bit much in light of the fact that Salmon has a '91 Bowman (which is the best card of the bunch here). Everything else is moderately priced and worth buying.

	NM	EX	VG
1991 Bowman Tiffany #203	5.00	2.25	1.00
1991 Impel/Line Drive AA #443	1.00	0.40	0.15
1991 ProCards Midland Angels (set)	9.00	3.75	1.75
1991 ProCards Tomorrow's Heroes #32	1.50	0.65	0.25
1992 Bowman Gold #259	8.00	3.50	1.50

Ryne Sandberg

The second-base, National League flip side of Cal Ripken Jr., Ryne Sandberg is durable, hits with power and for average, steals bases, and plays a practically perfect second base. Even though he's been helped by Wrigley Field a time or two in his career, Sandberg is one of those players who is not really affected by the thousand little shocks the flesh is heir to. He just keeps going and going and going — as do his cards, which show no signs of ever retreating from their current levels, and show every sign of advancing. If you're going to buy Ryne Sandberg cards, better buy them now while you can still afford them.

	NM	EX	VG
1981 TCMA Oklahoma City #17	150.00	75.00	35.00
1983 Donruss #277	42.00	20.00	10.00
1983 Fleer #507	42.00	20.00	10.00
1983 Topps #83	68.00	33.00	16.00
1984 7-Up Cubs #23	3.25	1.50	0.75
1984 Donruss #311	25.00	12.50	6.25
1984 Fleer #504	18.50	9.25	4.50
1984 Topps #596	9.50	4.50	2.25
1984 Topps Stickers #45	0.15	0.07	0.01
1984 Topps Tiffany #496	55.00	25.00	12.00
1984 Topps/Nestle #496 (sheet)	17.50	8.00	3.50
1985 7-Eleven Slurpee Disc #11 (Great Lakes)	3.25	1.50	0.50
1985 Donruss #67	10.00	4.75	2.25
1985 Donruss Diamond King #1	3.25	1.50	0.70
1985 Fleer #65	8.00	4.00	1.75
1985 Leaf-Donruss #1	1.25	0.60	0.24
1985 Topps #460	3.50	1.60	0.75
1985 Topps 3-D #7	0.65	0.30	0.12
1985 Topps Gallery of Champions (aluminum)	1.50	0.60	0.25
1985 Topps Gallery of Champions (bronze)	14.00	6.50	3.00
1985 Topps Gallery of Champions (silver)	75.00	35.00	15.00

1986 Donruss #67 .... 4.25	2.00	1.00
1986 Fleer #378 .... 4.25	2.00	1.00
1986 Fleer Star Stickers #186 .... 0.75	0.35	0.15
1986 Sportflics #20 .... 2.25	1.10	0.50
1986 Topps #690 .... 2.25	1.10	0.50
1987 Classic #35 .... 10.00	4.50	2.00
1987 David Berg Hot Dogs Cubs #23 .... 2.00	1.00	0.45
1987 Donruss #77 .... 1.10	0.50	0.20
1987 Donruss All-Stars #13 .... 0.65	0.30	0.12
1987 Donruss Opening Day #75 .... 0.25	0.12	0.05
1987 Donruss Pop-Up 0.75	0.35	0.15
1987 Fleer #572 .... 2.75	1.25	0.60
1987 Fleer League Leaders #39 .... 0.25	0.12	0.05
1987 Sportflics Team Preview #22 .... 0.50	0.20	0.08
1987 Topps #680 .... 1.00	0.45	0.20
1988 Classic Red #169 .... 2.25	1.10	0.50
1988 Fleer #431 .... 1.10	0.50	0.20
1989 Topps Tiffany #360 .... 1.50	0.70	0.30
1989 Upper Deck #120 .... 1.75	0.85	0.35
1990 Bowman Tiffany #30 .... 3.50	1.70	0.80
1990 Kenner Starting Lineup #29 .... 8.50	4.00	1.25
1990 Leaf #98 .... 4.00	1.75	0.80
1990 Score McDonald's #28 .... 27.50	12.50	6.00
1991 Donruss Elite (signature) 350.00	150.00	50.00
1991 Studio #158 .... 1.00	0.45	0.20
1991 Topps Stadium Club #230 .... 4.25	2.00	1.00
1991 Upper Deck Silver Sluggers #8 .... 6.00	2.50	1.10
1992 Fleer Lumber Co. #4 .... 3.50	1.50	0.50
1992 Fleer Ultra Award Winners #25 .... 12.00	5.50	2.50
1992 Kenner Starting Lineup #6 .... 12.50	6.00	2.50
1992 Upper Deck FanFest #39 .... 0.65	0.30	0.12

Deion Sanders

Love him or hate him, Deion Sanders is a talent. And surprise, surprise: he's
even becoming a baseball player. Sanders' assets are simple: tremendous foot
speed and bat speed. Some people feel Sanders could be a better all-around
ballplayer than Bo Jackson — the old Bo Jackson — if he applied himself more.
That doesn't seem likely. Sanders is doing everything in his power to apply
himself to football and baseball more or less equally, and until it catches up
with him Sanders will be fun to watch. And his cards will be too expensive to
seriously consider.

	NM	EX	VG
1989 Donruss #6	2.75	1.25	0.55
1989 Fleer Glossy Tin Update #53	2.75	1.25	0.50
1989 Fleer Update #53	2.25	1.00	0.45
1989 Topps Tiffany Traded #110	6.50	3.00	1.25
1989 Topps Tiffany Traded #110	6.50	3.00	1.25
1989 Topps Traded #110	2.00	0.85	0.35
1990 Classic #21	4.00	1.75	0.75
1990 Donruss #427	0.45	0.20	0.08
1990 Fleer #454	0.50	0.20	0.08
1990 Leaf #359	7.75	3.50	1.50
1990 Score #586	0.50	0.20	0.08
1990 Upper Deck #13	2.00	0.85	0.35
1991 Bowman #588	0.25	0.10	0.04
1991 Leaf #436	1.00	0.40	0.15
1991 Score Traded #34	0.30	0.10	0.04
1991 Topps Stadium Club #442	3.00	1.25	0.55
1991 Upper Deck #352	0.35	0.15	0.05
1992 Bowman #160	0.50	0.20	0.08
1992 Donruss #564	0.15	0.05	0.01
1992 Fleer Ultra #464	0.75	0.30	0.10
1992 Leaf #448	0.50	0.20	0.08
1992 Leaf Gold #448	2.00	0.80	0.30
1992 Pinnacle Team 2000 #31	0.75	0.30	0.10
1992 Studio #9	0.40	0.15	0.05
1992 Upper Deck #247	0.20	0.08	0.02
1993 Upper Deck #166	0.15	0.05	0.01

Reggie Sanders

Reggie Sanders, like Royce Clayton, has more cards than his performance to date would warrant. This is not to say that Sanders is a bad ballplayer; on the contrary, he has all the makings of a solid center fielder — like Jerome Walton had a chance to be. However, he hasn't become that solid center fielder yet, and he may never. But the cards keep on coming nonetheless. It's hard to recommend Reggie Sanders' cards for a lot of reasons. Overpopulation is just one of them.

	NM	EX	VG
1990 Best Cedar Rapids (set)	8.50	4.00	1.75
1991 Bowman #537	0.55	0.25	0.10
1991 Gold Leaf Rookies #10	7.25	3.50	1.50
1991 Impel Line Drive AA #167	3.50	1.50	0.55
1991 ProCards Tomorrow's Heroes #214	2.50	1.10	0.45

	NM	EX	VG
1991 Upper Deck #71	1.50	0.65	0.30
1991 Upper Deck Final Edition #11	0.50	0.20	0.08
1992 Bowman #118	0.45	0.20	0.03
1992 Bowman Gold #118	1.25	0.55	0.20
1992 Donruss #415	0.25	0.10	0.04
1992 Fleer #421	0.25	0.10	0.04
1992 Fleer Ultra #486	1.75	0.75	0.35
1992 Fleer Ultra All-Rookie Team #8	6.50	3.00	1.25
1992 Leaf #360	1.00	0.45	0.20
1992 Leaf Gold #360	5.00	2.25	1.00
1992 O-Pee-Chee Premier #25	0.50	0.20	0.08
1992 Pinnacle #440	0.75	0.30	0.10
1992 Pinnacle Rookie Idols #1	21.50	10.00	4.50
1992 Pinnacle Team 2000 #70	1.25	0.55	0.20
1992 Score Impact Players #76	0.75	0.30	0.10
1992 Studio #29	0.80	0.35	0.15
1992 Topps #283	0.30	0.10	0.04
1992 Topps Gold #283	5.00	2.25	1.00
1992 Upper Deck #27	0.35	0.15	0.05
1992 Upper Deck Scouting Report #20	3.25	1.50	0.65
1993 Fleer #44	0.25	0.10	0.04
1993 Fleer Rookie Sensations #10	2.50	1.00	0.45
1993 Score Select Dufex Inserts #3	1.25	0.50	0.20
1993 Topps Gold #83	2.00	0.85	0.35

Benito Santiago

Benito Santiago was the complete catching package — arm, bat, even a little bit of speed — until injuries and a surly attitude took some of it away. Now Santiago is sort of the Tony Fernandez of catchers — equal parts untapped potential and squandered potential. His cards used to be more expensive; they're realistically priced now, but could even fall further before they're done.

	NM	EX	VG
1985 TCMA Beaumont (set)	35.00	15.00	6.50
1986 Fleer #644	1.50	0.60	0.25
1987 Bohemian Hearth Bread #9	8.00	3.75	1.75
1987 Donruss #31	0.40	0.15	0.05
1987 Donruss Rookies #44	0.35	0.12	0.04
1987 Fleer #429	0.40	0.15	0.05
1987 Sportflics Rookies #19	0.50	0.20	0.08
1987 Topps Tiffany Traded #109	0.85	0.30	0.12
1988 Classic Red #160	0.25	0.10	0.04
1988 Fleer Baseball MVP #30	0.25	0.10	0.04

1988 Fleer Glossy Tin #596	0.25	0.10	0.04
1988 Fleer Star Stickers #125	0.30	0.12	0.05
1988 Kenner Starting Lineup	12.00	5.50	2.50
1988 Panini Stickers #402	0.12	0.05	0.01
1988 Score #25	1.80	0.85	0.40
1988 Sportflics #22	0.50	0.20	0.08
1988 Topps Big #12	0.12	0.05	0.01
1988 Topps Tiffany #693	0.75	0.30	0.12
1989 Bowman Tiffany #453	0.85	0.30	0.12
1989 Fleer Glossy Tin #316	0.45	0.20	0.08
1990 Donruss Learning Series #4	0.85	0.35	0.15
1990 Fleer Award Winners #33	0.10	0.04	0.01
1990 Leaf #207	0.35	0.15	0.05
1991 Fleer All-Stars #9	1.50	0.65	0.25
1991 Topps #105	0.30	0.12	0.05
1991 Upper Deck Silver Sluggers #17	1.00	0.45	0.20
1992 Leaf Gold Inserts #321	0.40	0.15	0.05
1992 Topps Gold Inserts #185	2.00	0.80	0.35

Mike Schmidt

Mike Schmidt may be the greatest at his position in history. His spot in Cooperstown is reserved and that means higher card prices — and soon.

	NM	EX	VG
1973 Topps #615	500.00	175.00	75.00
1974 Topps #283	110.00	45.00	20.00
1975 Topps #70	75.00	27.50	10.00
1976 Topps #480	32.75	13.50	5.00
1977 Topps #140	28.00	10.00	3.50
1978 Topps #360	16.25	7.50	2.50
1979 Topps #610	14.00	5.00	2.00
1980 Topps #270	7.50	2.50	0.75
1981 Donruss #11	3.00	0.75	0.25
1981 Fleer #5	2.75	1.00	0.25
1981 Fleer #640	2.50	1.00	0.25
1981 Topps #540	5.00	1.50	0.50
1982 Donruss #294	2.75	1.00	0.25
1982 Fleer #258	2.50	1.00	0.25
1982 Topps #100	3.35	1.25	0.30
1982 Topps #101	1.35	0.30	0.10
1983 Donruss #168	2.25	0.75	0.20
1983 Fleer #173	2.25	0.75	0.20

1983 Topps #300 .... 3.35	1.15	0.40
1983 Topps #301 .... 1.75	0.50	0.10
1984 Donruss #183 .... 14.00	2.25	0.50
1984 Fleer #265 .... 2.75	0.60	0.15
1985 Topps #500 .... 1.35	0.25	0.10
1986 Donruss #61 .... 2.25	0.45	0.10
1986 Fleer #450 .... 2.25	0.45	0.10
1989 Fleer Update 1.25	0.30	0.10
1989 Upper Deck #406 .... 2.25	0.45	0.10

Aaron Sele

No one in Boston is claiming Aaron Sele is another Roger Clemens. Sele is, however, a very poised pitcher — similar to the Orioles' Mike Mussina — who is making a rapid rise through the Boston system. Like Tyrone Hill, Sele is a sleeper; also like Hill, Sele is a pitcher, and you know what that means. Watch from a distance. His excellent 1993 season will have to be repeated a few times before we'll know if his cards are a good bet.

	NM	EX	VG
1991 Classic Draft Picks #19 .... 0.25	0.10	0.04
1991 Topps Stadium Club Dome #168 .... 1.75	0.75	0.35
1992 Bowman #311 .... 0.75	0.30	0.12
1992 Classic-Best Minor League #175 .... 0.75	0.30	0.12
1992 Front Row #2 .... 0.50	0.20	0.08
1992 Score #809 .... 0.50	0.20	0.08
1992 Topps #504 .... 0.50	0.20	0.08
1992 Upper Deck Minor League #20 .... 0.75	0.30	0.12
1992 Upper Deck Minor League #291 .... 0.75	0.30	0.12

Gary Sheffield

Gary Sheffield very nearly won a Triple Crown in 1992 with the Padres. Now with the Marlins, Sheffield is the exceptionally talented nephew of Mets pitcher Dwight Gooden, and along with Fred McGriff a product of the Tampa baseball factory. Sheffield is an awful fielder but a wonderful hitter. Every level his cards were hyped to initially is valid, because the guy can play, and play for a long time. He will be as good as his mind allows him to be. Make your buying judgments accordingly.

	NM	EX	VG
1987 ProCards Stockton (set) 25.00	12.00	5.50
1988 Best El Paso Diablos (set) 16.00	6.50	3.00
1989 Bowman #142 .... 1.00	0.40	0.15

1989 Bowman Tiffany #142	5.00	2.25	1.00
1989 Donruss #31	1.00	0.40	0.15
1989 Donruss Rookies #1	2.00	0.80	0.15
1989 Fleer #196	1.50	0.65	0.25
1989 Fleer Glossy Tin #196	3.75	1.50	0.65
1989 Score #625	1.00	0.40	0.15
1989 Sportflics #41	1.00	0.40	0.15
1989 Topps #343	1.00	0.40	0.15
1989 Topps Tiffany #343	6.25	3.00	1.25
1990 Kenner Starting Lineup	10.00	4.50	2.00
1990 Leaf #157	9.00	4.25	2.00
1990 Sportflics #52	0.75	0.30	12.00
1990 Upper Deck #157	0.75	0.30	0.12
1991 Donruss #76	1.00	0.40	0.15
1991 Donruss Elite #28	75.00	36.50	17.50
1991 Fleer Ultra #180	0.75	0.30	0.12
1991 Leaf #173	0.75	0.30	0.12
1991 Topps #95	3.50	1.50	0.65
1991 Topps Desert Storm #68	35.00	15.00	6.50
1992 Bowman #214	0.50	0.20	0.08
1992 Fleer Ultra #582	0.75	0.30	0.12
1992 Fleer Ultra #83	0.75	0.30	0.12
1992 Fleer Ultra All-Stars #14	5.00	2.25	1.00
1992 Leaf Gold Inserts #446	4.00	1.75	0.75
1992 Leaf Studio #108	0.50	0.20	0.08
1992 Score Pinnacle #235	0.50	0.20	0.08
1992 Score Pinnacle Team 2000 #59	1.00	0.40	0.15
1992 Topps #309	1.00	0.40	0.15
1992 Topps #766	0.75	0.30	0.12
1992 Topps Gold Inserts #695	2.00	0.80	0.30
1993 Donruss Diamond Kings #21	4.00	1.75	0.75
1993 Fleer NL All-Stars #3	3.00	1.25	0.50
1993 Fleer Pro Visions I #3	2.50	1.10	75.00
1993 Score Select Rookies #4	5.00	2.25	1.00
1993 Topps Gold Inserts #140	1.00	0.40	0.15
1993 Topps Black Gold Inserts #18	7.00	3.25	0.15
1993 Upper Deck Triple Crown #8	7.50	3.50	1.50

Al Shirley

The Mets are counting on Shirley to supply their outfield power starting in about 1995, and the Mets are talking through their collective hat when they say this. Shirley can hit — and he's an excellent athlete with some multifaceted tools, too. But like every other minor-league prospect who's been drafted out of high school, Shirley has some maturing to do. Once he gets that out of the way, though, watch out.

	NM	EX	VG
1991 Classic Draft Picks #14	0.75	0.30	0.12
1991 Front Row Draft Picks #43	0.50	0.20	0.08
1992 Classic-Best Kingsport (set)	5.00	2.25	1.00
1992 Score #802	0.15	0.05	0.01
1992 Score Pinnacle #297	0.50	0.20	0.08
1992 Topps #306	0.25	0.10	0.04
1992 Topps Gold Inserts #306	6.00	2.50	1.00
1993 Fleer #79	0.50	0.20	0.08

Ruben Sierra

Ruben Sierra has been compared to Roberto Clemente, and the comparisons are valid in more ways than one. Both are immensely talented players whose biggest enemies are themselves. Sierra in particular. There is literally nothing on a baseball field that Sierra cannot do exceptionally well except pitch, and he could probably do that in a pinch. But sometimes it seems as though Sierra lacks motivation and turns trivialities into career-threatening situations. For all his skills, Sierra probably won't win his long-coveted MVP award or make the Hall of Fame, all of which would tend to put a damper on his cards. But he's young; don't write him off quite yet.

	NM	EX	VG
1985 Team Tulsa Drillers (set)	175.00	85.00	40.00
1987 Mother's Cookies Rangers #13	1.75	0.75	0.30
1988 Fleer Baseball's Hottest Stars #38	0.50	0.20	0.08
1988 Fleer Star Stickers #69	0.25	0.10	0.04
1988 Topps Stickers #234	0.20	0.08	0.03
1989 Donruss Baseball's Best #111	0.30	0.12	0.05
1989 Fleer Baseball MVP #35	0.25	0.10	0.04
1989 Mother's Cookies Rangers #7	0.90	0.35	0.12
1989 Topps American Baseball #70	0.20	0.08	0.03
1989 Topps Big Baseball #82	0.20	0.08	0.03
1990 Donruss A.L. Best #143	0.20	0.08	0.03
1990 Fleer Award Winners #35	0.25	0.10	0.04
1990 Topps All-Star Glossy (60) #26	0.25	0.10	0.04

John Smiley

Good left-handed pitching is welcome wherever it goes, meaning that John Smiley has been more than welcome with the three teams he has pitched for in the last three years. Smiley is a maddeningly inconsistent pitcher who will never be a Hall of Famer for that reason alone. He's never less than entertaining, though his cards rightly tend toward the more mundane side of things.

	NM	EX	VG
1986 ProCards Prince William (set)	13.50	6.50	3.00
1987 Donruss Rookies #39	0.85	0.40	0.15
1987 Fleer Glossy Update #110	0.80	0.35	0.12
1987 Fleer Update #110	0.85	0.40	0.15
1987 Topps Tiffany Traded #114T	3.25	1.50	0.60
1987 Topps Traded #114T	0.65	0.30	0.12
1988 Fleer #340	1.00	0.45	0.20
1988 Score #287	0.30	0.12	0.05
1988 Score Glossy #287	3.25	1.50	0.65
1991 Topps Desert Storm #143	6.50	3.00	1.25
1992 Leaf Gold #526	0.50	0.20	0.08

Lee Smith

Lee Smith is currently the all-time leader in saves, which means card touts are going to be pitching his rookie cards as undervalued until someone comes along and beats his save record, at which time he'll become just another relief slug, like Jeff Reardon. Smith has had a remarkable career in the sense that he's never been thought of at any time as the absolute best No. 1 reliever in the game. Top five, certainly, but never numero uno. That would seem to keep him some distance from the Hall of Fame, and rightly so. Smith didn't have a single Classic card until 1990. It's fun to watch his cards make a little dash up the charts, and presumably it shall also be enjoyable to watch them slowly work their way down.

	NM	EX	VG
1990 Classic #137	0.10	0.04	0.01

Ozzie Smith

Like Luis Aparicio, Ozzie Smith will make it to Cooperstown on his glove. No one since Aparicio has reshaped a position in his own image like Ozzie, and perhaps no one in baseball history has reshaped it more completely. Smith is also a much more than competent hitter, though his career batting average isn't likely to top .270. His cards have moved up and are not bargains in general, though the things that remain bargains for virtually all players — stickers, Topps Big cards, Donruss Pop-Ups, and the like — remain good buys for Ozzie. Perhaps especially good ones, considering where he's going to end up.

	NM	EX	VG
1984 Cereal Series #2.	0.35	0.15	0.05
1986 Burger King #14	0.10	0.04	0.01
1986 Donruss Pop-Up	0.15	0.05	0.01
1986 Schnucks Milk Cardinals (21)	4.50	2.00	0.75
1987 Classic #32	0.75	0.35	0.15
1987 Donruss Diamond King Supers #5	0.25	0.10	0.04
1987 Smokey Bear Cardinals #17	0.75	0.35	0.15
1988 Fleer Star Stickers #120	0.20	0.08	0.03
1989 Donruss All-Stars #37	0.20	0.08	0.03
1989 Topps Big #110	0.10	0.04	0.01
1990 Fleer Award Winners #37	0.10	0.04	0.01
1990 Score McDonald's #24	10.00	4.50	2.00

John Smoltz

Yet another in the Braves' great stable of starting pitchers, Smoltz was stolen from the Tigers' organization in a trade for Doyle Alexander and has become one of the N.L.'s top strikeout pitchers, though not as consistent a winner as his arm and stuff might have you believe. Smoltz's card values have been inflated by the team he pitches for and the exposure he gets, though he is young enough that several 20-win seasons are not at all out of the question.

	NM	EX	VG
1987 ProCards Glens Falls Tigers #372	18.50	9.00	4.25
1988 CMC Richmond Braves #4	9.50	4.50	2.00
1988 Fleer Update #74U	5.00	2.25	1.00
1989 Bowman Tiffany #266	4.25	2.00	0.85
1989 Upper Deck #17	5.25	2.50	1.10
1990 Leaf #59	4.25	2.00	0.85
1990 Topps Big #306	0.10	0.04	0.01
1991 Topps Desert Storm #157	16.00	8.00	4.00
1991 Topps Stadium Club #365	1.25	0.60	0.25

J.T. Snow

Though baseball-card companies are rushing too many prospects into their card sets, every now and then a player slips through to have a rookie card in the very same year that he makes the bigs. Such is the case with J.T. Snow. He's more of a Wally Joyner type than a Fred McGriff — hits for more average than pop, in other words. But he can drive the ball out of the park if need be. He's part of an exciting, resurgent team in California, and that won't hurt, either. His cards are prime candidates for being caught up in a hype rush, so they're not the best buys. But Snow is a nice ballplayer, and over time may justify the prices being asked for his cards.

	NM	EX	VG
1990 Sportsprint Prince William (set)	10.00	4.50	2.00
1991 Impel Line Drive AA #18	0.75	0.35	0.15
1991 ProCards Albany (set)	7.50	3.50	1.50
1991 ProCards Tomorrow's Heroes #114	0.75	0.35	0.15

Terry Steinbach

One of the steadying influences on an otherwise disparate Oakland A's ballclub, Steinbach is just beginning to be recognized as one of the game's finest catchers. While he doesn't do any one thing superbly, he does all the right things well, and has the respect of his peers to boot. His cards just sort of tag along behind those of Ruben Sierra, Will Clark, et al., but over the long haul may outperform these cards substantially.

	NM	EX	VG
1986 Team Huntsville Stars (set)	15.00	6.50	2.50
1989 Mother's Cookies A's #3	0.65	0.25	0.10
1990 Mother's Cookies A's #3	0.45	0.20	0.08
1990 Topps All-Star Glossy (22) #20	0.12	0.05	0.01
1990 Topps Big #118	0.15	0.06	0.01

Dave Stewart

The line you hear about Dave Stewart is always the same: If he hadn't got off to such a late start, he'd be a lock for the Hall of Fame. But the truth is, Stewart's early career was a search for the proper stuff to go with his arm. His glory years were brief and spent with an exceptional team, and his decline appears to be swift. If it's not, there's justification for the prices of some of his early cards. If it is, there are some overpriced cards collectors should be aware of.

	NM	EX	VG
1979 TCMA Albuquerque Dukes #5	55.00	26.50	12.50
1982 Donruss #410	2.35	1.10	0.50
1982 Fleer #24	2.35	1.10	0.50
1983 Donruss #588	0.45	0.20	0.08
1983 Topps #532	0.50	0.20	0.08
1984 Donruss #343	1.00	0.45	0.20

1984 Fleer #430 .... 0.45	0.20	0.08
1985 Fleer #569 .... 0.45	0.20	0.08
1988 Fleer Baseball MVP #36 .... 0.10	0.04	0.01
1988 Fleer Mini #348 .... 0.12	0.05	0.01
1989 Donruss Baseball's Best #99 .... 0.50	0.20	0.08
1989 Fleer Baseball's Exciting Stars #39 .... 0.07	0.03	0.01
1990 Topps All-Star Glossy (22) #21 .... 0.20	0.08	0.03
1992 Topps Gold #410 .... 2.00	0.85	0.35

Darryl Strawberry

Supposedly Darryl Strawberry has the swing Ted Williams loves to watch. Too bad he doesn't have the fire in the belly anymore. For the longest time all you heard out of Darryl Strawberry was how much he wanted to go home to L.A. Now that he's home you don't hear much out of him at all, and you sure don't see the production he was capable of during his best years with the Mets. Strawberry's too young to self-destruct like this, and since his cards still show some residual carryover from his great days in New York, they're not worth buying, either.

	NM	EX	VG
1983 TCMA Tidewater (set)	125.00	55.00	253.00
1984 Nestle #182	70.00	32.50	15.00
1984 O-Pee-Chee #182	18.00	8.50	4.00
1984 Smokey Bear Jackson Mets in Majors	20.00	8.50	3.50
1984 Topps Tiffany #182	125.00	60.00	27.50
1985 Leaf-Donruss #159	1.75	0.75	0.35
1985 O-Pee-Chee #126	3.00	1.25	0.50
1986 Donruss All-Stars #5	0.60	0.25	0.10
1986 Donruss Pop-Ups (16)	0.65	0.30	0.12
1986 Fleer Mini #26	0.50	0.20	0.08
1986 Fleer Star Stickers #116	1.00	0.45	0.20
1986 Glossy All-Star (22) #19	0.80	0.35	0.15
1986 Mets Super Fan Club #8	1.25	0.50	0.20
1986 Topps Stickers #150	0.40	0.15	0.05
1987 Classic #3	5.00	2.25	1.00
1987 Drake's Panel (1)	4.00	1.75	0.75
1987 Fleer League Leaders #41	0.41	0.15	0.05
1987 Jiffy Pop #178	2.75	1.25	0.50
1987 Leaf #68	1.00	0.45	0.20
1988 Donruss Mets Team Book #439	0.70	0.30	0.12
1988 Drake's Panel (2)	3.75	1.75	0.75
1988 Kahn's Mets #18	2.00	0.80	0.35
1988 Kenner Starting Lineup	10.00	4.50	2.00

	NM	EX	VG
1988 Score Young Superstar II #20	0.40	0.15	0.05
1989 Classic #8	0.40	0.15	0.05
1989 Scoremasters #42	0.40	0.15	0.05
1989 Topps Big #139	0.25	0.10	0.04
1990 Fleer Baseball All-Stars #37	0.30	0.12	0.04
1990 Kahn's Mets #18	1.00	0.45	0.20
1991 Colla Darryl Strawberry (1–13)	10.00	4.50	2.00
1991 Donruss Grand Slammers #13	0.25	0.10	0.04

William Sunday

Billy Sunday was not known for what he did on the field, but by his preaching (which quicky ended his career). It happened in the late 1800s, but demand for Sunday cards remains — for now — far greater than the minimal supplies.

	NM	EX	VG
E223 G&B Chewing Gum	2500.00	1750.00	1200.00
N172	1500.00	1000.00	625.00
N173	2000.00	1500.00	1000.00
N284 Buchner Gold Coin	150.00	80.00	35.00
N403 Yum Yum	2500.00	1750.00	1200.00

Rick Sutcliffe

Rick Sutcliffe has fewer lives than a cat but more lives than a pitcher with a sneaky-fast fastball and an overhand curveball ought to. Sutcliffe has been around for 16 years in an up-and-down career. His cards aren't really expensive — $2.50 tops — but look at it this way: Do you really want to spend $2.50 on a Rick Sutcliffe rookie?

	NM	EX	VG
1985 Topps Supers #3	0.25	0.10	0.04
1986 Leaf #122	0.10	0.04	0.01
1986 Topps Stickers #61	0.08	0.03	0.01
1987 Donruss Opening Day #69	0.10	0.04	0.01
1987 Fleer Baseball's Best #41	0.10	0.04	0.01
1988 Classic Travel Blue #224	0.15	0.05	0.01
1988 Donruss Cubs Team Book #68	0.15	0.05	0.01
1988 Fleer Award Winners #41	0.10	0.04	0.01
1988 Fleer Star Stickers #51	0.15	0.05	0.01
1988 Kenner Starting Lineup	12.00	5.50	2.00
1988 Topps American Baseball Glossy #78	0.50	0.20	0.08
1988 Topps Big Baseball #128	0.10	0.04	0.01
1989 Marathon Cubs #40	0.40	0.12	0.04

Greg Swindell

Swindell is a big lefty out of the University of Texas, a Roger Clemens with a little less stuff. Swindell has also had to deal with the burden of pitching in Cleveland most of his career. He's not a bad pitcher when he's healthy, and pitching in Houston will certainly give his career a boost, but there's not a lot to him. Even if he hadn't been hurt a day in his life he'd still be ranked below the first echelon of pitchers.

	NM	EX	VG
1989 Topps Big Baseball #68	0.08	0.03	0.01
1990 Score Superstar #11	0.08	0.03	0.01

Kevin Tapani

Of all the pitchers sent from the Mets to the Twins in the Frank Viola deal, less was expected of Kevin Tapani than any of the others (Jack Savage, David West, Rick Aguilera, and Tim Drummond being the others). But ho! Kevin Tapani has proven to be one of the best of the bunch. So much for scouting reports. Tapani is a control pitcher who throws moderately hard, and if that's an indefinite way of describing Tapani, it's because he's an indefinite sort of pitcher. It would be a mistake to underestimate him, but until he wins 20 games or a Cy Young Award — both of which are improbable — it's going to be his lot. His cards are moderately priced and at this point are not bargains in any sense of the word.

	NM	EX	VG
1987 ProCards Modesto (set)	12.00	5.50	2.50
1989 ProCards Tidewater (set)	9.00	3.50	1.50
1990 Bowman Tiffany #407	1.25	0.50	0.20
1990 Donruss #473	0.30	0.10	0.04
1990 Donruss Rookies #35	0.35	0.10	0.04
1990 Fleer Update #110	0.35	0.10	0.04
1990 Leaf #269	1.50	0.60	0.25
1990 Score Traded #82	0.60	0.25	0.10
1990 Topps #227	0.30	0.10	0.04
1990 Upper Deck #87	0.60	0.25	0.10
1991 Bowman Tiffany #322	0.30	0.10	0.04
1991 Topps #161	0.75	0.30	0.12
1991 Topps Desert Storm #633	20.00	8.50	3.50
1992 Bowman Gold #552	0.50	0.20	0.04
1992 Leaf Gold Inserts #14	0.40	0.15	0.05
1992 Topps Gold Inserts #313	2.00	0.80	0.30
1993 Score Select Aces #24	3.00	1.25	0.50

Danny Tartabull

The Yankees thought they were getting guaranteed production in Tartabull, but they should have looked twice. Tartabull's career has been about nothing so much as inconsistency. From the start of his career with Seattle through his days with Kansas City to 1992 and 1993 with the Yankees, Tartabull's career has been on a rollercoaster of production covering everything from home runs to batting average. Things were so bad in 1992 with New York that Tartabull was offered around to the expansion teams but found no takers at the price. When you look at what the 30-year-old Tartabull has done in his career, you figure his cards are priced about where they should be, if not a little over.

	NM	EX	VG
1984 Cramer Salt Lake City (set)	25.00	11.00	5.00
1986 Mother's Cookies Mariners #22	1.75	0.75	0.35
1987 Topps Coins #25	0.20	0.08	0.03
1987 Topps Glossy All-Star (60) #19	0.35	0.15	0.05
1987 Topps Stickers #223	0.25	0.10	0.04
1988 Donruss Baseball's Best #287	0.20	0.08	0.03
1988 Fleer Award Winners #42	0.12	0.05	0.01
1988 Kenner Starting Lineup	13.50	6.00	2.50
1988 Topps American Baseball Glossy #78	0.75	0.30	0.10
1988 Topps Big #230	0.20	0.08	0.03
1988 Topps Mini League Leaders #16	0.25	0.10	0.04
1989 Donruss Baseball's Best #39	0.12	0.05	0.01
1989 Fleer Baseball MVP #37	0.09	0.04	0.01
1990 Score Superstar #72	0.10	0.04	0.01

Brien Taylor

The No. 1 pick in the 1991 baseball draft, Brien Taylor got the largest signing bonus ever paid to a high-school draftee, then went out and pitched like a high-school kid. Brien Taylor throws 90-mile-an-hour-plus fastballs from the left side at the knees with consistency. He hasn't worked out some inconsistencies in his delivery yet, but once he does, look out. His cards — the ones that were able to sneak in under the Classic embargo — are expensive and worth it, from a pure player-performance standpoint. Whether the cards are worth much as investments is a trickier call.

	NM	EX	VG
1991 Baseball Draft Pick Promo Card (signed)	100.00	45.00	20.00
1991 Classic Four-Sport Draft Pick Foil #51	3.50	1.50	0.50

	NM	EX	VG
1992 Bowman Gold #124	25.50	12.50	6.00
1992 Classic-Best Fort Lauderdale (set)	7.00	3.00	1.10

Bobby Thigpen

Bobby Thigpen's record-setting 1990 season, when he posted 57 saves in 77 appearances, must have really taken its toll. He hasn't been close to being the same since. Thigpen hit cleanup in the same Mississippi State lineup that included Will Clark and Rafael Palmiero, but in the pros the only things he cared about hitting were corners with his screaming fastball. The fastball isn't what it used to be and the breaking pitches that might help him are nowhere to be found, so the outlook isn't bright for Thigpen. His cards are likewise doomed. Who knows? Maybe he could go back to hitting cleanup.

	NM	EX	VG
1986 Team Birmingham (set)	90.00	42.50	20.00
1987 Coca-Cola White Sox #37	0.60	0.25	0.10
1987 Donruss #370	1.25	0.50	0.20
1987 Fleer #507	0.50	0.20	0.08
1987 Fleer Glossy Tin #507	0.55	0.25	0.10
1987 Topps Tiffany #61	0.50	0.20	0.08
1988 Fleer #410	0.30	0.10	0.04
1988 Fleer Glossy Tin #410	0.50	0.20	0.06
1988 Score Glossy Glossy #307	0.75	0.30	0.10
1989 Bowman Tiffany #55	0.25	0.10	0.04
1989 Fleer Baseball MVP #38	0.09	0.03	0.01
1989 Fleer Glossy Tin #512	0.25	0.10	0.04
1989 Kenner Starting Lineup	8.00	3.50	1.50
1989 Score Young Superstar I #29	0.12	0.05	0.01
1990 Bowman Tiffany #306	0.25	0.10	0.04
1990 Classic III #81.	0.08	0.03	0.01
1990 Donruss A.L. Best #32	0.10	0.04	0.01
1990 Fleer Baseball All Stars #40	0.10	0.04	0.01
1990 Topps Big #295	0.10	0.04	0.01
1991 Topps #256	0.50	0.20	0.08
1992 Leaf Gold Inserts #210	0.40	0.15	0.05
1992 Topps Gold Inserts #505	0.75	0.30	0.12

Frank Thomas

Thomas and Ken Griffey Jr. run neck-and-neck as far as modern players and baseball cards are concerned. Both have singlehandedly driven sets (Griffey the '89 Upper Deck set, Thomas the '90 Leaf and the 1992 Fleer Rookie

Sensations sets), and both are among the few modern players capable of building on their current card prices in the next three to five years.

	NM	EX	VG
1990 Best Birmingham Barons #1 (set)	55.00	28.00	15.00
1990 Best Minor League #1	40.00	20.00	10.00
1990 Bowman #320	5.50	3.00	1.50
1990 Bowman Tiffany #320	17.50	8.00	4.00
1990 CMC Pre-Rookie #818	25.00	12.50	6.00
1990 Leaf #300	72.50	40.00	20.00
1990 Score #663	7.25	3.50	1.50
1990 Score Rising Star #78	2.75	1.25	0.65
1990 Score Traded #86T	11.00	5.50	2.50
1990 Topps Tiffany #414	17.50	8.00	4.00
1991 Leaf #281	8.00	4.10	2.00
1991 Topps Desert Shield #79	250.00	150.00	80.00
1991 Topps Stadium Club #57	33.00	16.00	7.00
1991 Upper Deck #246	4.00	3.00	2.25
1992 Fleer Rookie Sensations #1	45.00	23.00	10.00
1992 Kenner Starting Lineup figurine and card	35.00	18.00	8.00

Jim Thome

Thome may eventually be the Cleveland Indians' starting third baseman and a hitting machine along the lines of Robin Ventura or even George Brett. But first he has to: (1) stop gettting injured, and (2) make the major-league roster. He hasn't done either, yet, and you can guess what that means for his cards.

	NM	EX	VG
1991 Bowman #6 8	0.20	0.08	0.03
1991 Bowman Tiffany #68	1.00	0.45	0.20
1991 Classic-Best Minor League #195	1.50	0.65	0.30
1991 Line Drive Pre-Rookie #96	1.00	0.45	0.20
1991 ProCards Canton-Akron (set)	6.50	2.50	1.00
1991 Upper Deck Final Edition #17	0.50	0.20	0.08
1992 Fleer Ultra #54	0.35	0.15	0.05
1992 Leaf Gold #299	1.50	0.65	0.25
1992 Pinnacle Team 200 #37	0.50	0.20	0.08
1992 Score Impact Player #36	0.25	0.12	0.04
1992 Topps Stadium Club #360	0.50	0.20	0.06
1992 Upper Deck #5	0.15	0.05	0.01
1992 Upper Deck Scouting Report #22	0.75	0.30	0.12

Jim Thorpe

Jim Thorpe couldn't hit a curve, but he's still considered the greatest athlete of all time by many admirers. His one baseball card was appropriately the M101-5 issue of The Sporting News. It's rare, it's in heavy demand, and it's not likely to get much cheaper unless collectors are willing to have their Thorpe card be a football card.

	NM	EX	VG
M101-5 176	5700.00	2000.00	950.00

Alan Trammell

Often mentioned in the same breath with Lou Whitaker, Trammell is actually closer in style to the player with whom Trammell shares a rookie card, Paul Molitor: an unstoppable hitter when healthy, but not healthy all that often. Trammell has put together some tremendous seasons, but the whole is less than the sum of its parts. He will likely be passed over for the Hall of Fame, and so some of the luster from the Trammell/Molitor rookie-card pairing is dissipated. However, Trammell has been a class player throughout his career and a credit to the game. Perhaps 50 years from now those considerations will get him enshrined. For the short term, though, there are too many negatives with Trammell for the buyer simply looking to make money. Collectors and fans of the game, of course, are advised to proceed full-speed ahead.

	NM	EX	VG
1978 Burger King Tigers #15	20.00	9.50	4.25
1979 O-Pee-Chee #184	5.00	2.25	1.00
1981 Kellogg's #51	0.30	0.10	0.04
1983 Topps Stickers #63	0.20	0.08	0.03
1984 Fleer Stickers #14	0.20	0.08	0.03
1985 Donruss Action All-Star #44	0.20	0.08	0.03
1985 Wendy's Tigers #20	1.00	0.40	0.15
1986 Leaf #101	0.25	0.10	0.04
1987 Baseball's Hottest Stars #41	0.20	0.08	0.03
1987 Coca-Cola Tigers Panel 2	1.25	0.50	0.20
1987 Topps Mini League Leaders #56	0.30	0.10	0.04
1988 Cain's Potato Chips Tigers	4.25	2.00	0.80
1988 Classic Travel Blue #231	0.35	0.15	0.05
1988 Donruss Baseball's Best #288	0.20	0.08	0.03
1988 Jiffy Pop #16	1.25	0.50	0.20
1988 Kenner Starting Lineup	12.00	5.50	2.00

Todd Van Poppel

Todd was the most hyped high-school pitcher since David Clyde when he was drafted out of high school by Oakland in 1990. But unlike Clyde, Van Poppel was not rushed to the major leagues, even though he did start one game for the A's in 1991. Some arm and shoulder problems have hindered Van Poppel's progress, but he still remains one of the A's brightest pitching hopes, and one of the top pitching prospects in baseball.

	NM	EX	VG
1990 Classic Draft Picks #11	1.00	0.45	0.20
1991 Classic Collector's Edition #151	1.00	0.45	0.20
1991 Classic I #75	1.00	0.45	0.20
1991 Classic II #77	1.00	0.45	0.20
1991 Classic-Best Foil #386	3.00	1.50	0.65
1991 Classic-Best Huntsville Stars #24	6.25	3.00	1.45
1991 Donruss Rookies #7	1.35	0.60	0.25
1991 Donruss Studio #109	2.50	1.25	0.60
1991 Gold Leaf Rookies #9	6.00	2.75	1.25
1991 Line Drive #296	2.25	1.10	0.50
1991 ProCards Huntsville Stars #1795	5.00	2.25	1.00
1991 ProCards Tomorrow's Heroes #129	3.00	1.35	0.60
1991 Score #389	0.60	0.25	0.12
1991 Upper Deck #53	2.25	1.10	0.50
1992 Donruss #9	0.25	0.10	0.04
1992 Fleer Rookie Sensations #2	9.50	4.50	2.25
1992 Score Impact Players #37	1.00	0.45	0.20

Andy Van Slyke

The good news for Andy Van Slyke was that 1992's back injury meant he couldn't pull everything, which resulted in Van Slyke's best offensive season ever. The bad news is that it is a back injury, it's not going to get better, and it's not going to continue to have a positive effect on his offensive production. Van Slyke has been the best offensive and defensive center fielder anyone could hope for for a lot of years now, but he's pushing 33 and he's probably not going to have too much more than 2,000 hits and 200 homers for his career — nice enough, but not Hall of Fame stuff. So what do you do with his cards? If you have them sell them; if you don't have them and don't have to buy them right this minute, don't. They're at a peak.

	NM	EX	VG
1983 Riley's Louisville (set)	30.00	13.50	6.00
1984 Donruss #83	13.00	6.00	2.50

1984 Fleer #339 .... 7.50	3.00	1.25
1984 Topps #206 .... 3.25	1.50	0.65
1985 Donruss #327 .... 2.75	1.25	0.50
1985 Fleer #242 .... 2.50	110.00	0.40
1985 Topps #551 .... 0.60	0.25	0.10
1986 Donruss #412 .... 0.60	0.25	0.10
1986 Fleer #48 .... 0.40	0.15	0.05
1986 Topps #683 .... 0.25	0.10	0.04
1987 Donruss #417 .... 0.40	0.25	0.10
1987 Donruss Opening Day #161 .... 0.10	0.04	0.01
1987 Fleer #311 .... 0.75	0.30	0.12
1987 Topps #33 .... 0.30	0.12	0.05
1987 Topps Traded #124 .... 0.25	0.10	0.04
1988 Fleer #341 .... 0.35	0.15	0.05
1988 Fleer Mini #108 .... 0.10	0.04	0.01
1988 Kenner Starting Lineup 18.50	8.50	4.00
1988 Leaf #102 .... 0.10	0.04	0.01
1988 O-Pee-Chee #142 .... 0.07	0.01	0.01
1988 Panini Stickers #388 .... 0.08	0.03	0.01
1988 Score Glossy #416 .... 0.60	0.20	0.07
1988 Topps American Baseball Glossy #81 ... 0.30	0.12	0.05
1988 Topps Stickers #126 .... 0.08	0.03	0.01
1989 Classic #111 .... 0.20	0.08	0.03
1989 Donruss Baseball's Best #45 .... 0.10	0.04	0.01
1989 Donruss MVP #10 .... 0.15	0.05	0.01
1989 Fleer Baseball MVP #40 .... 0.12	0.05	0.01
1989 Hills #30 .... 0.05	0.01	0.01
1989 Topps Big #255 .... 0.08	0.03	0.01
1989 Upper Deck #537 .... 0.40	0.12	0.05
1991 Donruss #230 .... 0.25	0.10	0.04
1991 Donruss Elite #36 .... 45.00	21.50	10.00
1991 Topps #118 .... 0.75	0.30	0.12
1992 Classic #92 .... 0.08	0.03	0.01
1992 Fleer Ultra #262 .... 1.00	0.45	0.20
1992 Fleer Ultra Awards #10 .... 2.50	1.10	0.50
1992 Leaf Gold Inserts #43 .... 0.40	0.15	0.05
1992 Leaf Studio Heritage #10 .... 0.75	0.35	0.15
1993 Donruss Diamond Kings #9 .... 2.00	0.80	0.30
1993 Fleer NL All-Stars #8 .... 1.50	0.65	0.25
1993 Score Select Rookies #6 .... 3.00	1.25	0.50
1993 Topps Gold Inserts #275 .... 0.25	0.10	0.04
1993 Topps Black Gold Inserts #21 .... 4.00	1.75	0.75
1993 Upper Deck Iooss Collection #18 .... 1.50	0.65	0.25

Mo Vaughn

Mo Vaughn is Phil Plantier all over again: Lots of power potential, signs of being able to hit for average, so-so glove, zero speed, Boston, overpriced cards. The only things that you can say about Vaughn that you can't say about Plantier is that Vaughn was rated a better power-hitting prospect than Frank Thomas coming out of college, and Vaughn is still with Boston. He only wishes he wasn't.

	NM	EX	VG
1991 Bowman #112	0.20	0.08	0.03
1991 Donruss #430	0.15	0.06	0.01
1991 Fleer Update #7	0.15	0.06	0.01
1991 Gold Leaf Rookies #7	2.50	1.15	0.50
1991 O-Pee-Chee #124	0.05	0.01	0.01
1991 Score #750	0.15	0.06	0.01
1991 Studio #20	0.60	0.25	0.10
1991 Topps Stadium Club #543	1.00	0.45	0.15
1992 Bowman Tiffany #397	0.50	0.20	0.08
1992 Fleer Ultra #23	0.25	0.10	0.04
1992 O-Pee-Chee Premier #50	0.05	0.01	0.01
1992 Pinnacle Team 2000 #54	0.25	0.10	0.04
1992 Score Impact Player #21	0.15	0.05	0.01
1992 Topps Gold #59	4.00	1.75	0.75
1992 Topps Stadium Club #325	0.25	0.10	0.04
1993 Topps Gold #51	0.50	0.20	0.06

Robin Ventura

The skeptics said that Robin Ventura would never be able to make the transition from college ball (Oklahoma State) to the pros, never would be able to make the transition from aluminum to wood bats, never would be able to make the transition from soft sliders to wicked breaking stuff. Boy, were they wrong. Ventura not only made transition, but he made it to the big leagues quickly and showed more power than almost anyone expected. He is now one of the top third basemen in the game, with power and average and a great glove. He could get better, and his cards could turn out to be some very good buys.

	NM	EX	VG
1988 Topps Traded #124	8.00	3.75	1.75
1988 Topps Tiffany Traded #124	25.00	12.00	5.50
1989 Best Birmingham (set)	20.00	9.50	4.25
1989 Best/Baseball America Prospects (set)	30.00	12.50	5.00

1989 Bowman #65 .... 0.60	0.20	0.08
1989 Bowman Tiffany #65 .... 3.00	1.25	0.50
1989 Classic Update #177 .... 1.75	0.75	0.30
1989 Fleer Update #23 .... 1.50	0.65	0.25
1989 Topps #764 .... 0.75	0.30	0.12
1989 Topps Big #65 .... 0.85	0.40	0.15
1989 Topps Major League Debut #129 .... 0.25	0.10	0.04
1990 Bowman #311 .... 0.35	0.15	0.05
1990 Classic #5 .... 0.85	0.35	0.15
1990 Coca-Cola White Sox #23 .... 0.75	0.30	0.10
1990 Donruss #28 .... 0.60	0.25	0.10
1990 Donruss Rookies #15 .... 0.50	0.20	0.08
1990 Donruss A.L. Best #60 .... 0.35	0.15	0.05
1990 Fleer #550 .... 0.35	0.15	0.05
1990 Leaf #167 .... 8.00	3.75	1.75
1990 Score #595 .... 0.50	0.20	0.08
1990 Sportflics #222 .... 0.50	0.20	0.08
1990 Topps #121 .... 0.50	0.20	0.08
1990 Upper Deck #21 .... 2.00	0.80	0.35
1991 Bazooka #15 .... 0.75	0.30	0.10
1991 Fleer Ultra #86 .... 0.60	0.25	0.10
1991 Leaf #271 .... 0.60	0.25	0.10
1991 Score Rising Star #48 .... 0.25	0.10	0.04
1991 Topps #274 .... 3.00	1.25	0.50
1991 Upper Deck #263 .... 0.40	0.15	0.05
1992 Bowman #275 .... 0.50	0.20	0.08
1992 Bowman #655 .... 1.25	0.50	0.20
1992 Fleer Ultra #343 .... 0.75	0.30	0.12
1992 Fleer Ultra Awards #15 .... 6.00	2.75	1.25
1992 Fleer All-Stars #19 .... 2.50	1.00	0.40
1992 Leaf #17 .... 0.35	0.15	0.05
1992 Leaf Gold Inserts #17 .... 2.50	1.10	0.45
1992 Leaf Studio #160 .... 0.50	0.20	0.08
1992 O-Pee-Chee Premier #132 .... 0.30	0.12	0.05
1992 Score Impact Players #42 .... 0.50	0.20	0.08
1992 Score Pinnacle #121 .... 0.50	0.20	0.08
1992 Score Pinnacle #286 .... 0.35	0.15	0.05
1992 Score Pinnacle Team 2000 #43 .... 0.75	0.30	0.12
1992 Topps #70 .... 0.60	0.25	0.10
1992 Topps Gold Inserts #255 .... 3.00	1.25	0.50
1992 Upper Deck Ted Williams' Best #20 ..... 2.50	1.10	0.50

Tim Wakefield

The pitcher flavor of the moment is the Pirates' Tim Wakefield, a light-hitting infielder turned knuckleball pitcher. Wakefield caught the public fancy during the 1992 N.L. Championship Series and maintained it through the off-season. The best a knuckleball pitcher can aspire to is being Phil Niekro — a probable Hall of Famer who gets no respect anyway. Wakefield's cards are too high-priced right now even if that ultimate scenario were to be realized. He's an interesting story, though, and as far as pitcher flavors of the month go, pretty neat.

	NM	EX	VG
1990 Star Co. Salem (set)	7.25	3.25	1.25
1991 ProCards Carolina (set)	7.00	3.25	1.25
1992 Donruss Rookies #121	3.00	1.25	0.50
1992 Fleer Update #117	2.00	0.80	0.35
1992 Score Traded #92	1.25	0.50	0.20
1993 Donruss #61	0.60	0.20	0.08
1993 Fleer #123	0.50	0.20	0.07
1993 Fleer #9	1.25	0.50	0.20
1993 Fleer Ultra #104	0.75	0.30	0.12
1993 Score #347	0.35	0.15	0.05
1993 Score Select #307	1.00	0.40	0.15
1993 Score Select Stars #16	12.00	5.50	2.50
1993 Topps #13	0.75	0.30	0.12
1993 Topps #163	0.50	0.20	0.08
1993 Topps Gold Inserts #163	5.00	1.75	0.75
1993 Topps Stadium Dome #51	1.75	0.75	0.30
1993 Upper Deck #66	0.25	0.10	0.04

Larry Walker

Larry Walker was a hockey player living outside of Vancouver and playing in some primitive sandlot leagues when he was discovered by Montreal scouts and signed to a contract. Since then Walker has blossomed into perhaps the greatest Canadian-born outfielder ever, a power-hitting, baserunning machine with an arm that can throw out baserunners at first with ease. Walker has some incredible tools and some cheap cards. We like his '90 Bowman card a lot, though all of his '90 cards except for his Leaf card have been caught up in that overproduction funk and have depressed values. Walker is the 100 percent genuine article, a real can't-misser. Go out and get him.

	NM	EX	VG
1987 ProCards Jacksonville (set)	15.00	6.50	3.00

1989 ProCards Indianapolis (set)	7.50	3.00	1.25
1989 Topps Major League Debut #133	0.40	0.15	0.05
1990 Bowman #117	0.60	0.25	0.10
1990 Bowman Tiffany #117	3.50	1.50	0.50
1990 Donruss #578	0.75	0.30	0.12
1990 Fleer #363	0.75	0.30	0.12
1990 Leaf #325	14.00	6.50	3.00
1990 Score #631	0.75	0.30	0.12
1990 Topps #757	0.75	0.30	0.12
1990 Topps Big #296	0.30	0.12	0.05
1990 Upper Deck #466	2.50	1.00	0.40
1991 Bowman Tiffany #442	0.75	0.35	0.10
1991 Donruss #359	0.25	0.10	0.04
1991 Donruss Elite #34	60.00	25.50	12.00
1991 Fleer #250	0.25	0.10	0.04
1991 Fleer Ultra Update #93	3.00	1.25	0.50
1991 Leaf #241	0.60	0.25	0.10
1991 Topps #339	0.25	0.10	0.04
1991 Topps #93	3.00	1.25	0.50
1991 Topps Desert Storm #339	50.00	20.00	8.50
1991 Toys 'R' Us #31	0.30	0.12	0.05
1991 Upper Deck #536	0.25	0.10	0.04
1992 Bowman #648	0.60	0.25	0.10
1992 Bowman Gold #648	1.25	0.50	0.20
1992 Fleer Ultra #525	0.75	0.30	0.10
1992 Leaf #201	0.40	0.15	0.05
1992 Leaf Gold Inserts #201	2.00	0.80	0.30
1992 Leaf Studio #59	0.30	0.12	0.04
1992 Score Impact Players #29	0.25	0.10	0.04
1992 Score Pinnacle #194	0.35	0.12	0.04
1992 Score Pinnacle Team 2000 #21	0.75	0.30	0.10
1992 Topps #256	1.00	0.30	0.10
1992 Topps Gold Inserts #531	0.75	0.30	0.10
1993 Donruss Diamond Kings #6	2.50	1.15	0.50
1993 Donruss MVPs #9	1.50	0.60	0.25
1993 Fleer NL All-Stars #6	150.00	0.60	0.25
1993 Topps Gold Inserts #95	1.00	0.40	0.15
1993 Topps Black Gold Inserts #22	6.00	2.50	1.00
1993 Upper Deck Triple Crown #10	5.00	2.25	1.00

Allen Watson

Of all the many fine young pitchers in the St. Louis farm system, Watson might be the best. He's a left-hander with a lot of stuff who breezed through the Cardinal farm system in 1992, gliding from Class-A ball to Double-A to Triple-A and never posting an ERA higher than 2.15. Watson's cards are cheap, mainly because he's a pitcher and he's not Brien Taylor and no one's been paying much attention. They appear to be pretty good buys on the whole.

	NM	EX	VG
1991 Classic Draft Pick #17	0.25	0.10	0.04

George "Buck" Weaver

Buck Weaver was a great ballplayer — not a Joe Jackson, but a potential Hall of Famer. Banished from the game for "guilty knowledge" and without the appeal of Jackson, Weaver got lost in the shuffle. Black Sox cards, however, are in demand, and Weaver has only one major card. It's probably a very good buy if you can find it.

	NM	EX	VG
T207	150.00	65.00	25.00

Lou Whitaker

Lou Whitaker is an amazing second baseman. His power has improved as he's aged, sometimes at the expense of his batting average, though Lou has managed to keep both going fairly strong for more than 15 years. He could finish his career with 250 home runs and 2,500 hits, both excellent figures for a second baseman and borderline Hall of Fame stuff. His cards are a speculator's buy right now. They're not cheap (though they are much cheaper than Alan Trammell's for no apparent reason), but if by some happenstance Whitaker makes it into the Hall they're going to go a lot higher a lot faster. A candid opinion? He won't make it. But we're hedging our bets.

	NM	EX	VG
1978 Burger King Tigers #13	15.00	6.50	2.50
1983 Topps Stickers #65	0.12	0.05	0.01
1984 Topps Stickers #264	0.12	0.05	0.01
1984 Topps Stickers Boxes #1	1.00	0.40	0.15
1985 Cain's Tigers	3.50	1.50	0.50
1985 Donruss Action All-Stars #42	1.15	0.05	0.01
1986 Cain's Tigers #4	3.50	1.50	0.50
1986 Fleer Star Stickers #126	0.25	0.10	0.04
1987 Cain's Tigers #8	2.00	0.80	0.30

1987 Donruss Opening Day #218 .... 0.15	0.05	0.01
1987 Fleer Mini #112 .... 0.15	0.05	0.01
1988 Kenner Starting Lineup 10.00	4.00	1.50
1990 Coca-Cola Tigers #1 .... 0.40	0.15	0.05

Rondell White

In the embarrassment of riches that is the Expos' farm system, Rondell White is just another top prospect. In any other organization, he'd be a crown jewel. White can hit for average and power, run, and play a superb center field — just like Moises Alou, just like Marquis Grissom, just like Larry Walker, and just like Cliff Floyd. His cards aren't too expensive right now, and the longer he languishes in the minors the better buys his cards will become.

	NM	EX	VG
1990 Classic Draft Picks #24 .... 0.50	0.20	0.08	
1991 Bowman #450 .... 0.40	0.15	0.05	
1991 Bowman Tiffany #450 .... 2.00	0.85	0.35	
1991 Classic-Best Minor-League Wax #360 ... 0.50	0.20	0.08	
1991 Classic-Best Sumter (set) 7.50	3.50	1.50	
1991 ProCards Tomorrow's Heroes #266 ..... 0.60	0.25	0.10	
1991 Score #390 .... 0.25	0.10	0.04	
1991 Upper Deck #10 .... 0.60	0.25	0.10	
1992 Bowman #436 .... 0.30	0.12	0.05	
1992 Classic -Best Minor League #305 .... 0.35	0.21	0.05	
1992 Classic-Best West Palm Beach Expos (set) 5.00	2.25	1.00	
1992 Upper Deck Minor League #276............ 0.60	0.25	0.10	
1992 Upper Deck Minor League #65 .... 0.20	0.08	0.03	
1993 Fleer #3 .... 5.00	2.25	1.00	
1993 Fleer #67 .... 0.85	0.35	0.12	

Mark Whiten

Yes, another ex-Blue Jay outfielder. This one has long-ball power and the best right-field arm since the heyday of Roberto Clemente (or, if you prefer to stay within the realm of ex-Blue Jay outfielders, Jesse Barfield). He also has an undisciplined bat and a less-than-superior noggin for the game, which might explain why he's with his third team in three years. A couple of expensive cards, but on the whole, nothing to get excited about.

	NM	EX	VG
1987 ProCards Myrtle Beach (set) 21.50	10.00	4.50	
1988 Star Co. Dun edin (set) 15.00	6.50	3.00	
1989 Best Knoxville Blue Jays (set) 14.00	6.50	3.00	

	NM	EX	VG
1990 CMC Pre-Rookie #350 .... 2.50	1.15	0.50
1990 CMC Syracuse (set) 25.00	11.50	5.00
1990 Leaf #396 .... 1.75	0.75	0.35
1990 ProCards AAA #367................................. 2.00	0.80	0.35
1990 ProCards Syracuse (set) 10.00	4.50	2.00
1991 Bowman Tiffany #13 .... 1.00	0.45	0.20
1991 Fleer Ultra Update #21 .... 0.40	0.15	0.05
1991 Topps #452 .... 1.00	0.40	0.15
1992 Leaf Gold Inserts #334 .... 0.75	0.30	0.12
1992 Topps Gold Inserts #671 .... 2.00	0.80	0.35

Bernie Williams

Not to be confused with Gerald Williams, Bernie Williams is the switch-hitting outfielder who got his chance in '93 with the Yankees. All the minor-league stats say he can play, though he probably can't hit .300 and drive in 100 runs every year. But Williams can hit for a good average, hit the occasional home run, and steal the odd base. There's not enough here to justify the prices Bernie's cards have been cataloging for, but what the heck — the guy's a Yankee.

	NM	EX	VG
1988 Star Co. Prince William (set) 30.00	12.00	5.00
1989 CMC Columbus (set) 10.00	4.50	2.00
1990 Best Albany Yankees (set) 9.00	3.50	1.50
1990 Best Minor League #26 .... 1.50	0.50	0.20
1990 ProCards A & AA Minor League			
Stars #31... 0.75	0.35	0.15
1990 ProCards Albany Yankees (set) 11.00	5.00	2.00
1991 Bowman Tiffany #173 .... 0.50	0.20	0.08
1991 Impel Line Drive AAA #123 .... 0.75	0.35	0.15
1992 Bowman Gold #407................................... 0.65	0.25	0.10

Gerald Williams

Gerald Williams should not be confused with Bernie, though Lord knows it's easy. Just so you know, Gerald does not switch-hit and is two years older, and if he doesn't make it to the majors sometime soon and do something profound a lot of people are going to be left holding the bag on his cards. Gerald has a multitude of tools but few opportunities to date to use them. His cards sell at prices they shouldn't.

	NM	EX	VG
1988 Star Prince William (set) 30.00	12.00	5.00
1989 Star Prince William (set) 12.00	5.50	2.50
1991 ProCards Tomorrow's heroes #115 ...... 1.00	0.40	0.15

Matt Williams

The occasionally slugging third baseman of the San Francisco Giants, Matt Williams has had all sorts of problems making consistent contact on the major-league level. When he does he's great; when he doesn't he's just another whiffer. For all his inconsistency on the field, his cards are the models of consistency — and also the perfect examples of cards that have had their values inflated by the power-hitting tendencies of the player they portray.

	NM	EX	VG
1986 Cramer Everett Giants #3	25.00	12.00	5.50
1987 Donruss Rookies #45	3.00	1.25	0.55
1987 Fleer Glossy Tin #129U	2.50	1.00	0.45
1987 Fleer Update #129	2.25	1.00	0.45
1987 Mother's Cookies Giants #22	1.75	0.75	0.35
1987 Topps Tiffany Traded #129T	4.50	2.00	0.85
1987 Topps Traded #129T	1.50	0.65	0.25
1988 Fleer #101	1.75	0.75	0.35
1988 Fleer Glossy Tin #101	2.50	1.00	0.45
1988 Score #118	0.75	0.35	0.15
1988 Score Glossy #118	4.50	2.00	0.85
1989 Mother's Cookies Giants #12	0.70	0.25	0.10
1989 Upper Deck #247	0.60	0.25	0.10
1990 Leaf #94	0.65	0.30	0.12
1990 Mother's Cookies Matt Williams (set of 4)	15.00	6.50	2.75
1991 Donruss Elite #8	75.00	35.00	16.50
1991 Upper Deck Silver Slugger #13	1.00	0.45	0.20
1992 Fleer Lumber Co. #6	1.00	0.45	0.20
1992 Fleer Ultra Award Winners #13	2.50	1.15	0.55
1992 Leaf Gold #373	0.75	0.30	0.10
1992 Topps Gold #445	2.00	0.85	0.35

Dave Winfield

Dave Winfield is a certain Hall of Famer now, and unlike some other talented ballplayers about to make Cooperstown, Winfield never fails to elicit a memorable image: diving into a pitch with that immense, scythe-like swing or diving over a fence trying to keep a home run in the park. Winfield has played on some high-profile teams, too: the Yankees, California, the World Champion Toronto Blue Jays. He has done the things that a Hall of Famer should do, and he has carried himself with complete dignity on and off the field. The fact that many of his early cards are quite valuable should not be unexpected. That they are not more valuable is a little surprising.

	NM	EX	VG
1974 Topps #456	150.00	72.50	35.00
1975 Topps #61	50.00	23.50	11.50
1976 Topps #160	23.50	11.50	5.50
1977 Topps #390	14.50	7.00	3.25
1978 Topps #530	10.00	4.75	2.25
1979 Topps #30	9.25	4.50	2.00
1980 Topps #230	8.00	3.75	1.75
1981 Donruss #364	2.25	1.00	0.45
1981 Fleer #484	1.75	0.75	0.35
1981 Topps #370	4.00	1.75	0.85
1982 Donruss #31	2.25	1.00	0.45
1982 Donruss (Diamond Kings) #18	1.25	0.55	0.25
1982 Fleer #56	2.25	1.00	0.45
1982 Topps #600	3.25	1.50	0.65
1983 Donruss #409	2.00	0.85	0.40
1983 Fleer #398	2.00	0.85	0.40
1983 Topps #770	3.00	1.40	0.60
1984 Donruss #51	8.25	4.00	1.75
1984 Fleer #143	4.25	2.00	0.75
1984 Topps #460	1.50	0.65	0.30
1984 Topps Tiffany #460	12.00	5.50	2.50
1985 Donruss #51	3.25	1.50	0.65
1985 Fleer #146	3.00	1.35	0.60
1985 Sportflics Prototype	35.00	16.50	7.50
1985 Topps #180	0.95	0.40	0.15
1985 Topps Tiffany #180	6.25	3.00	1.35
1986 Donruss #248	1.25	0.60	0.25
1986 Fleer #121	1.00	0.45	0.20
1986 Sportflics #49	0.75	0.30	0.10
1986 Topps #70	0.65	0.30	0.12
1987 Classic #11	0.45	0.20	0.08
1987 Fleer Glossy #120	0.45	0.20	0.08
1988 Score Box Panels #8	0.25	0.12	0.05
1988 Score Glossy #55	6.50	3.00	1.25
1989 Scoremasters #41	0.25	0.12	0.05
1989 Upper Deck #349	0.65	0.30	0.12
1990 Leaf #426	1.25	0.60	0.25
1991 Studio #30	0.30	0.12	0.05
1991 Topps Stadium Club #263	1.25	0.60	0.25
1992 Topps Gold #5	2.00	0.85	0.40
1992 Topps Gold #792	3.00	1.30	0.60
1993 Upper Deck Then and Now #9	4.25	2.00	0.85

Bobby Witt

Bobby Witt throws harder with less of an idea of where the ball is going than any other major-league pitcher — but at least Bobby Witt is a major-league pitcher. Other pitchers with Witt's brilliantly erratic stuff haven't been as fortunate. Witt has been subjected to any number of healers, with no discernable results. Nolan Ryan couldn't get him to throw the ball over the plate. Neither could pitching guru Tom House. Now it's the turn of A's pitching coach Dave Duncan, the guy who did it for Dave Stewart and Dennis Eckersley. Witt may be a tougher nut for Duncan to crack, but if he pulls it off Witt's cards ought to really accelerate. As it is they're not terrible buys — just erratic.

	NM	EX	VG
1987 Mother's Cookie Rangers #25	0.60	0.25	0.10
1988 Smokey Bear Rangers #7	0.60	0.25	0.10
1989 Mother's Cookies Rangers #145	0.30	0.12	0.04

Joseph "Smoky Joe" Wood

In 1912 Joe Wood produced one of the best seasons ever enjoyed by a pitcher and his Red Sox won the World Series. Years later, with a crippled arm, he became a solid outfielder. Many people say his achievements are Hall of Fame caliber, and to some extent the card market agrees, as his cards fetch nearly Hall of Fame prices.

	NM	EX	VG
M101-4	50.00	20.00	10.00
M101-5	50.00	20.00	10.00
M116	475.00	150.00	50.00
1914 Cracker Jack 22	475.00	50.00	25.00
1915 Cracker Jack 22	150.00	50.00	25.00
E120 American Caramel	60.00	25.00	10.00
E121 American Caramel Set of 80	65.00	25.00	10.00
E122 American Caramel	70.00	25.00	10.00
E254 Colgan's Chips	45.00	20.00	10.00
E270	45.00	20.00	10.00
E91 American Caramel Set C	75.00	25.00	15.00
T202 Hassan	575.00	150.00	75.00
T207	135.00	45.00	25.00

Dmitri Young

Dmitri Young is most often compared to Kevin Mitchell, which isn't ideal but which is sure better than being compared to Paul Mitchell. Young is a third baseman with an ungodly bat, weight problems and difficulties in the field. It may not be a magic combination but the bat is so good that you're willing to forgive everything else. Card collectors certainly are. Young's cards are some of the most valuable cards of Players Who Haven't Come Anywhere Close to Making the Majors that you're likely to find. Is Young worth it? Not at this point, but maybe soon.

	NM	EX	VG
1992 Classic-Best Springfield Cardinals (set)	9.25	4.50	2.00

Robin Yount

Yount has been heart and soul of the Milwaukee Brewers for almost 20 years. He is about as sure a Hall of Famer as you could hope for. Yount's hallmark has been consistency. He has been named the best player in the league twice, and has almost always been among the best. Basically the same thing can be said about his cards. They've never been spectacular, save for his rookie card, but they've been there year after year. The likelihood is very great that as Yount's career ends and the march toward Cooperstown begins, all his cards, not just his very early cards, will begin to rise in value.

	NM	EX	VG
1975 Topps #223	240.00	115.00	55.00
1975 Topps Mini #223	320.00	155.00	75.00
1976 Topps #316	60.00	28.00	12.50
1977 Topps #635	32.50	16.00	7.50
1977 Topps Cloth Stickers #54	27.50	13.00	6.00
1978 Topps #173	20.00	9.50	4.50
1979 Topps #95	11.50	5.50	2.50
1980 Topps #265	11.00	5.25	2.50
1981 Donruss #323	3.50	1.60	0.75
1981 Fleer #511	3.00	1.25	0.50
1981 Fleer Star Sticker #38	4.50	2.00	0.75
1981 Topps #515	6.00	2.75	1.25
1982 Brewers Police #19	1.75	0.75	0.35
1982 Donruss #510	1.75	0.75	0.35
1982 Fleer #155	1.75	0.75	0.35
1982 Fleer Stamps #135	0.12	0.05	0.01
1982 Topps #435	3.00	1.30	0.60
1983 Donruss #258	2.85	1.35	0.60
1983 Donruss Action All-Stars #56	0.75	0.35	0.15
1983 Fleer #51	2.85	1.35	0.60
1983 Kellogg's #14	0.45	0.20	0.08
1983 Topps #350	3.75	1.75	0.75

1984 Donruss #1 (Diamond King, reads "Perez-Steele" on back) 4.25	2.00	0.85
1984 Donruss #48 .... 9.75	4.75	2.10
1984 Fleer #219 .... 5.00	2.35	1.15
1984 Topps #10 .... 4.00	1.75	0.75
1984 Topps Glossy All-Star (22) #5 .... 0.45	0.20	0.08
1984 Topps Stickers #295 .... 0.15	0.07	0.01
1984 Topps Super #29 .... 0.40	0.15	0.06
1984 Topps Tiffany #10 .... 30.00	14.75	7.25
1985 Brewers Police #19 .... 1.25	0.60	0.25
1985 Donruss #48 .... 3.50	1.60	0.75
1985 Fleer #601 .... 3.50	1.60	0.75
1985 Gardner's Brewers #22 .... 4.25	2.00	1.35
1985 Topps #340 .... 1.00	0.45	0.20
1986 Donruss #48 .... 1.75	0.75	0.30
1986 Fleer #506 .... 1.75	0.75	0.30
1986 O-Pee-Chee #144 .... 0.40	0.20	0.08
1986 Sportflics #42 (Brewers logo on back) 0.75	0.30	0.12
1986 Sportflics #42 (Yankees logo on back) 32.00	15.00	7.00
1987 Classic Major #44 .... 4.00	1.75	0.75
1987 Fleer Glossy #361 .... 1.10	0.50	0.20
1987 Fleer Limited Edition #44 .... 0.25	0.10	0.04
1988 Score Glossy #160 .... 3.50	1.50	0.60
1989 Upper Deck #285 .... 0.65	0.30	0.12
1990 Kenner Starting Lineup #112 .... 10.00	4.50	2.00
1990 Leaf #71 .... 1.40	0.65	0.30
1990 Score McDonald's #25 .... 17.50	7.50	3.50
1991 Topps Stadium Club #509 .... 1.40	0.65	0.30
1992 Fleer Ultra #87 .... 0.40	0.18	0.08

Todd Zeile

For a long time in 1992, the best thing you could say about Todd Zeile was that he had a lovely and talented wife (former Olympic gymnast Julianne McNamara). You certainly couldn't say he was anything like the power-hitting catching prospect the Cardinals had so carefully nurtured through their system. Heck, he wasn't even catching but was playing third base, and he wasn't even playing for the Cardinals but was moldering down in Louisville. Those days are over, and while the returns on the new Todd Zeile are incomplete, so far, so good. He still has great home-run power, and he's not the threat to children and other living things around the bag that his past would suggest. His cards have been caught in the doldrums and are merely dull buys, though they could catch fire.

	NM	EX	VG
1987 Best Springfield (set)	22.50	10.50	4.50
1988 Grand Slam Arkansas (set)	12.50	6.00	2.50
1989 Team Louisville #2–5	8.50	4.00	1.50

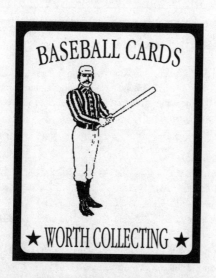

BASEBALL CARDS

★ WORTH COLLECTING ★

Hall of Famers

A note about the Hall of Famers listings

NOT ALL CARDS of the players included in this section are listed. Especially later issues of some players' cards may be considered common and can be priced according to sets. Also listed are a few managers, umpires, and baseball executives. Many of these had short, undistinguished playing careers but at least got their faces on a few cards. Elected to the Hall of Fame for their efforts in the dugout, behind the umpire's mask, or off the field, they make an interesting fringe area of Hall of Fame baseball-card collecting.

Almost from its inception in the 1880s until after World War II, "organized" baseball — that which eventually grew into today's major-league baseball — banned non-Caucasian players from its ranks. Many found an outlet for their sometimes prodigious baseball talents in international, semiprofessional, or entertainment teams barely a step up from traveling minstrel shows. For a time, a fairly well-organized and financed Negro league flourished, in which some of the greatest players ever — judged by today's standards and in many cases by their contemporaries in the "real" professional league — took baseball to new levels of skill and strategy. A few—very few—of these players broke through the color barrier in the late 1940s to join the recognized ranks of the major leagues, and thus drew the attention of baseball-card manufacturers. Some of the greatest Negro league legends have been inducted into the Hall of Fame based on their Negro league careers; almost none are remembered on baseball cards. They are listed here anyway, with the notation "(Negro leagues) No cards" to point out a rather large gap in card collecting.

Henry "Hank" Aaron

Elected HoF 1982. The all-time home-run king is a very popular player, as might be expected. Aaron cards are generally available, but demand keeps prices steady. Demand for some cards in top grades, such as his rookie card (which is notoriously poorly centered) is extremely high.

	NM	EX	VG
1954 Topps #128	1950.00	750.00	250.00
1955 Bowman #179	250.00	95.00	45.00
1955 Topps #47	375.00	150.00	65.00
1956 Topps #31	225.00	85.00	35.00
1957 Topps #20	250.00	100.00	45.00
1958 Topps #30	225.00	100.00	45.00
1958 Topps #488	45.00	17.50	10.00
1959 Topps #380	135.00	50.00	20.00
1959 Topps #561	140.00	55.00	25.00
1960 Topps #300	135.00	50.00	20.00
1960 Topps #566	115.00	45.00	17.50
1961 Topps #415	115.00	45.00	17.50
1961 Topps #577	145.00	55.00	25.00
1962 Topps #320	150.00	50.00	20.00
1962 Topps #394	35.00	15.00	5.00
1963 Topps #390	140.00	60.00	25.00
1964 Topps #300	95.00	40.00	15.00
1965 Topps #170	95.00	40.00	15.00
1966 Topps #500	100.00	40.00	15.00
1967 Topps #250	90.00	35.00	15.00
1968 Topps #110	90.00	35.00	15.00
1969 Topps #100	75.00	25.00	10.00
1970 Topps #500	55.00	17.50	7.50
1971 Topps #400	50.00	20.00	7.50
1972 Topps #299	40.00	10.00	5.00
1972 Topps #300	16.00	5.00	2.00
1973 Topps #100	22.50	7.50	3.50
1974 Topps #1	35.00	7.50	2.50
1975 Topps #660	27.50	10.00	3.00
1976 Topps #550	22.50	7.00	2.00

Grover Cleveland Alexander

Elected HoF 1938. Grover Cleveland Alexander is one of the great pitchers and colorful figures of all time. He had a lengthy career, but his cards are not particularly easy to obtain, and this is especially true in high grades.

	NM	EX	VG
1914 Cracker Jack #37	1500.00	250.00	100.00
1915 Cracker Jack #37	750.00	250.00	100.00
E120 American Caramel	225.00	50.00	15.00
E121 Series of 80 American Caramel	225.00	50.00	15.00
E121 Series of 120 American Caramel	225.00	50.00	15.00
E122 American Caramel	200.00	40.00	15.00
M101-4 #4	150.00	35.00	15.00
M101-5 #4	150.00	35.00	15.00
T222 Fatima	1000.00	200.00	75.00
1940 Play Ball #119	175.00	40.00	12.50

Walter Alston

Elected HoF 1983 (manager). Walt Alston's cards have a problem. Alston was named to the Hall of Fame as a manager. Collectors don't take that very seriously except when it's time to fire the one they've got. Alston was not a manager who was fired. He managed the Dodgers 23 years, from 1954 to 1976. Still, his cards remain affordable. (Alston cards not listed are priced less than 25¢ in Near Mint condition.)

	NM	EX	VG
1956 Topps #8	45.00	15.00	5.00
1960 Topps #212	12.00	4.00	1.50
1961 Topps #136	5.75	1.75	0.80
1962 Topps #217	5.00	1.50	0.75
1964 Topps #101	3.75	1.00	0.50
1965 Topps #217	3.75	1.00	0.50
1966 Topps #116	3.00	0.75	0.25
1967 Topps #294	2.50	0.75	0.25
1968 Topps #472	2.50	0.75	0.25
1969 Topps #24	2.50	0.75	0.25
1970 Topps #242	1.75	0.50	0.15
1971 Topps #567	3.75	1.00	0.25
1972 Topps #749	6.00	1.50	0.40

Adrian "Cap" Anson

Elected HoF 1939. Cap Anson stands as the most famous name of all pre-1900 cards. Along with King Kelly his cards also rank as the most expensive of all pre-1900 players despite being among the most readily available.

	NM	EX	VG
E223	7000.00	2000.00	1000.00
N28	1750.00	700.00	300.00
N162	5000.00	1700.00	1000.00
N172	2200.00	500.00	200.00
N173	3500.00	1000.00	500.00
N284	500.00	150.00	100.00
N300	2500.00	750.00	300.00
N403	7500.00	3000.00	1500.00

Luis Aparicio

Elected HoF 1984. Luis Aparicio was the classic fielding shortstop of his day. That translated into a Hall of Fame spot, but not particularly heavy demand for his cards.

	NM	EX	VG
1956 Topps #292	130.00	50.00	22.50
1957 Topps #7	35.00	15.00	5.00
1958 Topps #85	20.00	6.50	2.00
1958 Topps #483	10.00	3.50	1.50
1959 Topps #310	17.50	5.00	1.50
1959 Topps #560	17.50	5.00	1.50
1960 Topps #240	12.00	5.00	1.50
1960 Topps #559	17.50	5.00	1.50
1961 Topps #440	12.50	5.00	1.50
1961 Topps #574	40.00	17.50	7.50
1962 Topps #325	17.50	6.50	2.00
1962 Topps #469	7.50	2.50	1.00
1963 Topps #205	8.50	2.50	1.00
1964 Topps #540	15.00	3.50	1.00
1965 Topps #410	8.50	2.50	0.75
1966 Topps #90	8.00	2.25	0.75
1967 Topps #60	7.50	2.25	0.75
1968 Topps #310	6.50	1.75	0.65
1969 Topps #75	6.00	1.75	0.60
1970 Topps #315	5.50	1.50	0.50

1971 Topps #740	21.00	6.00	1.00
1972 Topps #313	3.50	1.00	0.35
1972 Topps #314	1.75	0.65	0.25
1973 Topps #165	2.75	1.25	0.45
1974 Topps #61	2.75	1.00	0.25

Lucius "Luke" Appling

Elected HoF 1964. Luke Appling is on surprisingly few cards despite a long career. He had no power; consequently he is overlooked by many collectors. His card prices will be fairly modest for the immediate future.

	NM	EX	VG
Diamond Star #95	250.00	75.00	25.00
1934 Goudey #27	150.00	50.00	20.00
1935 Goudey	125.00	50.00	20.00
1948 Leaf #59	100.00	35.00	15.00
1949 Bowman #175	125.00	40.00	15.00
1950 Bowman #37	75.00	25.00	10.00

Earl Averill

Elected HoF 1975. There is low demand and a strong supply for Earl Averill cards, hence relatively low prices. A few cards exist that are tough to get, but they seem to get lost in the shuffle.

	NM	EX	VG
1933 Goudey #194	175.00	75.00	25.00
1934 Batter Up #24	100.00	40.00	20.00
1934 Batter Up #113	275.00	100.00	50.00
Diamond Star #100	450.00	175.00	75.00
1935 Goudey	125.00	50.00	25.00
George Miller	375.00	135.00	50.00
1939 Play Ball #143	245.00	100.00	35.00
1940 Play Ball #46	65.00	30.00	15.00

John Franklin "Home Run" Baker

Elected HoF 1955. The "Home Run" nickname belongs to a Hall of Famer whose cards bring big bucks. He was *the* power hitter of the dead-ball era until Ruth arrived on the scene. Home Run Baker was a natural for every card set. By the standards of the early 1900s his cards are in good supply.

	NM	EX	VG
E90-1 American Caramel	575.00	200.00	65.00
E91 Set B American Caramel	250.00	95.00	35.00
E96 Philadelphia Caramel	450.00	150.00	50.00
E120 American Caramel	175.00	65.00	30.00
E121 Series of 80	175.00	65.00	30.00
E122 American Caramel	175.00	65.00	30.00
E220 National Caramel	175.00	65.00	30.00
E224 Texas Tommy	950.00	350.00	200.00
E254 Colgan's Chips	100.00	35.00	15.00
D328 Weil Baking #11	350.00	150.00	65.00
D329 Weil Baking #9	350.00	150.00	65.00
T201 Mecca with Collins	325.00	125.00	75.00
T202 Hassan	425.00	150.00	85.00
T205	525.00	200.00	75.00
T206	395.00	125.00	40.00
T208	1350.00	500.00	250.00
T213 Type 2	300.00	125.00	50.00
T213 Type 3	375.00	150.00	75.00
T215	750.00	250.00	150.00
T227	1000.00	350.00	200.00
1914 Cracker Jack #2	1750.00	300.00	100.00
1915 Cracker Jack #2	850.00	300.00	100.00
Turkey Red (T3) #78	1400.00	650.00	250.00
1940 Play Ball #177	125.00	45.00	25.00

David Bancroft

Elected HoF 1971. Bancroft is not well known. He is a Hall of Famer whose cards are tough to find because he appeared in no significant gum or tobacco sets. That leaves candy and baking cards as the only source of supply.

	NM	EX	VG
E120 American Caramel	125.00	55.00	35.00
E121 Series of 80	125.00	55.00	35.00
E121 Series of 120	125.00	55.00	35.00
E210 York Caramel #19	75.00	40.00	25.00
E220 National Caramel	225.00	100.00	45.00
D328 Weil Baking #12	325.00	150.00	60.00
D329 Weil Baking #10	325.00	150.00	60.00

Ernie Banks

Elected HoF 1977. Mr. Cub is at least as popular today as he was during his career. There is a good supply of Banks cards, but the loyal legions of Wrigley keep buying them, with no change in sight.

	NM	EX	VG
1954 Topps #94	800.00	350.00	150.00
1955 Bowman #242	375.00	150.00	50.00
1955 Topps #28	185.00	75.00	35.00
1956 Topps #15	110.00	40.00	15.00
1957 Topps #55	110.00	40.00	15.00
1958 Topps #310	75.00	30.00	10.00
1958 Topps #482	25.00	10.00	3.50
1959 Topps #350	75.00	30.00	10.00
1960 Topps #10	60.00	20.00	7.50
1960 Topps #560	55.00	20.00	5.00
1961 Topps #350	27.50	10.00	3.50
1961 Topps #485	20.00	5.00	1.50
1961 Topps #575	85.00	35.00	10.00
1962 Topps #25	45.00	15.00	5.00
1963 Topps #380	55.00	20.00	7.50
1964 Topps #55	25.00	10.00	5.00
1965 Topps #510	65.00	25.00	10.00
1966 Topps #110	20.00	7.50	2.50
1967 Topps #215	17.50	7.00	2.00
1968 Topps #355	20.00	7.50	2.50
1969 Topps #20	17.50	7.00	2.00
1970 Topps #630	33.00	10.00	3.50
1971 Topps #525	37.50	10.00	3.50

Albert J. Barlick

One of only seven umpires elected to the Hall of Fame for meritorious service, Al Barlick is one of the few Hall of Fame umpires depicted on 1955 Bowman cards. There's fairly strong demand for this card, which bodes well for its future price.

	NM	EX	VG
1955 Bowman #265	90.00	45.00	20.00

Jacob "Jake" Peter Beckley

Elected HoF 1971. Jake Beckley appears on only a few cards. That's the bad news. The good news is that a Jake Beckley card can be acquired for less than the price of a new sports car because at least two of his cards were heavily produced. Don't be tempted to take Jake for granted, however, as his cards are tougher than average to find.

	NM	EX	VG
N172	750.00	350.00	250.00
E107	650.00	350.00	250.00
T206	450.00	150.00	50.00

James "Cool Papa" Bell

Elected HoF 1974 (Negro leagues).

	NM	EX	VG
No cards			

Johnny Bench

Elected HoF 1989. Bench is the standard by which modern catchers are judged. Johnny Bench cards are generally in good supply with the exception of those from his first few seasons.

	NM	EX	VG
1968 Topps #247	325.00	125.00	50.00
1969 Topps #95	165.00	75.00	27.50
1969 Topps #430	15.00	5.00	1.50
1970 Topps #464	12.50	4.50	1.25
1970 Topps #660	175.00	75.00	30.00
1971 Topps #250	60.00	20.00	7.50
1972 Topps #433	40.00	10.00	5.00
1972 Topps #434	17.500	5.00	3.25
1973 Topps #380	25.00	7.50	4.50
1974 Topps #10	12.50	3.50	1.50
1975 Topps #260	11.50	3.25	1.25
1976 Topps #300	10.00	2.75	1.00
1977 Topps #70	9.50	2.50	0.75
1978 Topps #700	4.50	1.25	0.50
1979 Topps #200	1.50	0.40	0.20
1980 Topps #100	2.50	1.00	0.35

1981 Donruss #62	1.00	0.35	0.15
1981 Donruss #182	1.00	0.35	0.15
1981 Fleer #196	0.90	0.25	0.10
1981 Topps #600	1.50	0.50	0.15
1982 Donruss #400	0.75	0.30	0.10
1982 Fleer #57	0.80	0.25	0.10
1982 Topps #400	1.50	0.35	0.10
1983 Donruss #500	0.75	0.30	0.10
1983 Fleer #584	0.75	0.30	0.10
1983 Topps #60	0.90	0.35	0.15
1984 Donruss #660	6.00	2.00	1.00

Charles "Chief" Bender

Elected HoF 1953. Chief Bender was a star pitcher of his day. As such he appeared on most of the cards issued during the early 1900s. Hence, an ample supply of his cards is available. Unless the Chief Bender marching and chowder society drums up some enthusiasm for his cards they are likely to remain at or near current prices for some time.

	NM	EX	VG
T201 Mecca with Oldring	250.00	100.00	35.00
T202 Hassan	375.00	125.00	75.00
T204 Ramly	1350.00	500.00	200.00
T205	650.00	225.00	75.00
T206 (pitching, no trees)	450.00	100.00	35.00
T206 (pitching, with trees)	450.00	100.00	35.00
T206 (portrait)	550.00	125.00	50.00
T207	650.00	200.00	55.00
T208	1350.00	500.00	250.00
T213 Type 1	350.00	100.00	35.00
T213 Type 2	250.00	75.00	35.00
T213 Type 3	350.00	100.00	35.00
T214	2000.00	1000.00	750.00
T215 Type 1	250.00	75.00	35.00
T215 Type 2	400.00	125.00	50.00
T216 (all varieties)	300.00	100.00	40.00
Turkey Red (T3) #80	950.00	350.00	175.00
E90-1 American Caramel	500.00	125.00	50.00
E91 American Caramel Set A	180.00	75.00	25.00
E91 American Caramel Set B	200.00	90.00	30.00
E92 Croft's Candy	525.00	150.00	50.00
E92 Dockman	375.00	125.00	35.00
E93 Standard Caramel	475.00	135.00	50.00

E95 Philadelphia Caramel	475.00	135.00	50.00
E98	550.00	175.00	60.00
E101	550.00	150.00	50.00
E102	550.00	150.00	50.00
E103 Williams Caramel	650.00	200.00	75.00
E104 Nadja	350.00	100.00	30.00
E105 Mello-Mint	275.00	70.00	25.00
E106 American Caramel	450.00	100.00	35.00
E107 Breisch Williams	575.00	125.00	50.00
E224 Texas Tommy	775.00	250.00	100.00
E286 Ju Ju Drums	750.00	150.00	100.00
D303 General Baking	250.00	75.00	25.00
D304 (various backs)	175.00	50.00	20.00
D329 Weil Baking #13	275.00	125.00	35.00
1914 Cracker Jack #19	1000.00	150.00	75.00
1915 Cracker Jack #19	450.00	150.00	75.00
M101-4	90.00	35.00	15.00
M116 (blue background)	775.00	250.00	75.00
M116 (pastel background)	450.00	175.00	50.00
1940 Play Ball #172	125.00	30.00	10.00

Lawrence "Yogi" Berra

Elected HoF 1972. Yogi Berra is one of the great catchers and most interesting quotes in baseball history. His cards are popular, and a diverse supply in all price ranges is available. Berra cards not listed are 25¢ or less in Near Mint condition.

	NM	EX	VG
1948 Bowman #6	575.00	225.00	100.00
1949 Bowman #60	275.00	125.00	50.00
1950 Bowman #46	350.00	135.00	60.00
1951 Bowman #2	380.00	145.00	65.00
1952 Bowman #1	650.00	200.00	75.00
1952 Topps #191	375.00	140.00	65.00
1953 Bowman #121	525.00	200.00	90.00
1953 Topps #104	285.00	100.00	45.00
1954 Bowman #161	165.00	60.00	25.00
1954 Topps #50	235.00	85.00	35.00
1955 Bowman #168	95.00	35.00	15.00
1955 Topps #198	250.00	100.00	35.00
1956 Topps #110	115.00	55.00	25.00
1957 Topps #2	175.00	65.00	25.00

1958 Topps #370 .... 95.00	40.00	15.00
1959 Topps #180 .... 80.00	27.50	10.00
1960 Topps #480 .... 75.00	25.00	10.00
1961 Topps #425 .... 65.00	20.00	7.50
1962 Topps #360 .... 75.00	25.00	10.00
1963 Topps #340 .... 75.00	25.00	10.00
1964 Topps #21 .... 32.50	10.00	3.50
1965 Topps #470 .... 45.00	17.50	3.50

James LeRoy Bottomley

Elected HoF 1974. "Sunny Jim" Bottomley has been passed over by the market for years. He was a deserving Hall of Famer, but he wasn't in the Ruth class and wasn't on many good teams. That leaves his cards at the lower end of the 1930s price range of Hall of Famers.

	NM	EX	VG
1934 Batter Up #8 .... 175.00	60.00	15.00
1934 Batter Up #115 .... 325.00	75.00	30.00
Diamond Star #59 .... 165.00	50.00	25.00
1933 Goudey #44 .... 195.00	75.00	35.00
1935 Goudey 125.00	35.00	20.00
George Miller 350.00	150.00	50.00
1940 Play Ball #236 .... 125.00	35.00	10.00

Lou Boudreau

Elected HoF 1970. Lou Boudreau would have had many more cards were it not for his military service during World War II. He appeared in the 1941 Double Play set and promptly vanished until the late 1940s. His cards are scarce, but demand for them is low so prices are just about right.

	NM	EX	VG
1941 Double Play #132 .... 145.00	50.00	20.00
1948 Leaf #106 .... 85.00	35.00	20.00
1949 Bowman #11 .... 70.00	25.00	7.50
1950 Bowman #94 .... 40.00	15.00	5.00
1951 Bowman #62 .... 45.00	15.00	5.00
1953 Bowman (color) #57 .... 65.00	20.00	7.50
1955 Bowman #89 .... 22.50	7.50	3.50

Roger Philip Bresnahan

Elected HoF 1945. He may not be well known today, but Roger Bresnahan was a star in his day and it shows. Tobacco, candy, and other types of cards featured him along with Cobb and Johnson. He doesn't bring their prices, but for a decade he was one of the greats.

	NM	EX	VG
T201 Mecca with Huggins	275.00	125.00	50.00
T202 Hassan	375.00	125.00	75.00
T202 Hassan with McGraw	450.00	150.00	75.00
T204 Ramly	650.00	175.00	75.00
T205	650.00	150.00	50.00
T206 (Portrait)	625.00	75.00	25.00
T206 (with bat)	425.00	75.00	25.00
T213 Type 2	190.00	75.00	25.00
T213 Type 3	275.00	75.00	25.00
T215 Type 2	375.00	75.00	25.00
T214	2000.00	1000.00	750.00
T216	300.00	100.00	40.00
T222 Fatima	500.00	125.00	50.00
E90-1 American Caramel	575.00	125.00	50.00
E91 Set A	175.00	65.00	25.00
E98	550.00	175.00	60.00
E103 Williams Caramel	650.00	200.00	75.00
E106 American Caramel	450.00	100.00	35.00
E254 Colgan's Chips	100.00	35.00	15.00
E270	150.00	50.00	15.00
D303 General Baking	225.00	75.00	25.00
1914 Cracker Jack #17	1500.00	175.00	50.00
1915 Cracker Jack #17	500.00	175.00	50.00
M101-5 #16	90.00	35.00	15.00
M116	450.00	150.00	35.00
Turkey Red (T3)	950.00	350.00	175.00

Louis Clark "Lou" Brock

Elected HoF 1985. Stolen bases don't equal home runs in the card market. That's about all you will ever need to know about Lou Brock's card prices. Brock got on base and then advanced. It was good enough for the Hall of Fame but it does not make him a high-demand card, so prices can be expected to stay modest.

	NM	EX	VG
1962 Topps #287	185.00	75.00	30.00
1963 Topps #472	130.00	50.00	20.00
1964 Topps #29	35.00	15.00	5.00
1965 Topps #540	45.00	20.00	7.50
1966 Topps #125	20.00	8.50	3.00
1967 Topps $285	19.00	8.00	2.75
1968 Topps #372	5.50	2.00	0.95
1968 Topps #520	19.00	8.00	2.75
1969 Topps #85	17.50	7.50	2.50
1969 Topps #428	4.00	1.00	0.35
1970 Topps #330	7.50	2.50	1.00
1971 Topps #625	27.50	7.50	2.00
1972 Topps #200	4.50	1.50	0.50
1973 Topps #320	5.00	1.75	0.75
1974 Topps #60	4.00	1.00	0.35
1975 Topps #540	3.50	1.00	0.35
1976 Topps #10	3.50	1.00	0.35
1977 Topps #355	2.50	0.75	0.25
1978 Topps #170	2.50	0.75	0.25
1979 Topps #655	2.50	0.75	0.25
1980 Topps #1	1.50	0.50	0.15

Dennis Joseph "Big Dan" Brouthers

Elected HoF 1945. Brouthers was actually called Dan, and by any name it's a tough card to get. Demand isn't great, but supplies are very limited so prices are on the rise.

	NM	EX	VG
N162 Goodwin Champions	1750.00	650.00	250.00
N172	475.00	2550.00	100.00
N173	1600.00	750.00	300.00
N284	200.00	75.00	25.00
N300	1000.00	325.00	125.00
N403 Yum Yum	1250.00	750.00	500.00
N526 Diamond S Cigars	950.00	375.00	200.00

Mordecai "Three Finger" Brown

Elected HoF 1949. If nothing else, Mordecai Peter Centennial "Three Finger" Brown has one of the great names (and nicknames) in sports. Once you've heard "Three Finger" you remember it, and that translates into demand for his cards. In his case the demand is justified, as he was one of the great pitchers of his era.

	NM	EX	VG
T201 Mecca with Holman	175.00	100.00	50.00
T202 Hassan	425.00	150.00	75.00
T204 Ramly	750.00	250.00	100.00
T205	650.00	150.00	50.00
T206 (Chicago on shirt)	375.00	75.00	35.00
T206 (Cubs on shirt)	625.00	140.00	65.00
T206 Portrait	500.00	100.00	50.00
T213 Type 2	190.00	75.00	25.00
T215 Type 2	375.00	75.00	25.00
E90-1 American Caramel	575.00	125.00	50.00
E90-3 American Caramel	550.00	100.00	50.00
E91 Set A	175.00	65.00	25.00
E91 Set B	175.00	65.00	25.00
E93 Standard Caramel	375.00	100.00	25.00
E98	550.00	175.00	60.00
E300 Plow's Candy	725.00	250.00	125.00
D329 Weil Baking #17	350.00	150.00	50.00
1914 Cracker Jack #32	1500.00	175.00	50.00
1915 Cracker Jack #32	500.00	175.00	50.00
M101-4 #17	75.00	25.00	10.00
M101-5 #23	100.00	35.00	20.00
M116 (blue background)	750.00	275.00	125.00
M116 (pastel background)	450.00	125.00	50.00
Turkey Red (T3)	950.00	350.00	175.00

Jesse Cail "The Crab" Burkett

Elected HoF 1946. Jesse Burkett certainly fell through the card crack. The fact is that there is really only one Burkett card — the uncommon T204 Ramly. The good news is that Burkett is one of the five players known to appear on both square and round Ramlys. Square Ramlys are virtually unknown, so it doesn't help the supply problem. Burkett is the bluest of blue chips. If you see him, you're lucky. If you own one of his cards, you are one of the very few.

	NM	EX	VG
T204 Ramly (round frame)	11750.00	1000.00	750.00
T204 Ramly (square frame)	2750.00	1500.00	1000.00

Roy "Campy" Campanella

Elected HoF 1969. Campy's major-league career was shortened by a tragic automobile accident. That combined with years in the Negro Leagues make his cards among the more difficult to find of the stars of the 1950s. Campy died in 1993, but that will have more effect on the autograph market than on his card prices.

	NM	EX	VG
1949 Bowman #84	725.00	275.00	125.00
1950 Bowman #75	285.00	100.00	35.00
1951 Bowman #31	275.00	100.00	35.00
1952 Bowman #44	235.00	85.00	30.00
1952 Topps #314	1475.00	650.00	275.00
1953 Bowman #46	265.00	110.00	35.00
1953 Topps #27	225.00	85.00	30.00
1954 Bowman #90	145.00	65.00	25.00
1955 Bowman #22	115.00	45.00	15.00
1956 Topps #101	125.00	40.00	10.00
1957 Topps #210	95.00	35.00	10.00
1959 Topps #550	135.00	45.00	15.00
1961 Topps #480	20.00	7.50	2.50

Rodney Cline "Rod" Carew

Elected HoF 1991. By surpassing 3000 hits, Rod Carew's Hall of Fame spot was automatic. His career extended into the mid-1980s, so supplies of Carew cards are plentiful; hence prices for all but his first few cards are very reasonable. Carew cards not listed are less than $1.00 in Near Mint condition.

	NM	EX	VG
1967 Topps #569	475.00	200.00	85.00
1968 Topps #80	145.00	55.00	20.00
1968 Topps #363	12.50	3.50	1.00
1969 Topps #419	8.50	2.00	0.75
1969 Topps #510	70.00	20.00	7.50
1970 Topps #290	65.00	20.00	7.50
1970 Topps #453	3.50	1.00	0.35
1971 Topps #210	65.00	20.00	7.50
1972 Topps #695	100.00	35.00	15.00
1972 Topps #696	35.00	10.00	2.75
1973 Topps #330	17.50	8.50	3.00
1974 Topps #50	12.50	3.00	0.50

1975 Topps #600	10.00	2.50	0.50
1976 Topps #400	7.50	2.00	0.45
1977 Topps #120	7.50	2.00	0.45
1978 Topps #580	4.50	1.25	0.40
1979 Topps #300	3.75	1.00	0.35
1980 Topps #700	1.75	0.75	0.25
1981 Donruss #49	1.50	0.50	0.20
1981 Donruss #169	1.50	0.50	0.20
1981 Fleer #268	1.50	0.50	0.20
1981 Topps #100	2.50	1.00	0.35
1982 Topps #500	1.50	0.45	0.15
1984 Donruss #352	3.00	1.00	0.35
1984 Fleer #511	1.75	0.85	0.25

Max Carey

Elected HoF 1961. Carey cards are not in high demand, and plenty of cards exist for his time. His cards are readily available and not likely to increase significantly in price anytime soon.

	NM	EX	VG
T206	275.00	50.00	20.00
T207	400.00	125.00	35.00
T213 Type 1	300.00	125.00	50.00
E120 American Caramel	85.00	35.00	15.00
E121 Set of 80	70.00	30.00	10.00
E121 Set of 120	70.00	30.00	10.00
E122 American Caramel	100.00	35.00	15.00
E210 York Caramel #32	75.00	30.00	10.00
E220 National Caramel	100.00	35.00	15.00
1914 Cracker Jack #73	1350.00	150.00	50.00
1915 Cracker Jack #73	350.00	150.00	50.00
D329 Weil Baking #28	275.00	125.00	45.00
M101-4 #28	60.00	20.00	10.00
M101-5 #26	60.00	20.00	10.00
Yuengling's Ice Cream #32	20.00	10.00	5.00
1940 Play Ball #178	125.00	40.00	15.00

Frank LeRoy Chance

Elected HoF 1946. The famous anchor of Tinker to Evers to Chance — the last of the great Cubs teams was Chance's. That plus a little poetry keep demand for his cards high despite an especially large number of cards for the time.

	NM	EX	VG
T201 Mecca With Evers	425.00	150.00	75.00
T202 Hassan	375.00	125.00	75.00
T204 Ramly	1425.00	350.00	125.00
T205	725.00	225.00	100.00
T206 (batting)	425.00	100.00	35.00
T206 (portrait, red background)	625.00	125.00	55.00
T206 (portrait, yellow background)	525.00	100.00	40.00
T207	675.00	200.00	90.00
T213 Type 1	300.00	125.00	50.00
T213 Type 2	225.00	100.00	50.00
T213 Type 3	250.00	125.00	60.00
T215 Type 1	775.00	185.00	85.00
T215 Type 2	425.00	175.00	75.00
T216	275.00	125.00	50.00
T222 Fatima	550.00	200.00	85.00
Turkey Red (T3) #47	950.00	350.00	150.00
E90-1 American Caramel	625.00	150.00	65.00
E90-3 American Caramel	875.00	350.00	125.00
E91 Set A	200.00	75.00	35.00
E91 Set B	200.00	75.00	35.00
E92 Croft's Candy	500.00	175.00	75.00
E92 Dockman	175.00	75.00	35.00
E93 Standard Caramel	475.00	150.00	60.00
E94	475.00	150.00	60.00
E95	475.00	150.00	60.00
E98	550.00	200.00	85.00
E101	475.00	150.00	60.00
E103 Williams Caramel	600.00	175.00	75.00
E105 Mello-Mint	425.00	150.00	60.00
E107 Breisch Williams	475.00	150.00	60.00
E224 Texas Tommy	750.00	275.00	125.00
E254 Colgan's Chips	75.00	25.00	10.00
E270	100.00	35.00	15.00
E286 Ju Ju Drums	525.00	175.00	75.00
D304 General Baking	175.00	75.00	35.00
1914 Cracker Jack #99	2750.00	750.00	200.00
M101-5 #28	100.00	35.00	15.00
M116 (blue background)	1000.00	300.00	100.00
M116 (pastel background)	450.00	125.00	50.00
1940 Play Ball #234	150.00	60.00	25.00

Oscar Charleston

Elected HoF 1976 (Negro leagues).

	NM	EX	VG
No cards			

John Dwight "Happy Jack" Chesbro

Elected HoF 1946. It's a good thing Chesbro appeared on a T206 card; otherwise his situation would be similar to Jesse Burkett's. Chesbro cards deserve even higher prices than he currently commands, since supply is very limited.

	NM	EX	VG
T206	750.00	200.00	75.00
E107 Breisch Williams	600.00	175.00	50.00

Fred Clifford "Cap" Clarke

Elected HoF 1945. He's not well known, but he has appeared on a number of cards. Fred Clarke is tough to find and sometimes difficult to afford.

	NM	EX	VG
T201 Mecca with Gaspar or Byrnes	200.00	90.00	50.00
T205	425.00	150.00	50.00
T206 (holding bat)	450.00	125.00	40.00
T206 (portrait)	500.00	150.00	50.00
E90-2 American Caramel	450.00	165.00	75.00
E91 Set A	175.00	65.00	30.00
E93 Standard Caramel	200.00	90.00	35.00
E96 Philadelphia Caramel	525.00	225.00	100.00
E98	500.00	175.00	75.00
E107 Breisch Williams	450.00	200.00	85.00
E254 Colgan's Chips	65.00	20.00	10.00
E270	90.00	30.00	15.00
E300 Plow's Candy	800.00	325.00	125.00
1914 Cracker Jack #70	1350.00	150.00	50.00
1915 Cracker Jack #70	400.00	150.00	50.00
M116	425.00	175.00	65.00
Turkey Red (T3) #8	925.00	350.00	125.00

John Gibson Clarkson

Elected HoF 1963. Clarkson cards are of average difficulty to obtain for the pre-1900 Hall of Famers. Clarkson was not one of the biggest names of the era, but he was a star pitcher, so he appears in quite a few sets. Enough cards exist to meet the current limited demand.

	NM	EX	VG
N28	850.00	350.00	125.00
N172	600.00	250.00	100.00
N173	1750.00	1000.00	450.00
N300	850.00	275.00	125.00
N403 Yum Yum	1500.00	700.00	325.00

Roberto Clemente

Elected HoF 1973. The demand for Clemente cards is high, which keeps the prices for his cards stable. His cards are no more scarce than the average player's cards. As time passes, Clemente's reputation as a player and as a man seems to be growing, and that makes for real blue-chip cards.

	NM	EX	VG
1955 Topps #164	1650.00	750.00	275.00
1956 Topps #33	425.00	175.00	65.00
1957 Topps #76	255.00	85.00	30.00
1958 Topps #52	255.00	85.00	25.00
1959 Topps #478	110.00	35.00	10.00
1960 Topps #326	100.00	30.00	10.00
1961 Topps #388	90.00	35.00	10.00
1962 Topps #10	100.00	30.00	10.00
1963 Fleer #56	85.00	30.00	10.00
1963 Topps #540	190.00	75.00	25.00
1964 Topps #440	115.00	45.00	15.00
1965 Topps #160	75.00	30.00	10.00
1966 Topps #300	90.00	35.00	15.00
1967 Topps #400	75.00	30.00	10.00
1968 Topps #150	50.00	20.00	7.50
1968 Topps #374	12.50	5.00	2.00
1969 Topps #50	45.00	17.50	7.50
1970 Topps #350	45.00	17.50	7.50
1971 Topps #630	70.00	25.00	10.00
1972 Topps #309	25.00	10.00	3.50
1972 Topps #310	12.50	5.00	1.75
1973 Topps #50	30.00	10.00	3.50

Tyrus Raymond "Ty" Cobb

Elected HoF 1936. The dominant player of the era is also the dominant player in terms of demand for his cards. Everyone wants a Ty Cobb card, but they come at a steep price. Despite the fact that he was represented in nearly every card set issued during his playing days, demand still keeps prices high today.

	NM	EX	VG
T201 Mecca with Crawford	1750.00	1000.00	350.00
T202 Hassan	2750.00	1000.00	350.00
T205	6000.00	1500.00	400.00
T206 (bat off shoulder)	2275.00	425.00	275.00
T206 (bat on shoulder)	2300.00	450.00	300.00
T206 (portrait, green background)	5000.00	1000.00	450.00
T206 (portrait, red background)	2250.00	400.00	250.00
T213 Type 1	2750.00	1000.00	350.00
T213 Type 2	1400.00	500.00	225.00
T213 Type 3	2500.00	900.00	325.00
T214	5500.00	2000.00	1500.00
T215 Type 1	2500.00	900.00	325.00
T215 Type 2	2500.00	900.00	325.00
T216	2500.00	900.00	325.00
E90-1 American Caramel	3250.00	1000.00	375.00
E92 Croft's Candy	3900.00	1000.00	375.00
E92 Croft's Cocoa	3900.00	1000.00	375.00
E93 Standard Caramel	3250.00	1000.00	375.00
E94	3500.00	900.00	350.00
E95	3500.00	900.00	350.00
E98	4000.00	1200.00	400.00
E101	3250.00	1000.00	375.00
E102	3750.00	1000.00	375.00
E103 Williams Caramel	3750.00	1000.00	375.00
E105 Mello-Mint	2500.00	825.00	325.00
E106 American Caramel	5000.00	1500.00	600.00
E120 American Caramel	950.00	275.00	200.00
E121 Set of 80	725.00	225.00	150.00
E121 Set of 120	725.00	225.00	150.00
E122 American Caramel	800.00	250.00	150.00
E210 York Caramel	725.00	225.00	150.00
E224 Texas Tommy	3750.00	1000.00	375.00
E254 Colgan's Chips	1000.00	300.00	125.00
E270	1100.00	300.00	125.00
E300 Plow's Candy	3400.00	950.00	350.00

D303 General Baking 1250.00	450.00	175.00
D304 General Baking 1000.00	300.00	175.00
D329 Weil Baking #38 .... 1250.00	450.00	175.00
1914 Cracker Jack #30 .... 17000.00	2500.00	1000.00
1915 Cracker Jack #30 .... 8500.00	2500.00	1000.00
M101-4 .... 1250.00	450.00	150.00
M101-6 .... 2250.00	750.00	250.00
M116 (blue background) 4900.00	1200.00	750.00
M116 (pastel background) 2750.00	1000.00	650.00
Turkey Red (T3) #9 .... 9000.00	2500.00	1500.00
1933 Sport Kings 2000.00	800.00	300.00

Gordon Stanley "Mickey" Cochrane

Elected HoF 1947. Mickey Cochrane does not have the glamour of a Cobb or Ruth. With less demand and a solid supply of cards there's not a lot of upward potential with Cochrane.

	NM	EX	VG
1933 Delong #6 .... 350.00	125.00	75.00
Diamond Star 200.00	75.00	35.00
1933 Goudey #76 .... 225.00	100.00	40.00
1934 Goudey #2 .... 275.00	100.00	40.00
1935 Goudey 150.00	70.00	25.00
1936 Goudey 150.00	55.00	25.00
1940 Play Ball #180 .... 135.00	50.00	20.00
1933 Tatoo Orbit 75.00	30.00	15.00

Edward Collins

Elected HoF 1939. A few years ago Eddie Collins was viewed as one of the game's real elites. Somehow his stock has been slipping, and with it the premiums for his cards relative to other Hall of Famers for the same period.

	NM	EX	VG
T202 Hassan ....,................................ 425.00	150.00	75.00
T204 Ramly 1900.00	450.00	150.00
T205 .... 700.00	175.00	75.00
T206 .... 550.00	150.00	60.00
T208 Fireside 1350.00	400.00	150.00
T213 Type 2 .... 225.00	100.00	50.00
T213 Type 3 .... 275.00	125.00	75.00
T215 Type 1 .... 750.00	200.00	100.00

T215 Type 2	425.00	175.00	75.00
T216	275.00	125.00	50.00
E90-1 American Caramel	600.00	125.00	55.00
E92 Croft's Candy	450.00	100.00	50.00
E92 Croft's Cocoa	450.00	100.00	50.00
E93 Standard Caramel	475.00	150.00	60.00
E98	550.00	200.00	85.00
E101	475.00	150.00	60.00
E102	550.00	200.00	85.00
E105 Mello-Mint	425.00	150.00	60.00
E106 Breisch Williams	225.00	90.00	40.00
E120 American Caramel	135.00	45.00	20.00
E121 Set of 120	135.00	45.00	20.00
E121 Set of 80	135.00	45.00	20.00
E122 American Caramel	135.00	45.00	20.00
E220 National Caramel	135.00	45.00	20.00
E254 Colgan's Chips	100.00	35.00	15.00
D303 General Baking	225.00	100.00	35.00
D304 General Baking	200.00	90.00	25.00
D329 Weil Baking #34	325.00	125.00	50.00
1914 Cracker Jack #7	1500.00	225.00	100.00
1915 Cracker Jack #7	625.00	225.00	100.00
M101-4 #34	100.00	25.00	15.00
M101-5 #33	65.00	20.00	15.00
M116 (blue background)	950.00	275.00	100.00
M116 (pastel background)	500.00	125.00	50.00
Turkey Red (T3) #87	1200.00	350.00	150.00
1933 Goudey #42	250.00	100.00	35.00

James Joseph Collins

Elected HoF 1945. Jimmy Collins cards are tougher to find than Eddie Collins cards, but they're also in far less demand. Of the two Collinses in the Hall of Fame, this one's cards might be the better bet.

	NM	EX	VG
T204 Ramly	1250.00	325.00	125.00
T205	950.00	325.00	125.00
T206	425.00	125.00	40.00
E91 American Caramel Set A	150.00	50.00	20.00
E107 Breisch Williams	550.00	175.00	80.00

Earle Bryan Combs

Elected HoF 1970. Earle is certainly not a marquee name in the Hall of Fame. Combs cards are somewhat depressed in price, especially since two were made after he was finished as a player. That provides collectors with a cheap alternative to his otherwise very limited appearances.

	NM	EX	VG
1933 Goudey #103	225.00	85.00	35.00
Yuengling's Ice Cream #21	35.00	15.00	7.50
1940 Play Ball #124	150.00	50.00	20.00
1954 Topps #183	37.50	12.50	5.00

Charles Albert Comiskey

Elected HoF 1939 (manager). Comiskey was well known, but not well liked due to his stingy pay for players. Though elected to the Hall as a manager, his cards still bring high prices, especially those on which he is depicted as a player.

	NM	EX	VG
N28	1250.00	450.00	200.00
N172	700.00	300.00	125.00
N173	1750.00	750.00	250.00
N284 Buchner Gold Coin	400.00	175.00	60.00
N370 Lone Jack	2750.00	1500.00	1000.00
D329 Weil Baking #36	225.00	100.00	40.00
1914 Cracker Jack #23	1600.00	175.00	90.00
1915 Cracker Jack #23	550.00	175.00	90.00

J.B. "Jocko" Conlan

Electer HoF 1974. Although he played briefly, Jocko Conlan made the Hall of Fame not as a player, but as one of the game's leading umpires. No cards of Conlan as a player exist, and he was only on one Bowman card as an umpire. So if you include Conlan in a Hall of Fame set you only need one card, but so does everyone else — a very desirable card.

	NM	EX	VG
1955 Bowman #303	115.00	50.00	25.00

Roger Connor

Elected HoF 1976. Connor cards are probably the most difficult of the pre-1900 stars' cards to acquire. He does not appear on many cards and most of them are scarce. Those assembling a Hall of Fame collection should make Connor one of their high priorities.

	NM	EX	VG
N167	3200.00	1500.00	850.00
N172	900.00	500.00	350.00
N173	2500.00	1250.00	750.00
N284 Buchner Gold Coin	250.00	100.00	50.00
N690 Kalamazoo Bats	1100.00	650.00	400.00
E223 G&B Chewing Gum	1750.00	1250.00	850.00

Stanley Coveleski

Elected HoF 1969. Stan Coveleski is one of those players who was ignored in terms of cards. His cards should some of the more common of his era, but instead they are tough to find. His appearance in a couple of the more common "E" sets is the only factor keeping his cards from being surprisingly expensive.

	NM	EX	VG
E120 American Caramel	125.00	40.00	15.00
E121 Set of 120	125.00	40.00	15.00
E220 National Caramel	175.00	65.00	30.00
Yuengling's Ice Cream #57	35.00	20.00	10.00

Samuel Earl Crawford

Elected HoF 1957. Sam Crawford is another big star who seems to have lost a bit of his appeal over the years. Although his cards still bring a slight premium over average Hall of Famers, his are no longer among the really high priced cards of the era.

	NM	EX	VG
T201 Mecca with Cobb (See Ty Cobb prices)			
T206 (batting)	500.00	125.00	40.00
T206 (throwing)	550.00	150.00	50.00
T213 Type 2	275.00	125.00	75.00
T213 Type 3	325.00	150.00	75.00
T215 Type 1	750.00	200.00	100.00
T216	275.00	125.00	50.00
E92 Croft's Candy	450.00	100.00	50.00

E92 Croft's Cocoa	450.00	100.00	50.00
E94	550.00	150.00	75.00
E95	550.00	150.00	75.00
E101	475.00	150.00	60.00
E102	550.00	200.00	85.00
E103 Williams Caramel	750.00	225.00	100.00
E104 Nadja Type 3	475.00	175.00	85.00
E106 Breisch Williams	225.00	90.00	40.00
D303 General Baking	225.00	100.00	35.00
D304 General Baking	200.00	90.00	25.00
1914 Cracker Jack #14	1500.00	150.00	75.00
1915 Cracker Jack #14	500.00	150.00	75.00
M101-4	80.00	35.00	20.00
M101-5	80.00	35.00	20.00
M116 (blue background)	950.00	375.00	150.00
M116 (pastel background)	550.00	225.00	100.00
Turkey Red (T3) #5	1350.00	500.00	200.00

Joseph Edward Cronin

Elected HoF 1956. Average or even slightly below-average demand coupled with a good supply of different cards is an equation for modest prices now and in the future.

	NM	EX	VG
1933 Goudey #63	200.00	85.00	35.00
1933 Goudey #109	175.00	75.00	25.00
1933 Goudey #189	175.00	75.00	25.00
1935 Goudey	120.00	35.00	20.00
1934 Batter Up #32	125.00	50.00	25.00
1934 Batter Up #183	325.00	100.00	50.00
George Miller	450.00	200.00	100.00
1941 Double Play #59	150.00	60.00	25.00
1941 Double Play #82	525.00	150.00	100.00
1940 Play Ball #134	125.00	50.00	20.00
1941 Play Ball #15	185.00	80.00	35.00

William Arthur "Candy" Cummings

Elected HoF 1939.

	NM	EX	VG
No cards			

Hazen Shirley "Kiki" Cuyler

Elected HoF 1968. Small wonder Hazen Shirley Cuyler became Kiki! His cards are numerous enough to make Cuyler owners wish they weren't, but it's too late. Don't expect great things from your Cuylers.

	NM	EX	VG
Diamond Star #31	110.00	45.00	20.00
1933 Delong #8	275.00	125.00	45.00
1933 Goudey #23	325.00	125.00	40.00
1934 Goudey #90	525.00	150.00	50.00
1935 Goudey	75.00	30.00	20.00
1936 Goudey	115.00	40.00	20.00

Ray Dandridge

Elected HoF 1987 (Negro leagues).

	NM	EX	VG
No cards			

Jay Hanna "Dizzy" Dean

Elected HoF 1953. Dizzy Dean was many things, but never boring. Though there were only a few glorious seasons, there are many anecdotes. His cards are a popular choice today, even at premium prices.

	NM	EX	VG
1934 Batter Up #64	625.00	275.00	125.00
1933 Goudey #223	850.00	350.00	175.00
1934 Goudey #6	625.00	275.00	125.00
1935 Goudey	300.00	125.00	50.00
George Miller	850.00	350.00	150.00

Edward James Delahanty

Elected HoF 1945. A tragic figure from the pre-1900 period. Delahanty died early, but he is certainly not forgotten by today's collectors. There is very solid demand for very few cards, and prices are going up fast.

	NM	EX	VG
N142	7500.00	3250.00	1500.00
N172	1500.00	700.00	350.00

	NM	EX	VG
N173	3000.00	1250.00	500.00
N300	1200.00	450.00	225.00

William Malcolm Dickey

Elected HoF 1954. The dominant catcher of his day is starting to fade slightly in recognition. Even so, as part of those great Yankee teams any softening in demand should be modest.

	NM	EX	VG
1934 Batter Up #30	225.00	100.00	45.00
1934 Batter Up #117	450.00	200.00	75.00
1941 Double Play #66	100.00	45.00	20.00
Diamond Star #11	250.00	100.00	35.00
Diamond Star #103	725.00	300.00	125.00
1933 Goudey #19	535.00	200.00	90.00
1935 Goudey	225.00	100.00	45.00
George Miller	575.00	225.00	85.00
1939 Play Ball #30	175.00	85.00	35.00
1940 Play Ball #7	175.00	85.00	35.00
1941 Play Ball #70	750.00	275.00	125.00
1952 Topps #400	575.00	250.00	100.00

Martin DiHigo

Elected HoF 1977 (Negro leagues).

	NM	EX	VG
No cards			

Joseph Paul "Joltin' Joe" DiMaggio

Elected HoF 1955. Class is always worth money. That seems to be the current market message with regard to The Yankee Clipper. DiMaggio cards are hot and getting hotter despite big price tags. Demand explains part of the prices, but the very limited supply is also a factor.

	NM	EX	VG
1935 Zeenut with coupon	13500.00	6250.00	2750.00
1938 Goudey #250	3750.00	1500.00	600.00
1938 Goudey #274	4300.00	1700.00	750.00
1939 Play Ball #26	1900.00	900.00	400.00
1940 Play Ball #1	2600.00	1100.00	525.00

	NM	EX	VG
1941 Double Play #63	725.00	300.00	125.00
1941 Play Ball #71	3500.00	1300.00	550.00
1948 Leaf #1	1800.00	850.00	350.00

Robert Pershing Doerr

Elected HoF 1986. Bobby Doerr is not a high demand card. Moreover, supplies are fairly good since his career extended into the 1950s. He may be a friend of Ted Williams, but don't expect them to share the same price levels or even price direction.

	NM	EX	VG
1938 Goudey #258	300.00	125.00	50.00
1938 Goudey #282	325.00	125.00	50.00
1939 Play Ball #7	95.00	45.00	20.00
1940 Play Ball #38	95.00	45.00	20.00
1941 Double Play #106	160.00	75.00	35.00
1941 Play Ball #64	240.00	100.00	35.00
1948 Leaf #83	90.00	40.00	15.00
1949 Bowman #23	75.00	25.00	10.00
1950 Bowman #43	75.00	25.00	10.00

Donald Scott Drysdale

Elected HoF 1984. Another popular Dodger and baseball personality who died unexpectedly in 1993. Demand for Drysdale cards is good, although supplies are adequate to meet current needs without significant price increases.

	NM	EX	VG
1957 Topps #18	210.00	85.00	30.00
1958 Topps #25	65.00	25.00	10.00
1959 Topps #387	25.00	10.00	3.50
1960 Topps #475	25.00	10.00	3.50
1960 Topps #570	17.50	5.00	1.75
1961 Topps #260	20.00	7.50	2.50
1962 Topps #340	32.50	10.00	3.50
1962 Topps #398	8.00	2.50	1.00
1963 Fleer #41	25.00	7.50	2.25
1963 Topps #360	27.50	12.50	3.00
1964 Topps #120	15.00	5.50	2.00
1965 Topps #260	15.00	5.50	2.00
1966 Topps #430	12.50	4.50	1.75
1967 Topps #55	10.00	2.50	1.00

1968 Topps #145	8.50	2.00	0.75
1969 Topps #400	7.50	2.00	0.75

Hugh Duffy

Elected HoF 1945. Hugh Duffy is interesting. He has cards in two distinct eras. Some date from before 1900 and bring the sort of prices associated with that era. A small number, however, are in the major sets of the tobacco era. It gives you some interesting choices, but it also keeps Hugh Duffy's card prices below where they might be if he had never appeared on a card after 1900.

	NM	EX	VG
N172	600.00	200.00	100.00
N173	1750.00	1000.00	650.00
N300	1000.00	275.00	150.00
T205	850.00	250.00	75.00
T206	575.00	175.00	75.00
E90-1 American Caramel	1750.00	600.00	250.00
M116	650.00	200.00	90.00

Johnny Evers

Elected HoF 1946. Evers is a lot like Frank Chance and Joe Tinker, with whom he is forever linked. He retains solid popularity today. Featured on many cards, supplies remain plentiful.

	NM	EX	VG
T201 Mecca (See Frank Chance)			
T202 Hassan with Archer	325.00	150.00	75.00
T202 Hassan with Chance	550.00	225.00	100.00
T204 Ramly	1800.00	750.00	275.00
T205	650.00	275.00	100.00
T206 (Chicago on shirt)	450.00	150.00	50.00
T206 (Cubs on shirt)	525.00	175.00	75.00
T206 (portrait)	725.00	225.00	100.00
T213 Type 1	325.00	125.00	75.00
T213 Type 2	250.00	100.00	50.00
T213 Type 3	300.00	115.00	65.00
T215 Type 2	250.00	100.00	50.00
T216	350.00	135.00	75.00
E91 Set A	150.00	65.00	30.00
E91 Set B	150.00	65.00	30.00
E92 Croft's Candy	625.00	250.00	100.00
E92 Croft's Cocoa	625.00	250.00	100.00

E93 Standard Caramel	475.00	150.00	60.00
E94	425.00	125.00	50.00
E95	425.00	125.00	50.00
E98	550.00	200.00	85.00
E101	475.00	150.00	60.00
E102	550.00	200.00	85.00
E105 Mello-Mint	425.00	150.00	60.00
E106 Breisch Williams	225.00	90.00	40.00
E121 Set of 80	135.00	45.00	20.00
E122 American Caramel	135.00	45.00	20.00
E254 Colgan's Chips	100.00	35.00	15.00
E270	130.00	40.00	20.00
D303 General Baking	225.00	100.00	35.00
D304 General Baking	200.00	90.00	25.00
D329 Weil Baking #54	200.00	90.00	25.00
M101-4 #54	75.00	25.00	15.00
M101-5 #55	80.00	25.00	15.00
M116	525.00	175.00	85.00
1914 Cracker Jack #18	1700.00	200.00	100.00
1915 Cracker Jack #18	475.00	175.00	90.00
1940 Play Ball #174	125.00	50.00	20.00
Turkey Red (T3)	1100.00	400.00	175.00

William "Buck" Ewing

Elected HoF 1946. Everything about Buck Ewing is medium and relative. His fame is medium in relation to other players from before 1900. His card prices are middling relative to other players of that period, and his future prices have about average prospects for pre-1900 cards.

	NM	EX	VG
N29	3750.00	1250.00	500.00
N172	650.00	300.00	175.00
N173	2500.00	1100.00	700.00
N284 Buchner Gold Coin	275.00	125.00	50.00
N300	950.00	450.00	225.00
N403 Yum Yum	1750.00	1200.00	850.00
E223 G&B Chewing Gum	1750.00	1200.00	850.00

Urban Charles "Red" Faber

Elected HoF 1964. Red Faber cards are not as common as you might think. If he hadn't made the 1933 Goudey set it would be fairly difficult to get his cards. As it is, he's a little tougher to find than average, but he seems to have a strong following. Maybe there are more Fabers out there than we know about.

	NM	EX	VG
D329 Weil Baking #55	225.00	90.00	25.00
E120 American Caramel #56	125.00	40.00	20.00
E121 Set of 80	125.00	40.00	20.00
E121 Set of 120	125.00	40.00	20.00
E220 National Caramel	135.00	50.00	25.00
1933 Goudey #79	225.00	85.00	35.00
1940 Play Ball #230	135.00	50.00	25.00
Yuengling's Ice Cream	35.00	15.00	10.00

Robert William Andrew Feller

Elected HoF 1962. The dominant pitcher of the 1940s and early 1950s has lost no luster. People go for speed in pitchers, and Rapid Robert was one of the hardest throwers of all time. In addition, his cards are scarce due to his absence from baseball in service to World War II.

	NM	EX	VG
1938 Goudey #264	450.00	200.00	85.00
1938 Goudey #288	925.00	350.00	150.00
1948 Bowman #5	225.00	100.00	45.00
1948 Leaf #93	1000.00	300.00	125.00
1949 Bowman #27	175.00	65.00	25.00
1950 Bowman #6	215.00	90.00	35.00
1951 Bowman #30	120.00	50.00	20.00
1952 Bowman #43	100.00	40.00	15.00
1952 Topps #88	185.00	75.00	30.00
1953 Bowman #114	275.00	125.00	50.00
1953 Topps #54	125.00	45.00	20.00
1954 Bowman #132	75.00	30.00	12.50
1955 Bowman #134	55.00	20.00	7.50
1956 Topps #200	95.00	35.00	15.00

Richard Benjamin Ferrell

Elected HoF 1984. There aren't many Rick Ferrell cards; he's not very popular. In fact, Rick Ferrell is one of the few Hall of Famers who raises eyebrows — just how did he get picked? Under the circumstances, don't expect price increases for Ferrell's cards.

	NM	EX	VG
1933 Goudey #197	225.00	85.00	35.00
1934 Batter Up #10	135.00	50.00	20.00
1934 Batter Up #126	375.00	130.00	55.00
Diamond Star #48	140.00	50.00	20.00
1935 Goudey	125.00	40.00	20.00
1936 Goudey	135.00	45.00	25.00
1939 Play Ball #39	130.00	40.00	20.00
1940 Play Ball #21	75.00	30.00	15.00

Roland Glen "Rollie" Fingers

Elected HoF 1992. Rollie Fingers is one of the rarest of all breeds in Cooperstown: a relief pitcher. That tends to mean lower-than-average prices. Very few of his cards cost over $10. (Rollie Fingers cards not listed are worth 25¢ or less.)

	NM	EX	VG
1969 Topps #597	130.00	35.00	15.00
1970 Topps #502	40.00	12.50	5.00
1971 Topps #384	15.00	3.50	1.50
1972 Topps #241	8.75	3.00	1.00
1973 Topps #84	5.00	1.75	0.50
1974 Topps #212	4.50	1.50	0.50
1975 Topps #21	4.75	1.50	0.50
1976 Topps #405	4.25	1.25	0.35
1977 Topps #523	2.25	1.00	0.25
1978 Topps #140	2.50	1.00	0.35
1979 Topps #390	2.25	1.00	0.25
1980 Topps #651	1.00	0.25	0.10
1981 Topps #229	1.00	0.25	0.10
1981 Topps Traded	2.00	0.35	0.10

Elmer Harrison Flick

Elected HoF 1963. Yes, Elmer Flick. He's in the Hall of Fame and he deserves it. He doesn't exactly create a lot of talk in hot-stove league discussions, but he's still in Cooperstown and his is not exactly an easy card to find.

	NM	EX	VG
T206	475.00	200.00	85.00
E107 Breisch Williams	650.00	250.00	100.00
E254 Colgan's Chips	125.00	50.00	20.00
E270	150.00	50.00	20.00
M116	475.00	175.00	75.00

Edward Charles "Whitey" Ford

Elected HoF 1974. Whitey Ford had the advantage of playing for great Yankee teams. Of course, he played a significant role in helping to make them great. His cards are not as easy to get as you might expect, especially his Bowman rookie in top grade.

	NM	EX	VG
1951 Bowman #1	1600.00	500.00	200.00
1953 Bowman #153	525.00	200.00	85.00
1953 Topps #207	225.00	80.00	35.00
1954 Bowman #177	110.00	35.00	15.00
1954 Topps #37	110.00	45.00	20.00
1955 Bowman #59	80.00	30.00	10.00
1956 Topps #240	135.00	45.00	15.00
1957 Topps #25	60.00	20.00	5.00
1958 Topps #320	42.00	15.00	5.00
1959 Topps #430	35.00	15.00	5.00
1960 Topps #35	37.50	15.00	5.00
1961 Topps #160	35.00	15.00	5.00
1961 Topps #586	100.00	35.00	10.00
1962 Topps #310	35.00	10.00	4.00
1962 Topps #475	15.00	3.50	1.00
1963 Topps #446	42.50	12.00	3.00
1964 Topps #380	27.00	10.00	3.00
1965 Topps #330	25.00	7.50	2.00
1966 Topps #160	23.00	7.00	1.50
1967 Topps #5	21.00	5.00	1.50

James Emory Foxx

Elected HoF 1951. If it wasn't for Babe Ruth, Jimmie "The Beast" Foxx cards might cost a fortune due to his popularity. As it is, they aren't cheap. But what might have been!

	NM	EX	VG
Diamond Star #64	375.00	150.00	70.00
1933 Delong #21	575.00	225.00	100.00
1933 Goudey #29	750.00	275.00	125.00
1933 Goudey #154	500.00	175.00	85.00
1934 Goudey #1	1200.00	400.00	150.00
1934 Batter Up #28	275.00	125.00	50.00
1934 Batter Up #144	650.00	275.00	100.00

1935 Goudey	225.00	85.00	35.00
1938 Goudey #249	525.00	200.00	100.00
1938 Goudey #273	625.00	275.00	100.00
George Miller	575.00	225.00	100.00
1940 Play Ball #133	250.00	100.00	50.00
1941 Play Ball #13	425.00	150.00	50.00
1941 Double Play #60	165.00	75.00	30.00

Ford Frick

Elected HoF 1959 (special). For those of you who want a complete Hall of Fame set, you'll need Ford Frick, an executive elected to Cooperstown in 1959. He was baseball commissioner from 1951 to 1965.

	NM	EX	VG
1959 Topps #1	65.00	10.00	3.50

Frank Francis Frisch

Elected HoF 1947. Some Hall of Famers appear on very few cards. Frank Frisch doesn't have that problem. Instead, he seems to appear on too many cards, and that will keep the prices for his cards under control for some time.

	NM	EX	VG
E120 American Caramel	135.00	45.00	20.00
E121 Set of 120	135.00	45.00	20.00
E121 Set of 80	135.00	45.00	20.00
E210 York Caramel	75.00	25.00	10.00
E220 National Caramel	135.00	45.00	20.00
1933 Goudey #49	425.00	150.00	50.00
1934 Batter Up #33	185.00	75.00	30.00
1934 Batter Up #173	375.00	150.00	50.00
Diamond Star #17	125.00	45.00	20.00
George Miller	425.00	150.00	50.00
1934 Goudey #13	235.00	90.00	35.00
1935 Goudey (See Dizzy Dean)			
1940 Play Ball #167	135.00	45.00	20.00
1950 Bowman #229	55.00	20.00	7.50
1951 Bowman #282	75.00	30.00	10.00

James Francis "Pud" Galvin

Elected HoF 1965. A tough player to find. As people learn about pre-1900 players, Pud Galvin becomes one of the keys. Prices actually realized for players like Pud are sometimes well in excess of any catalog prices and should climb higher.

	NM	EX	VG
N172	2200.00	1000.00	500.00
N173	3500.00	1250.00	750.00

Henry Louis Gehrig

Elected HoF 1939. Lou Gehrig cards are tremendously popular. His card prices have been rising for years and seem to show no signs of abating.

	NM	EX	VG
1925 Exhibit Supply	15000.00	6000.00	2500.00
1928 Yuengling's Ice Cream #26	350.00	125.00	100.00
1933 Delong #7	4500.00	1500.00	500.00
1933 Goudey #92	5000.00	1500.00	750.00
1933 Goudey #160	5000.00	1500.00	750.00
1934 Goudey #37	4500.00	1250.00	700.00
1934 Goudey #61	4200.00	1000.00	600.00

Charles Gehringer

Elected HoF 1949. The owner of one of the sweetest swings in the history of the game still brings solid premiums. He was, however, not a power hitter, so his cards may not improve in price.

	NM	EX	VG
Diamond Star #77	225.00	85.00	30.00
George Miller	475.00	125.00	75.00
1933 Delong #5	435.00	150.00	75.00
1933 Goudey #222	400.00	135.00	55.00
1934 Batter Up #42	225.00	80.00	35.00
1934 Batter Up #130	400.00	140.00	65.00
1934 Goudey #23	225.00	100.00	35.00
1935 Goudey (See Gordon Cochrane)			
1938 Goudey #241	475.00	175.00	75.00
1938 Goudey #265	400.00	140.00	65.00
1939 Play Ball #50	235.00	85.00	35.00

1940 Play Ball #41	150.00	50.00	25.00
1941 Play Ball #19	325.00	135.00	45.00
1941 Double Play	100.00	35.00	20.00

Bob Gibson

Elected HoF 1981. Gibson's commanding presence on the mound has not yet translated into unusually heavy demand for his cards. Although supplies are currently adequate for most of his years as a player, Gibson's cards are not as common as one might expect for a player from the period.

	NM	EX	VG
1959 Topps #514	425.00	175.00	75.00
1960 Topps #73	50.00	17.50	7.50
1961 Topps #211	42.50	15.00	6.00
1962 Topps #530	175.00	40.00	17.50
1963 Fleer #61	25.00	8.00	3.00
1963 Topps #415	27.50	10.00	3.50
1964 Topps #460	22.00	7.00	2.50
1965 Topps #320	22.00	7.00	2.50
1966 Topps #320	22.00	7.00	2.50
1967 Topps #210	15.00	6.50	2.00
1968 Topps #100	22.50	7.50	2.50
1968 Topps #378	7.50	2.50	1.25
1969 Topps #200	12.50	4.00	1.00
1970 Topps #530	10.00	2.75	0.95
1971 Topps #450	16.00	5.00	2.00
1972 Topps #130	4.50	1.50	0.75
1973 Topps #190	4.50	1.50	0.75
1974 Topps #350	2.50	1.00	0.35
1975 Topps #150	2.75	1.25	0.40

Josh Gibson

Elected HoF 1972 (Negro leagues).

	NM	EX	VG
No cards			

Warren Giles

In 1956 Topps decided to include a few baseball executives in their regular sets. Warren Giles was one of them, and as luck would have it he also made the Hall of Fame. If you like guys in suits, this card is for you. It also makes sense if you are determined to have a complete Hall of Fame set.

	NM	EX	VG
1956 Topps #2	12.50	2.50	1.00

Vernon Louis "Lefty" Gomez

Elected HoF 1972. One of the original characters of the game and a solid pitcher, too. Moderate demand and a smaller-than-average supply of cards should mean modest future price increases.

	NM	EX	VG
1933 Goudey #216	450.00	175.00	75.00
1934 Batter Up #23	235.00	85.00	35.00
1934 Batter Up #86	500.00	175.00	75.00
1936 Goudey	225.00	75.00	30.00
1939 Play Ball #48	225.00	80.00	30.00
1940 Play Ball #6	175.00	75.00	25.00
1941 Play Ball #72	750.00	250.00	100.00
1941 Double Play #61	225.00	100.00	40.00

Leon Allen "Goose" Goslin

Elected HoF 1968. Life is a happy medium for Goose Goslin cards. There aren't a lot of them, but there isn't overwhelming demand either. You won't get rich with Goose, but you have nothing to lose.

	NM	EX	VG
E120 American Caramel	85.00	35.00	15.00
E210 York Caramel	65.00	25.00	15.00
1933 Goudey #110	235.00	75.00	25.00
1933 Goudey #168	235.00	75.00	25.00
1934 Batter Up #85	375.00	125.00	50.00
1935 Goudey	85.00	35.00	15.00
George Miller	375.00	125.00	50.00
1940 Play Ball #232	140.00	50.00	20.00

Henry "Hank" Greenberg

Elected HoF 1956. Hank Greenberg, like Jimmie Foxx, was a power hitter who was overshadowed by Babe Ruth. His cards bring some premiums, but nothing like they might have brought out of the shadows of Ruth and Foxx.

	NM	EX	VG
Diamond Star #54	350.00	150.00	75.00
1934 Batter Up #57	275.00	125.00	50.00
1934 Goudey #62	400.00	150.00	75.00
1935 Goudey	135.00	40.00	20.00
1936 Goudey	225.00	80.00	35.00
1938 Goudey #253	435.00	175.00	75.00
1938 Goudey #277	450.00	175.00	75.00
1939 Play Ball #56	140.00	50.00	25.00
1940 Play Ball #40	235.00	85.00	35.00
1941 Play Ball #18	400.00	150.00	50.00
1941 Double Play #52	85.00	30.00	15.00
1941 Double Play #85	85.00	30.00	15.00

Clark Calvin Griffith

Elected HoF 1946 (manager). Clark Griffith cards are diverse, but they do not abound. Enough are available to take care of his limited following. Though his playing career spanned 20 years, he was elected to the Hall of Fame as a manager.

	NM	EX	VG
N172	600.00	250.00	100.00
T202 Hassan	475.00	175.00	75.00
T204 Ramly	1250.00	450.00	150.00
T205	575.00	150.00	65.00
T206 (batting)	475.00	100.00	35.00
T206 (portrait)	575.00	125.00	40.00
T213 Type 2	195.00	75.00	35.00
T213 Type 3	225.00	85.00	35.00
T214	1750.00	850.00	650.00
T215 Type 1	675.00	225.00	100.00
T215 Type 2	350.00	125.00	50.00
E93 Standard Caramel	450.00	150.00	50.00
D329 Weil Baking #72	250.00	100.00	35.00
M101-4 #72	85.00	35.00	15.00
M116	550.00	150.00	50.00
Turkey Red (T3) #19	950.00	300.00	125.00

Burleigh Arland Grimes

Elected HoF 1964. Burleigh Grimes made his living as a spitball pitcher back when it was legal. Even when it was outlawed, Old Stubblebeard was still allowed to throw the controversial pitch. Actually, that was just a technicality. Anyone who knew Burleigh also knew that he would have spit and fired anyway. It made for a long career, so he appears on a fair number of cards. (We just don't respect a good spitballer the way we used to.)

	NM	EX	VG
E120 American Caramel	90.00	35.00	15.00
E210 York Caramel #1	145.00	35.00	15.00
1933 Goudey #64	250.00	80.00	25.00
1935 Goudey (See Kiki Cuyler)			
Yuengling's Ice Cream	45.00	10.00	5.00

Robert Moses "Lefty" Grove

Elected HoF 1947. Lefty Grove cards are not rare. They are, however, expensive thanks to solid demand. Whether his premiums will continue to hold over the years remains to be seen.

	NM	EX	VG
Diamond Star #11	1450.00	375.00	150.00
George Miller	475.00	150.00	75.00
1933 Delong #23	535.00	175.00	75.00
1933 Goudey #220	650.00	175.00	100.00
1934 Batter Up #31	225.00	85.00	40.00
1934 Batter Up #153	575.00	200.00	100.00
1934 Goudey #19	450.00	150.00	85.00
1941 Double Play #105 (See Bobby Doerr)			

Charles "Chick" Hafey

Elected HoF 1971. Chick Hafey is just one of those guys good enough to make the Hall of Fame but not good enough to create excitement today. He didn't appear on many cards, but you could cut the number in half and have enough Hafey cards for current demand.

	NM	EX	VG
Diamond Star #18	130.00	45.00	20.00
George Miller	350.00	125.00	50.00
1933 Delong #19	275.00	125.00	50.00
1934 Batter Up #16	135.00	50.00	25.00
1934 Batter Up #163	135.00	50.00	25.00
1934 Goudey #34	215.00	80.00	30.00

Jesse Haines

Elected HoF 1970. Jesse Haines is only on a few cards. If he was Babe Ruth that would be a problem. As it is, the few are plenty — enough to make his cards slightly more difficult to find than many, but with such limited demand that supply is not a problem.

	NM	EX	VG
E120 American Caramel	85.00	35.00	15.00
E121 Set of 120	85.00	35.00	15.00
E210 York Caramel #30	75.00	30.00	15.00
1933 Goudey #73	225.00	80.00	30.00
1940 Play Ball #227	125.00	40.00	20.00

William Robert Hamilton

Elected HoF 1961. Billy Hamilton cards are tough to find. It's just that simple. A nice Billy Hamilton is going to cost you dearly. If you find one and can afford it, buy it, because you probably won't find another one.

	NM	EX	VG
N172	2750.00	1300.00	800.00
N173	3500.00	1500.00	1000.00

William Harridge

Harridge is in the Hall of Fame as an executive selected for his business service (see the explanation for Warren Giles). The difference with Harridge is not popularity but the fact that his is a No. 1 card, a condition rarity. Were it not for that he'd be about the same price as Giles.

	NM	EX	VG
1956 Topps #1	95.00	7.50	2.50

Stanley Raymond "Bucky" Harris

Elected HoF 1975 (manager). Though Harris played 12 years, he managed for 29 and is in the Hall of Fame as a manager. Bucky Harris has a diverse assortment of cards that will provide an ample supply for anyone seeking a single Harris and an interesting challenge for anyone wanting them all.

	NM	EX	VG
E120 American Caramel	55.00	20.00	10.00
E210 York Caramel #41	65.00	25.00	10.00

	NM	EX	VG
E220 National Caramel	125.00	40.00	20.00
Yuengling's Ice Cream #41	35.00	15.00	10.00
Diamond Star #91	160.00	60.00	25.00
1936 Goudey	110.00	35.00	10.00
1940 Play Ball #129	95.00	35.00	10.00
1951 Bowman #275	65.00	25.00	10.00
1952 Bowman #158	35.00	12.50	5.00
1953 Bowman (black & white)	50.00	17.50	7.50

Charles "Gabby" Hartnett

Elected HoF 1955. Gabby Hartnett is not on a lot of cards, but for an average 1930s Hall of Famer, it's enough to satisfy demand.

	NM	EX	VG
E120 American Caramel	125.00	45.00	20.00
E210 York Caramel #5	65.00	30.00	15.00
Yuengling's Ice Cream #5	35.00	15.00	10.00
1933 Goudey #202	225.00	85.00	30.00
1934 Batter Up #136	325.00	125.00	50.00

Harry Edwin Heilmann

Elected HoF 1952. Harry Heilmann cards are not abundant. He was a top batter, so fortunately the cards that are available tend to be common.

	NM	EX	VG
E120 American Caramel	95.00	35.00	15.00
E121 Set of 120	125.00	45.00	20.00
E122 American Caramel	125.00	45.00	20.00
E210 York Caramel#22	65.00	30.00	15.00
E220 National Caramel	125.00	40.00	20.00

William Jennings Bryan Herman

Elected HoF 1975. Among the players of the 1930s and 1940s, Billy Herman is one of the least difficult cards to acquire. That's because his association with baseball continued into the 1950s, and that landed him on a variety of Topps cards. His cards are very affordable, given his caliber of player.

	NM	EX	VG
1933 Goudey #227	225.00	85.00	30.00
1934 Batter Up #138	325.00	125.00	35.00
1941 Double Play #3	55.00	20.00	10.00

1952 Topps #394	225.00	75.00	30.00
1954 Topps #86	35.00	15.00	5.00
1955 Topps Doubleheaders #53	27.50	10.00	3.50
1955 Topps #19	15.00	5.00	1.75
1960 Topps #456	3.50	1.25	0.50
1965 Topps #251	1.75	0.75	0.25
1966 Topps #37	3.50	1.25	0.35

Harry Bartholomew Hooper

Elected HoF 1971. Hooper was an extraordinary defensive outfielder in the early teens, but he was overshadowed by such teammates as Tris Speaker and even a non-Hall of Famer, Joe Wood.

	NM	EX	VG
T207	750.00	200.00	85.00
E91 American Caramel Set C	150.00	50.00	25.00
E120 American Caramel	85.00	35.00	20.00
E121 Set of 80	75.00	30.00	15.00
E121 Set of 120	75.00	30.00	15.00
E220 National Caramel	135.00	45.00	20.00
E254 Colgan's Chips	100.00	35.00	15.00
E270	100.00	35.00	15.00
D329 Weil Baking #84	250.00	100.00	40.00
1914 Cracker Jack #35	1650.00	175.00	75.00
1915 Cracker Jack #35	575.00	175.00	75.00
M101-4	65.00	30.00	15.00
M101-5 #83	65.00	30.00	15.00
M101-6 #40	65.00	30.00	15.00
M116	750.00	250.00	100.00
1940 Play Ball #226	125.00	45.00	20.00

Rogers Hornsby

Elected HoF 1942. One of the greatest hitters of all time, "The Rajah" also has one of the greatest selections of cards. That's important, because if the selection wasn't plentiful, his would be among the most expensive cards.

	NM	EX	VG
E120 American Caramel	225.00	85.00	35.00
E121 American Caramel Set of 120 #47	175.00	75.00	30.00
E121 American Caramel Set of 80 #45	175.00	75.00	30.00
E122 American Caramel	175.00	75.00	30.00

E220 National Caramel	175.00	75.00	30.00
Diamond Star #44	375.00	150.00	75.00
1933 Tatoo Orbit	225.00	75.00	30.00
Yuengling's Ice Cream #13	100.00	30.00	20.00
1933 Goudey #119	625.00	225.00	100.00
1933 Goudey #188	625.00	225.00	100.00
1934 Batter Up #35	375.00	150.00	75.00

Waite Charles "Schoolboy" Hoyt

Elected HoF 1969. Hoyt spent his life in baseball winning games and talking about Babe Ruth. He was bright, articulate, and featured on plenty of cards. Prices are likely to move with the general market.

	NM	EX	VG
E120 American Caramel	85.00	35.00	20.00
E220 National Caramel	85.00	35.00	20.00
Yuengling's Ice Cream	35.00	15.00	10.00
1933 Goudey #60	225.00	80.00	30.00
1935 Goudey	175.00	65.00	25.00
1940 Play Ball #118	95.00	35.00	20.00

Cal Hubbard

Cal is another of the umpires pictured by Bowman in 1955 who made the Hall of Fame. That means solid demand for this, his only card.

	NM	EX	VG
1955 Bowman #315	90.00	45.00	20.00

Carl Owen Hubbell

Elected HoF 1947. The 1930s are not remembered for great pitchers. Carl Hubbell is one of the few exceptions, along with Dizzy Dean. Hubbell is in great demand, and that means higher-than-usual prices for his cards.

	NM	EX	VG
Diamond Star #39	175.00	75.00	35.00
Sport Kings #42	475.00	200.00	75.00
1933 Goudey #230	425.00	175.00	85.00
1933 Goudey #234	425.00	175.00	85.00
1934 Batter Up #5	250.00	100.00	45.00
1934 Goudey #12	325.00	125.00	50.00

1939 Play Ball #53	250.00	100.00	40.00
1940 Play Ball #87	250.00	100.00	40.00
1941 Double Play #140	125.00	59.00	25.00
1941 Goudey #20	200.00	80.00	35.00
1941 Play Ball #6	325.00	125.00	50.00

Miller James Huggins

Elected HoF 1964 (manager). An average player for 13 years, Huggins managed for 17, most notably with the Yankees of the 1920s. Miller Huggins appeared on a lot of cards in the tobacco era. He lacks the popularity of Cobb or Speaker, which leaves him with fairly low prices and prospects.

	NM	EX	VG
T201 Mecca (See Roger Bresnahan)			
T202 Hassan	450.00	150.00	75.00
T204 Ramly	1550.00	350.00	125.00
T205	500.00	150.00	75.00
T206 (hands to mouth)	425.00	150.00	50.00
T206 (portrait)	475.00	175.00	60.00
T213 Type 1	325.00	125.00	50.00
T213 Type 2	225.00	85.00	35.00
T213 Type 3	325.00	125.00	50.00
T215 Type 1	725.00	200.00	100.00
T215 Type 2	400.00	125.00	75.00
T222 Fatima	500.00	150.00	60.00
E121 Set of 80	75.00	35.00	15.00
E121 Set of 120	75.00	35.00	15.00
E270	100.00	30.00	10.00
E300 Plow's Candy	775.00	250.00	100.00
D329 Weil Baking #86	225.00	100.00	50.00
1914 Cracker Jack #75	1450.00	175.00	80.00
1915 Cracker Jack #75	475.00	175.00	80.00
M101-4	75.00	25.00	15.00
M101-5	75.00	25.00	15.00
M116	550.00	200.00	85.00

James Augustus "Catfish" Hunter

Elected HoF 1987. It's hard to be gifted with a more memorable nickname than "Catfish" (see "Three Finger" Brown), and it doesn't hurt card prices one bit. Nor does years of winning on both coasts. Hunter's cards are solid and likely to remain that way.

	NM	EX	VG
1965 Topps #526 .... 155.00	155.00	50.00	20.00
1966 Topps #36 .... 33.00	33.00	10.00	4.00
1967 Topps #369 .... 19.00	19.00	5.00	2.00
1968 Topps #385 .... 12.50	12.50	3.50	1.00
1969 Topps #235 .... 12.00	12.00	3.25	1.00
1970 Topps #565 .... 12.00	12.00	3.25	1.00
1971 Topps #45 .... 7.50	7.50	2.50	0.75
1972 Topps #330 .... 4.00	4.00	1.00	0.25
1973 Topps #235 .... 4.00	4.00	1.00	0.25
1974 Topps #7 .... 4.00	4.00	1.00	0.25
1975 Topps #230 .... 3.00	3.00	0.50	0.15
1976 Topps #100 .... 2.75	2.75	0.40	0.15
1977 Topps #280 .... 2.25	2.25	0.35	0.10
1978 Topps #460 .... 2.00	2.00	0.30	0.10
1979 Topps #670 .... 1.00	1.00	0.25	0.10

Monford "Monte" Irvin

Elected HoF 1973. Cards of Monte Irvin should continue to appreciate over the years. Irvin spent the prime years of his career in the Negro leagues, for which there are no cards. It was 1951 before he appeared on a card, and by then there were only five years left in his career. By the standards of the 1950s Irvin is a somewhat difficult card to find.

	NM	EX	VG
1951 Bowman #198 .... 125.00	125.00	55.00	30.00
1952 Bowman #162 .... 55.00	55.00	25.00	15.00
1952 Topps #26 .... 95.00	95.00	50.00	25.00
1953 Bowman #51 .... 50.00	50.00	20.00	10.00
1953 Topps #62 .... 50.00	50.00	25.00	10.00
1954 Topps #3 .... 40.00	40.00	15.00	5.00
1955 Topps #100 .... 30.00	30.00	15.00	5.00
1956 Topps #194 .... 25.00	25.00	10.00	5.00

Reginald "Reggie" Jackson

Elected HoF 1993. One of the dominant names of the 1970s, "Mr. October" was the guiding force behind championship teams in Oakland and New York, and that gave him a huge national following. The demand for Jackson cards is important, as supplies for all but his earliest cards are equally large. All Reggie Jackson cards not listed are 50¢ or less in Near Mint condition.

	NM	EX	VG
1969 Topps #260	675.00	300.00	125.00
1970 Topps #140	165.00	75.00	35.00
1970 Topps #459	25.00	10.00	3.00
1971 Topps #20	125.00	40.00	15.00
1972 Topps #435	44.00	20.00	7.50
1972 Topps #436	25.00	10.00	3.00
1973 Topps #255	40.00	15.00	7.50
1974 Topps #130	25.00	10.00	5.00
1975 Topps #300	27.50	10.00	5.00
1976 Topps #500	20.00	7.50	3.00
1977 Topps #10	12.50	5.00	2.50
1978 Topps #200	10.00	3.50	1.00
1979 Topps #700	5.00	1.50	0.40
1980 Topps #600	7.50	2.50	0.75
1981 Donruss #228	2.25	0.50	0.25
1981 Donruss #348	2.25	0.50	0.25
1981 Donruss #468	3.00	0.75	0.35
1981 Fleer #650	2.50	0.60	0.30
1981 Topps #400	3.00	0.75	0.35
1982 Donruss #535	2.50	0.50	0.25
1982 Fleer #39	2.25	0.50	0.25
1982 Topps #300	2.50	0.50	0.25
1982 Topps #301	1.25	0.30	0.10
1982 Topps #551	0.50	0.10	0.05
1982 Topps Traded #47	11.00	3.50	1.00
1983 Donruss #115	1.50	0.25	0.10
1983 Fleer #93	1.50	0.25	0.10
1983 Topps #500	1.50	0.25	0.10
1984 Donruss #57	6.50	2.00	0.50
1984 Fleer #520	1.75	0.25	0.10
1984 Topps #100	1.50	0.25	0.10
1985 Donruss #57	1.00	0.15	0.05
1985 Fleer #303	0.75	0.10	0.05
1985 Topps #200	1.00	0.15	0.05

Travis Calvin "Stonewall" Jackson

Elected HoF 1982. Travis Jackson is definitely not on the high-demand list. That is countered to some degree by the fact that Jackson was somewhat overlooked by the card makers of his day, so supplies are modest at best.

	NM	EX	VG
Diamond Star #63	135.00	50.00	20.00
1933 Goudey #102	225.00	85.00	30.00
1934 Batter Up #180	325.00	125.00	50.00
1935 Goudey	165.00	75.00	30.00
1940 Play Ball #158	95.00	35.00	15.00

Ferguson Arthur Jenkins

Elected HoF 1991. Fergie has always been a popular Cubs pitcher. He's not a marquee name, yet his cards are somewhat more difficult to get than other stars of the 1970s and 1980s. He retired just prior to huge increases in card production. Cards not listed here are worth 25¢ or less in Near Mint condition.

	NM	EX	VG
1966 Topps #254	135.00	45.00	30.00
1967 Topps #333	30.00	10.00	5.00
1968 Topps #410	25.00	7.50	3.50
1969 Topps #640	22.50	7.00	2.50
1970 Topps #240	12.50	5.00	2.50
1971 Topps #280	17.50	5.00	2.50
1972 Topps #410	6.00	1.75	0.75
1973 Topps #180	4.50	1.25	0.50
1974 Topps #87	3.75	1.00	0.40
1975 Topps #60	3.25	0.85	0.35
1976 Topps #250	2.25	0.75	0.25
1977 Topps #430	2.30	0.95	0.40
1978 Topps #720	2.00	0.75	0.25
1979 Topps #544	1.65	0.60	0.20
1980 Topps #390	1.40	0.55	0.15
1981 Donruss #146	0.55	0.15	0.05
1981 Fleer #622	0.55	0.15	0.05
1981 Topps #158	1.10	0.20	0.05
1982 Topps Traded #49	2.25	0.40	0.25
1984 Donruss #189	1.00	0.20	0.05
1984 Fleer #494	0.75	0.10	0.05

Hugh Ambrose Jennings

Elected HoF 1945. There aren't many men like Hugh Jennings. Ty Cobb, Walter Johnson, and just a few others appear with such regularity in cards of the tobacco era. Moreover, he made it onto almost all the candy cards as well. In fact, he could have been the poster child for card collecting in 1912. The good news is that unless you want to be the only one in the hemisphere with a complete Hugh Jennings collection, his cards are comparatively cheap.

	NM	EX	VG
T201 Mecca	225.00	75.00	25.00
T202 Hassan with Cobb (See Ty Cobb)			
T202 Hassan with McGraw	575.00	225.00	100.00
T205	750.00	225.00	75.00
T206 (portrait)	525.00	150.00	75.00
T206 (all others)	425.00	100.00	50.00
T213 Type 2	200.00	100.00	50.00
T213 Type 3	275.00	125.00	75.00
T215 Type 1	675.00	200.00	100.00
T215 Type 2	350.00	100.00	50.00
T216	275.00	125.00	50.00
T222 Fatima	450.00	125.00	50.00
E90-1 American Caramel	475.00	125.00	50.00
E92 Croft's Candy	375.00	100.00	40.00
E92 Croft's Cocoa	375.00	100.00	40.00
E92 Dockman	325.00	75.00	35.00
E93 Standard Caramel	475.00	150.00	60.00
E94	425.00	100.00	50.00
E96	425.00	100.00	50.00
E98	550.00	200.00	85.00
E101	475.00	150.00	60.00
E103 Williams Caramel	650.00	225.00	90.00
E104 Nadja	450.00	125.00	55.00
E105 Mello-Mint	350.00	85.00	35.00
E106 American Caramel	400.00	135.00	50.00
E121 Set of 80	75.00	30.00	15.00
E254 Colgan's Chips	100.00	35.00	15.00
E270	100.00	35.00	15.00
D303 General Baking	225.00	100.00	35.00
D329 Weil Baking #90	325.00	125.00	50.00
1914 Cracker Jack #77	1450.00	150.00	50.00
1915 Cracker Jack #77	450.00	150.00	50.00
M101-5 #88	70.00	30.00	15.00
M116 (blue background)	750.00	225.00	100.00
M116 (pastel background)	500.00	150.00	75.00
Turkey Red (T3)	1000.00	350.00	100.00
1940 Play Ball #223	125.00	50.00	25.00

Judy Johnson

Elected HoF 1975 (Negro leagues).

	NM	EX	VG
No cards			

Walter Perry Johnson

Elected HoF 1936. With the exception of Ty Cobb, Walter Johnson is the key to the tobacco era. He was the standard by which pitchers were measured and his popularity remains unchanged to the present day. His cards will cost you, but legends never come cheap.

	NM	EX	VG
T201 Mecca	700.00	250.00	100.00
T202 Hassan	825.00	275.00	125.00
T204 Ramly	5500.00	1500.00	650.00
T205	3250.00	850.00	275.00
T206 (portrait)	1750.00	650.00	200.00
T206 (ready to pitch)	1100.00	450.00	175.00
T207	1900.00	650.00	200.00
T213 Type 2	1250.00	450.00	200.00
T213 Type 3	1100.00	400.00	175.00
T214	4000.00	1900.00	1000.00
T215 Type 1	1100.00	400.00	175.00
T215 Type 2	1100.00	400.00	175.00
T222 Fatima	750.00	225.00	100.00
E91 American Caramel Set C	475.00	150.00	60.00
E120 American Caramel	450.00	175.00	75.00
E121 American Caramel Set of 80	300.00	100.00	50.00
E121 American Caramel Set of 120	350.00	125.00	75.00
E122 American Caramel	325.00	100.00	50.00
E210 York Caramel #45	225.00	75.00	35.00
E224 Texas Tommy	4000.00	1000.00	450.00
E300 Plow's Candy	1800.00	750.00	250.00
D329 Weil Baking #91	450.00	125.00	75.00
1914 Cracker Jack #57	4500.00	1000.00	400.00
1915 Cracker Jack #57	2250.00	1000.00	400.00
M101-4 #91	425.00	150.00	75.00
M101-5 #90	450.00	150.00	75.00
M101-6 #44	550.00	200.00	75.00
M116	1750.00	650.00	275.00

Turkey Red (T3) #99	4500.00	1500.00	750.00
1940 Play Ball #120	300.00	100.00	50.00

Adrian "Addie" Joss

Elected HoF 1978. His tragic death meant a short career, so Addie Joss does not appear on many cards. Fortunately, the few he does appear on are fairly common, so prices are not out of line with the cards of other players from the era.

	NM	EX	VG
T205	850.00	250.00	100.00
T206 (hands at chest)	525.00	100.00	50.00
T206 (portrait)	625.00	200.00	75.00
E90-1 American Caramel (pitching)	1800.00	650.00	275.00
E90-1 American Caramel (portrait)	575.00	125.00	50.00
E93 Standard Caramel	475.00	150.00	60.00
E107 Breisch Williams	550.00	200.00	100.00
E254 Colgan's Chips	100.00	35.00	15.00
M116	625.00	250.00	100.00
Turkey Red (T3) #19	950.00	350.00	125.00

Albert Kaline

Elected HoF 1980. Al Kaline remains popular today as one of the great players of the 1950s. He's not quite in the Mantle class, but he's right up there with Ernie Banks, Hank Aaron, and Yogi Berra.

	NM	EX	VG
1954 Topps #201	850.00	250.00	100.00
1955 Bowman #23	135.00	45.00	20.00
1955 Topps #4	210.00	75.00	25.00
1956 Topps #20	115.00	35.00	15.00
1957 Topps #125	85.00	30.00	12.00
1958 Topps #70	85.00	30.00	12.00
1959 Topps #360	55.00	17.50	6.00
1960 Topps #50	45.00	15.00	5.00
1960 Topps #561	42.00	12.00	4.00
1961 Topps #429	48.00	15.00	5.00
1961 Topps #580	85.00	30.00	10.00
1962 Topps #150	37.50	11.00	4.00
1962 Topps #470	17.50	6.00	2.50
1963 Topps #25	32.50	10.00	3.50

1964 Topps #250	27.50	10.00	3.50
1965 Topps #130	23.00	8.00	2.50
1966 Topps #410	24.00	8.00	2.50
1967 Topps #30	22.00	7.50	2.00
1968 Topps #240	20.00	6.00	1.50
1969 Topps #410	17.50	5.00	1.25
1970 Topps #640	55.00	15.00	5.00
1971 Topps #180	25.00	5.00	1.25
1972 Topps #600	15.00	3.50	1.00
1973 Topps #280	6.00	1.50	0.50
1974 Topps #215	5.50	1.25	0.50
1975 Topps #4	1.50	0.50	0.15

Timothy John Keefe

Elected HoF 1964. Like Cap Anson and King Kelly, Tim Keefe appears on a reasonable number of cards from the pre-1900 era. He's not cheap, but he's available.

	NM	EX	VG
N28	950.00	350.00	200.00
N162	1500.00	650.00	200.00
N172	750.00	250.00	100.00
N173	2250.00	1000.00	500.00
N284 Buchner Gold Coin	275.00	125.00	75.00
N690 Kalamazoo Bats	2300.00	1000.00	500.00
E223 G&B Chewing Gum	1500.00	550.00	250.00

William Henry "Wee Willie" Keeler

Elected HoF 1939. As you might imagine from his nickname, Wee Willie Keeler was not a long-ball hitter. But how can anyone fail to take notice of Wee Willie? In fact, no one did fail to notice him — and Keeler still has a decent following today. Moreover, there aren't too many cards, so the prospects are good if you're looking for an investment.

	NM	EX	VG
T204 Ramly	1950.00	750.00	300.00
T206 (batting)	750.00	250.00	100.00
T206 (portrait)	800.00	275.00	125.00
E90-1 (horizontal, throwing)	2250.00	900.00	500.00
E90-1 (portrait, pink background)	600.00	175.00	75.00
E90-1 (portrait, red background)	1450.00	500.00	200.00
E97 Briggs	850.00	350.00	150.00

	NM	EX	VG
E254 Colgan's Chips	100.00	35.00	15.00
E270	100.00	35.00	15.00
Turkey Red (T3) #101	900.00	350.00	150.00
1940 Play Ball #237	200.00	85.00	35.00

George Clyde Kell

Elected HoF 1983. George Kell is one of the lesser known players of the 1950s. He also had relatively few cards so there is a balance of sorts between supply and demand.

	NM	EX	VG
1948 Leaf #120	500.00	175.00	75.00
1949 Bowman #26	50.00	20.00	10.00
1950 Bowman #8	75.00	30.00	10.00
1951 Bowman #46	70.00	25.00	10.00
1952 Bowman #75	45.00	15.00	7.50
1952 Topps #246	55.00	20.00	10.00
1953 Bowman #61	35.00	15.00	7.50
1953 Topps #138	75.00	25.00	10.00
1954 Bowman #50	20.00	10.00	5.00
1955 Bowman #213	20.00	10.00	5.00
1956 Topps #195	35.00	15.00	5.00
1957 Topps #230	20.00	7.50	3.00
1958 Topps #40	12.50	5.00	1.75

Joseph Kelley

Elected HoF 1971. Joe Kelley came very close to being a key card in a Hall of Fame set. After all, he only has two, and were it not for the confusion as to which Kelley is which, he'd probably be a lot more expensive even, though one of his cards is a T206.

	NM	EX	VG
T206	450.00	150.00	50.00
E107 Breisch Williams	650.00	250.00	100.00

George Kelly

Elected HoF 1973. George Kelly is a little more available than Joe, but not much. If Hall of Fame collecting ever gains more popularity, starting with Kelley and Kelly is a good idea.

	NM	EX	VG
E120 American Caramel	85.00	35.00	15.00
E121 American Caramel Set of 120	90.00	40.00	20.00
E121 American Caramel Set of 80	75.00	35.00	15.00
E210 York Caramel #20	65.00	25.00	10.00
E220 National Caramel	125.00	50.00	20.00
Yuengling's Ice Cream #20	35.00	15.00	7.50
1940 Play Ball #142	90.00	35.00	15.00

Michael Joseph "King" Kelly

Elected HoF 1945. King Kelly ranks right up there with Cap Anson as a dominant name of the pre-1900 era. That means more-than-average numbers of cards and higher-than-average prices.

	NM	EX	VG
N28	1900.00	750.00	350.00
N162	4000.00	1500.00	500.00
N172	850.00	350.00	150.00
N173	3750.00	1500.00	1000.00
N284 Buchner Gold Coin	300.00	100.00	50.00
N403 Yum Yum (photo)	6500.00	1500.00	800.00
N526 Diamond S Cigars	1000.00	350.00	150.00
E223 G&B Chewing Gum (batting)	1250.00	500.00	250.00
E223 G&B Chewing Gum (standing by urn)	2800.00	1350.00	750.00

Harmon Clayton "Killer" Killebrew

Elected HoF 1984. Harmon Killebrew is extremely popular despite never playing in a media center. It would be unrealistic to expect his cards to rival those of Mantle and Mays, but they should hold their own for the short term.

	NM	EX	VG
1955 Topps #124	400.00	135.00	40.00
1956 Topps #164	130.00	35.00	15.00
1958 Topps #288	75.00	25.00	10.00
1959 Topps #515	135.00	40.00	15.00
1960 Topps #210	27.50	10.00	3.50
1961 Topps #80	23.00	8.00	3.00
1962 Topps #70	22.50	8.00	3.00
1963 Topps #500	120.00	35.00	12.50
1964 Topps #177	25.00	8.00	2.50

1965 Topps #400	28.00	9.00	3.00
1966 Topps #120	17.50	6.00	2.00
1967 Topps #460	48.00	15.00	5.00
1968 Topps #220	16.00	5.00	1.75
1968 Topps #361	5.50	1.50	0.50
1969 Topps #375	17.50	6.00	2.00
1970 Topps #150	8.50	2.50	1.00
1971 Topps #550	28.00	5.00	1.25
1972 Topps #51	5.25	1.50	0.50
1972 Topps #52	2.50	1.00	0.35
1973 Topps #170	5.25	1.50	0.50
1974 Topps #400	4.50	1.25	0.35
1975 Topps #640	5.50	1.50	0.50

Ralph McPherran Kiner

Elected HoF 1975. The power-hitting Kiner's cards are among the most difficult of all players from his era to find. His career was relatively short. The demand for his cards doesn't equal that of Mantle's, but the short supply should keep prices rising.

	NM	EX	VG
1948 Bowman #3	165.00	75.00	35.00
1948 Leaf #91	165.00	75.00	35.00
1949 Bowman #29	85.00	35.00	15.00
1950 Bowman #33	100.00	40.00	20.00
1952 Bowman #11	65.00	25.00	10.00
1953 Bowman #80	75.00	25.00	10.00
1953 Topps #191	70.00	25.00	10.00
1954 Bowman #45	45.00	15.00	7.50
1955 Bowman #197	25.00	7.50	5.00

Charles Herbert "Chuck" Klein

Elected HoF 1980. Chuck Klein isn't on a lot of cards, but it is enough to meet the current modest demand. His cards have slightly below-average prospects for Hall of Famers.

	NM	EX	VG
George Miller 375.00	150.00	65.00	
1933 Delong #22	325.00	125.00	50.00
1933 Goudey #128	250.00	85.00	35.00
1934 Batter-Up #185	325.00	125.00	50.00

1934 Goudey #10	225.00	85.00	35.00
1935 Goudey (see Kiki Cuyler)			
1936 Goudey	135.00	50.00	20.00
1939 Play Ball #82	155.00	65.00	25.00
1940 Play Ball #102	125.00	50.00	20.00
1941 Play Ball #60	325.00	125.00	50.00

Sanford "Sandy" Koufax

Elected HoF 1972. Sandy Koufax ranks among the most popular pitchers of the modern era. His card prices are boosted by his brief career. Sandy's cards are definitely blue chips in the card market.

	NM	EX	VG
1955 Topps #123	1200.00	400.00	150.00
1956 Topps #79	400.00	150.00	50.00
1957 Topps #302	425.00	175.00	75.00
1958 Topps #187	135.00	50.00	20.00
1959 Topps #163	155.00	60.00	25.00
1960 Topps #343	100.00	40.00	15.00
1961 Topps #344	90.00	35.00	12.00
1962 Topps #5	115.00	45.00	17.00
1963 Fleer #42	120.00	45.00	20.00
1963 Topps #210	155.00	60.00	25.00
1964 Topps #200	100.00	40.00	15.00
1965 Topps #300	130.00	55.00	20.00
1966 Topps #100	100.00	40.00	15.00

Napoleon "Nap" Lajoie

Elected HoF 1937. Nap Lajoie has one of the most famous of all cards: the controversial 1933 Goudey that was withheld just to keep kids buying gum to try to complete their sets. The following year it was available by mail but almost no one knew about it. Today, it's an easy five-figure card. Other Lajoie cards haven't suffered either. Despite a lot of cards there is plenty of demand and higher-than-average prices.

	NM	EX	VG
T201 Mecca	450.00	175.00	85.00
T206 (batting)	650.00	200.00	85.00
T206 (portrait)	750.00	250.00	100.00
T206 (throwing)	650.00	200.00	85.00
T213 Type 2	350.00	150.00	70.00
T213 Type 3	350.00	150.00	70.00

T214	3500.00	1500.00	1000.00
T215 Type 1	850.00	300.00	125.00
T215 Type 2	350.00	150.00	70.00
T216	500.00	200.00	100.00
E90-1 American Caramel	850.00	225.00	75.00
E92 Croft's Candy	750.00	200.00	70.00
E92 Croft's Cocoa	750.00	200.00	70.00
E92 Dockman	550.00	125.00	50.00
E93 Standard Caramel	900.00	325.00	125.00
E94	950.00	335.00	125.00
E96 Philadelphia Caramel	950.00	325.00	125.00
E98	950.00	325.00	125.00
E101	950.00	325.00	125.00
E102	1100.00	400.00	150.00
E103 Williams Caramel	1600.00	500.00	200.00
E105 Mello-Mint	750.00	200.00	70.00
E106 American Caramel	950.00	325.00	125.00
E107 Breisch Williams	850.00	225.00	75.00
E254 Colgan's Chips	300.00	100.00	50.00
E270	175.00	75.00	35.00
E300 Plow's Candy	400.00	150.00	65.00
D303 General Baking	425.00	125.00	75.00
D304 General Baking	325.00	90.00	45.00
D329 Weil Baking #97	325.00	90.00	45.00
1914 Cracker Jack #66	4750.00	1750.00	850.00
1915 Cracker Jack #66	1900.00	850.00	375.00
M101-4 #97	175.00	75.00	35.00
M101-5 #95	200.00	85.00	40.00
M116 (blue background)	1575.00	650.00	225.00
M116 (pastel background)	935.00	375.00	125.00
Turkey Red (T3) #23	2550.00	1100.00	500.00
1933 Goudey #106	45000.00	15000.00	6500.00
1940 Play Ball #173	300.00	125.00	65.00

Anthony Lazzeri

Elected HoF 1991. Tony Lazzeri is another member of the long line of Yankee dynasty products to find his way to the walls of Cooperstown. He's not in the Ruth or Gehrig class, but he's still a Yankee and that means there's always demand.

	NM	EX	VG
Diamond Star #74	150.00	55.00	25.00
Yuengling's Ice Cream	35.00	15.00	10.00

1933 Goudey #31	175.00	75.00	30.00
1934 Batter-Up #45	135.00	55.00	25.00
1935 Goudey (see Bill Dickey)			
1940 Play Ball #238	115.00	45.00	20.00

Robert Granville Lemon

Elected HoF 1976. Bob Lemon cards bring good prices for cards prior to 1960. The prices for his cards after 1960 are very reasonable. It's hard to figure trends when they seem to point in opposite directions. The best guess is that his pre-1960s card prices may be at or near their peaks. (All other Lemon cards not listed are priced under $1.00 in Near Mint condition.)

	NM	EX	VG
1949 Bowman #238	250.00	100.00	35.00
1950 Bowman #40	115.00	40.00	15.00
1951 Bowman #53	45.00	17.50	7.50
1952 Bowman #23	60.00	20.00	8.00
1952 Topps #268	185.00	65.00	22.00
1953 Bowman (black and white) #27	120.00	40.00	15.00
1954 Bowman #196	37.50	13.00	4.50
1955 Bowman #191	24.00	7.50	2.50
1956 Topps #255	30.00	10.00	2.00
1957 Topps #120	17.50	5.00	1.50
1958 Topps #2	28.00	6.50	2.00
1960 Topps #460	3.75	1.25	0.30
1971 Topps #91	2.50	0.75	0.20
1972 Topps #449	1.25	0.35	0.15
1977 Topps #418	1.00	0.30	0.10

Buck Leonard

Elected HoF 1972 (Negro leagues).

	NM	EX	VG
No cards			

Frederick Charles "Lindy" Lindstrom

Elected HoF 1976. If there was any demand at all for Fred Lindstrom, his prices would soar. As it is, that's not likely, although he remains a fairly tough card to find.

	NM	EX	VG
1933 Delong #11	225.00	100.00	35.00
1933 Goudey #133	225.00	100.00	35.00
1934 Batter Up #122	325.00	125.00	50.00

John Henry Lloyd

Elected HoF 1977 (Negro leagues).

	NM	EX	VG
No cards			

Ernesto Lombardi

Elected HoF 1986. Ernie Lombardi had one of those faces — not exactly pretty, but memorable. He's not well known, but he's a Hall of Famer who is fun to have around. With a decent number of cards it's possible to get one at a modest price. You won't get rich off Lombardi, but money isn't everything.

	NM	EX	VG
Diamond Star #36	225.00	85.00	35.00
Diamond Star #105	475.00	175.00	75.00
1933 Tatoo Orbit	65.00	25.00	10.00
1934 Batter Up #129	325.00	125.00	50.00
1934 Goudey #35	225.00	100.00	35.00
1938 Goudey #246	200.00	85.00	35.00
1938 Goudey #270	250.00	100.00	40.00
1941 Double Play #12	55.00	25.00	10.00

Alfonso Lopez

Elected HoF 1977 (manager). Al Lopez can be a little confusing. He has cards as a player, but he also has quite a few as a manager. It's an ideal situation, since his cards are inexpensive and he's a Hall of Famer from the 1930s. The only problem with Lopez cards is that with the diversity there's little upward price potential at present.

	NM	EX	VG
Diamond Star #28	250.00	100.00	35.00
Diamond Star #97	450.00	175.00	80.00
1934 Batter Up #3	175.00	75.00	30.00
1938 Goudey #257	175.00	75.00	35.00
1938 Goudey #281	225.00	85.00	40.00

1951 Bowman #295 .... 100.00	35.00	15.00
1953 Bowman #143 .... 70.00	25.00	10.00
1955 Bowman $308 .... 45.00	20.00	7.50
1960 Topps #222 .... 6.50	2.00	0.75
1961 Topps #132 .... 5.50	1.75	0.50
1962 Topps #286 .... 4.75	1.50	0.50
1963 Topps #458 .... 12.50	3.50	1.25
1964 Topps #232 .... 2.75	1.00	0.35
1965 Topps #414 .... 1.75	0.60	0.25
1969 Topps #527 .... 0.80	0.30	0.15

Theodore Amar "Ted" Lyons

Elected HoF 1955. Poor Ted Lyons. A great man, he labored for years on a White Sox team that aspired to such lofty goals as next-to-last place. He made the Hall of Fame, but losing doesn't make you famous (the 1962 Mets being one exception). Consequently, despite relatively few cards, the Ted Lyons demand just isn't there to produce significant price increases. He certainly deserves better, however.

	NM	EX	VG
Diamond Star #43 .... 125.00		45.00	20.00
1933 Goudey #7 .... 325.00		125.00	35.00
1933 Tatoo Orbit 75.00		30.00	15.00
1934 Batter Up #36 .... 200.00		85.00	35.00
1934 Batter Up #111 .... 425.00		150.00	50.00
1934 Batter Up #119 .... 285.00		125.00	50.00
1935 Goudey 110.00		35.00	20.00

Cornelius "Connie" Mack

Elected HoF 1937 (manager). Let's face it, Connie Mack should have been in every baseball set from the time the game was invented. When you talk about baseball being someone's life, the standard is Mack and no one else comes close. His career spanned eight years as a player, three as player-manager, and 50 (!) as manager of the Philadelphia Athletics. Despite more years in baseball than most people live, Mack is not on a lot of cards. There are enough to keep prices reasonable, but most of them are not common, and that keeps the pressure on prices.

	NM	EX	VG
N172 .... 1750.00		900.00	500.00
N173 .... 5500.00		2500.00	1000.00
T208 Fireside 2500.00		1100.00	500.00

E96 Philadelphia Caramel	1000.00	350.00	150.00
E98	1050.00	375.00	150.00
E104 Nadja	450.00	165.00	75.00
E223 G&B Chewing Gum	3000.00	1250.00	750.00
E224 Texas Tommy	1150.00	450.00	175.00
1914 Cracker Jack #12	1750.00	300.00	100.00
1915 Cracker Jack #12	750.00	300.00	100.00
M101-4 #107	100.00	35.00	20.00
M101-5 #105	165.00	65.00	30.00
M116	975.00	325.00	125.00
1933 Tatoo Orbit	110.00	35.00	20.00
1940 Play Ball #132	215.00	85.00	35.00

Mickey Charles Mantle

Elected HoF 1974. You don't really price Mantle cards, you make educated guesses — due, of course, to the extremely volatile nature of the Mantle market. As fast as you can read, a Mantle card can change direction dramatically. Learn all you can about the market before buying or selling Mantle.

	NM	EX	VG
1951 Bowman #253	14000.00	3000.00	1000.00
1952 Bowman #101	2300.00	750.00	350.00
1952 Topps #311	35000.00	12000.00	3500.00
1953 Bowman #59	2100.00	700.00	300.00
1953 Topps #82	2750.00	1200.00	450.00
1954 Bowman #65	825.00	325.00	150.00
1955 Bowman #202	425.00	165.00	75.00
1956 Topps #135	875.00	350.00	125.00
1957 Topps #95	825.00	325.00	150.00
1958 Topps	100.00	30.00	10.00
1958 Topps #150	550.00	200.00	85.00
1959 Topps #10	435.00	150.00	65.00
1959 Topps #564	275.00	125.00	40.00
1960 Topps #350	375.00	150.00	35.00
1960 Topps #563	225.00	85.00	35.00
1961 Topps #300	375.00	150.00	35.00
1961 Topps #475	95.00	30.00	10.00
1961 Topps #578	425.00	175.00	65.00
1962 Topps #200	435.00	165.00	60.00
1962 Topps #471	120.00	40.00	15.00
1963 Topps #200	365.00	125.00	40.00
1964 Topps #50	225.00	85.00	30.00
1965 Topps #350	435.00	170.00	65.00

	NM	EX	VG
1966 Topps #50	210.00	80.00	30.00
1967 Topps #150	225.00	85.00	35.00
1968 Topps #280	185.00	65.00	25.00
1969 Topps #500	225.00	85.00	35.00
1969 Topps #500 (name in white)	450.00	175.00	75.00

Henry Emmett "Heinie" Manush

Elected HoF 1964. Heinie Manush was one of the great hitters of his day. He is on a large number of cards that haven't commanded very high prices. Overlooked at present, he has good potential.

	NM	EX	VG
Diamond Star #30	155.00	55.00	25.00
1933 Goudey #47	375.00	150.00	60.00
1933 Goudey #107	225.00	85.00	35.00
1933 Goudey #187	225.00	85.00	35.00
1934 Batter Up #77	115.00	45.00	20.00
1934 Goudey #18	225.00	85.00	35.00
1935 Goudey	110.00	40.00	20.00
1939 Play Ball #94	115.00	40.00	20.00
1940 Play Ball #176	135.00	50.00	25.00
1954 Topps #187	40.00	15.00	6.50

Walter "Rabbit" Maranville

Elected HoF 1954. Everyone knows about Rabbit Maranville. The problem is that not enough people want his cards. In fairness, there are many of them, so the future for his cards looks modest by any standard.

	NM	EX	VG
E120 American Caramel	90.00	35.00	15.00
E121 American Caramel Set of 80	75.00	30.00	15.00
E121 American Caramel Set of 120	85.00	30.00	15.00
E122 American Caramel	120.00	45.00	20.00
E220 National Caramel	120.00	45.00	20.00
D329 Weil Baking #112	225.00	85.00	35.00
Diamond Star #3	115.00	45.00	20.00
George Miller	365.00	125.00	50.00
1914 Cracker Jack #136	1575.00	175.00	65.00
1915 Cracker Jack #136	575.00	175.00	65.00
1933 Delong #13	265.00	125.00	50.00
1933 Goudey #117	225.00	85.00	35.00
1935 Goudey	1900.00	850.00	350.00

Juan Marichal

Elected HoF 1983. Juan Marichal does not have as many key cards as you might expect, considering current price levels. At these prices, his cards are a good deal, even if his upward potential is limited.

	NM	EX	VG
1961 Topps #417	135.00	40.00	15.00
1962 Topps #505	40.00	17.50	7.75
1963 Topps #440	22.00	7.50	2.50
1964 Topps #280	11.00	4.00	1.50
1965 Topps #50	11.00	4.00	1.50
1966 Topps #420	10.00	3.50	1.25
1967 Topps #500	22.00	8.00	2.50
1968 Topps #205	8.50	2.75	1.00
1969 Topps #370	7.50	2.50	1.00
1970 Topps #210	9.00	3.00	1.25
1970 Topps #466	4.25	1.50	0.50
1971 Topps #325	6.50	1.50	0.65
1972 Topps #567	6.50	1.50	0.65
1972 Topps #568	3.25	1.25	0.40
1973 Topps #480	4.25	1.75	0.65
1974 Topps #330	3.00	1.00	0.35

Richard "Rube" Marquard

Elected HoF 1971. Another of the colorful characters of the early 1900s. In recent years demand for Marquard seems to have softened. Perhaps people aren't reading their baseball history as they should. If that trend reverses, look for good price gains. Marquard should bring premium prices.

	NM	EX	VG
T202 Hassan	525.00	200.00	100.00
T205	650.00	250.00	100.00
T206 (hands at thighs)	575.00	150.00	75.00
T206 (pitching)	500.00	125.00	50.00
T206 (portrait)	550.00	135.00	65.00
T207	675.00	125.00	45.00
T213 Type 1	375.00	125.00	50.00
T213 Type 2	300.00	100.00	40.00
T213 Type 3	335.00	110.00	45.00
T215 Type 1	775.00	250.00	100.00
T215 Type 2	450.00	150.00	65.00

T216	325.00	100.00	45.00
T222 Fatima	525.00	125.00	50.00
T227	1300.00	350.00	150.00
E90-1 American Caramel	575.00	175.00	75.00
E91 American Caramel Set B	175.00	65.00	30.00
E96 Philadelphia Caramel	550.00	135.00	50.00
E106 American Caramel	425.00	90.00	30.00
E120 American Caramel	135.00	45.00	20.00
E254 Colgan's Chips	100.00	35.00	15.00
D303 General Baking	225.00	100.00	35.00
D304 General Baking	200.00	90.00	25.00
D329 Weil Baking #113	325.00	125.00	50.00

Edwin Lee Mathews

Elected HoF 1978. Eddie Mathews cards are priced for literally every pocket-book. From his expensive 1952 Topps rookie to his cards of the late 1960s, there is enough of a price difference to suit everyone. All his cards are fairly priced. Just as he was on the field, the cards of Eddie Mathews are steady, but not spectacular.

	NM	EX	VG
1952 Topps #407	2450.00	1000.00	375.00
1953 Bowman #97	185.00	75.00	30.00
1953 Topps #37	125.00	50.00	20.00
1954 Bowman #64	60.00	25.00	10.00
1954 Topps #30	110.00	35.00	15.00
1955 Bowman #103	48.00	17.00	7.00
1955 Topps #155	120.00	55.00	22.00
1956 Topps #107	57.00	20.00	7.50
1957 Topps #250	45.00	18.00	7.25
1958 Topps #440	37.50	17.50	7.50
1958 Topps #480	12.00	3.00	1.00
1959 Topps #450	32.00	12.00	4.00
1960 Topps $420	28.00	10.00	3.50
1960 Topps #558	26.00	10.00	3.00
1961 Topps #120	23.00	8.00	2.75
1962 Topps #30	25.00	6.50	2.00
1963 Topps #275	22.00	6.00	1.85
1964 Topps #35	20.00	5.00	1.50
1965 Topps #500	32.00	12.00	4.00
1966 Topps #200	13.00	4.00	1.00
1967 Topps #166	12.00	4.00	1.00

1968 Topps #58	9.50	3.25	0.80
1973 Topps #237	2.25	0.80	0.25
1974 Topps #634	1.00	0.35	0.15

Christopher "Christy" Mathewson

Elected HoF 1936. Christy Mathewson is in that small group of giants who stand far above mere Hall of Famers. His popularity is huge and his card prices are high and rising.

	NM	EX	VG
T201 Mecca	775.00	250.00	100.00
T202 Hassan	850.00	300.00	125.00
T205	1750.00	450.00	150.00
T206 (dark cap)	900.00	150.00	100.00
T206 (white cap)	1750.00	600.00	250.00
T206 (portrait)	1550.00	350.00	150.00
T213 Type 1	950.00	250.00	100.00
T213 Type 2	1200.00	350.00	150.00
T213 Type 3	1000.00	300.00	125.00
T215 Type 1	1000.00	300.00	125.00
T215 Type 2	1000.00	300.00	125.00
T216	750.00	250.00	100.00
E90-1 American Caramel	1350.00	350.00	125.00
E91 American Caramel Set A	325.00	100.00	50.00
E91 American Caramel Set B	125.00	100.00	50.00
E93 Standard Caramel	1100.00	350.00	125.00
E95	1650.00	400.00	150.00
E98	1650.00	400.00	150.00
E224 Texas Tommy	1450.00	400.00	175.00
E286 Ju Ju Drums	900.00	375.00	200.00
D303 General Baking	750.00	350.00	100.00
D304 General Baking	700.00	200.00	100.00
1914 Cracker Jack #88	4500.00	750.00	350.00
1915 Cracker Jack #88	1550.00	650.00	300.00
Turkey Red (T3) #27	4250.00	1750.00	750.00
M116 (blue background)	3000.00	1200.00	500.00
M116 (pastel background)	1450.00	650.00	300.00
1940 Play Ball #175	250.00	125.00	60.00

Willie Mays

Elected HoF 1979. One of the eternal questions in baseball is, Was Mantle better than Mays? The answer from the card market is Yes. Mantle cards always cost about 30 percent more than Mays. Nevertheless, it pays to buy Mays cards as the prices will only go up.

	NM	EX	VG
1951 Bowman #305	3200.00	1300.00	550.00
1952 Bowman #218	1150.00	450.00	200.00
1952 Topps #261	2200.00	850.00	350.00
1953 Topps #244	2250.00	875.00	375.00
1954 Bowman #89	345.00	140.00	50.00
1954 Topps #90	475.00	200.00	85.00
1955 Bowman #184	215.00	90.00	35.00
1955 Topps #194	525.00	225.00	85.00
1956 Topps #130	315.00	125.00	50.00
1957 Topps #10	240.00	100.00	35.00
1958 Topps #5	175.00	75.00	25.00
1958 Topps #486	45.00	17.00	5.50
1959 Topps #50	165.00	60.00	22.00
1959 Topps #563	135.00	45.00	20.00
1960 Topps #200	110.00	40.00	15.00
1960 Topps #564	95.00	35.00	10.00
1961 Topps #150	100.00	35.00	10.00
1961 Topps #482	37.50	15.00	5.00
1961 Topps #579	155.00	50.00	15.00
1962 Topps #300	160.00	50.00	15.00
1962 Topps #395	32.00	13.00	5.00
1963 Fleer #5	90.00	35.00	10.00
1963 Topps #300	155.00	50.00	15.00
1964 Topps #150	95.00	30.00	10.00
1965 Topps #250	90.00	30.00	10.00
1966 Topps #1	175.00	50.00	15.00
1967 Topps #200	85.00	35.00	15.00
1968 Topps #50	55.00	17.00	5.00
1969 Topps #190	50.00	15.00	3.50
1970 Topps #600	75.00	25.00	10.00
1971 Topps #600	95.00	30.00	10.00
1972 Topps #49	27.00	10.00	3.50
1972 Topps #50	15.00	5.00	2.00
1973 Topps #305	32.00	10.00	3.50

Joseph Vincent McCarthy

Elected HoF 1957 (manager). Joe McCarthy made it to the Hall because he was arguably the best manager in the history of the game. He began a twenty-four year career in 1926 and he still holds the record for best career winning percentage for a manager. Too bad he was never portrayed on a card

	NM	EX	VG
No cards			

Thomas McCarthy

Elected HoF 1946. Hold on to your wallet. Tommy McCarthy is one of the toughest cards to find of all Hall of Famers. You can expect to pay through the nose, if you can find one. On average, few appear on the market each year, and they routinely bring record prices.

	NM	EX	VG
N172	1800.00	1000.00	750.00
N173	3500.00	1750.00	1000.00

Willie Lee McCovey

Elected HoF 1986. McCovey is a Giant's team great from the 1960s. His cards are in demand and prices are still reasonable for a Hall of Famer of his stature.

	NM	EX	VG
1960 Topps #316	225.00	65.00	25.00
1960 Topps #554	50.00	17.00	7.50
1961 Topps #517	65.00	25.00	10.00
1962 Topps #544	150.00	35.00	12.00
1963 Topps #490	115.00	40.00	17.00
1964 Topps #350	22.00	7.50	2.50
1965 Topps #176	19.00	6.50	2.00
1966 Topps #550	120.00	40.00	15.00
1967 Topps #480	33.00	12.00	3.00
1968 Topps #290	12.50	3.00	1.25
1969 Topps #416	3.75	1.25	0.40
1969 Topps #440	17.50	5.00	1.50
1970 Topps #250	11.00	3.00	1.00
1970 Topps #450	5.50	1.50	0.50
1971 Topps #50	10.00	2.00	0.50
1972 Topps #280	5.00	1.50	0.50

1973 Topps #410	5.25	1.50	0.50
1974 Topps #250 (San Diego)	5.00	1.50	0.50
1974 Topps #250 (Washington)	30.00	12.00	5.00
1975 Topps #450	4.25	1.25	0.50
1976 Topps #520	2.75	1.00	0.25
1977 Topps #547	2.75	1.00	0.25
1978 Topps #34	2.75	1.00	0.25
1979 Topps #215	2.00	0.75	0.15
1980 Topps #335	1.75	0.75	0.15
1981 Fleer #434	0.85	0.30	0.10

Joseph Jerome McGinnity

Elected HoF 1946. Iron Man Joe McGinnity has cards that seem a lot more common than they are due to his T206 card. Were it not for that, McGinnity cards would rank above average in difficulty and price. As it stands, his cards are average on both counts.

	NM	EX	VG
T201 Mecca	175.00	75.00	35.00
T206	325.00	100.00	35.00
E91 American Caramel Set A	150.00	50.00	25.00
E107 Breisch Williams	650.00	200.00	75.00
E 254 Colgan's Chips	100.00	35.00	15.00
E270	100.00	35.00	15.00

John McGraw

Elected HoF 1937. Baseball cards don't get much more common than John McGraw's. For some reason, he appeared on the cards Connie Mack should have. You will have little trouble finding a McGraw. Which one to buy and how much to pay are the more realistic concerns.

	NM	EX	VG
T202 Hassan	575.00	175.00	75.00
T205	775.00	225.00	75.00
T206 (finger in air)	475.00	150.00	40.00
T206 (glove at hip)	475.00	150.00	40.00
T206 (portrait, no cap)	550.00	175.00	45.00
T206 (portrait, with cap)	425.00	125.00	35.00
T207	825.00	200.00	65.00
T213 Type 2	200.00	75.00	35.00
T213 Type 3	325.00	100.00	50.00
T216	200.00	75.00	35.00

E91 American Caramel Set A	200.00	75.00	30.00
E92 American Caramel Set B	200.00	75.00	30.00
E92 Croft's Candy	525.00	150.00	75.00
E92 Croft's Cocoa	525.00	150.00	75.00
E92 Nadja	635.00	200.00	100.00
E93 Standard Caramel	575.00	125.00	65.00
E94	550.00	125.00	65.00
E98	800.00	250.00	100.00
E101	450.00	100.00	50.00
E104 Nadja	475.00	135.00	65.00
E105 Mello-Mint	400.00	100.00	45.00
E106 American Caramel	825.00	275.00	140.00
E107 Breisch Williams	550.00	135.00	60.00
E121 American Caramel Set of 80	115.00	40.00	15.00
E121 American Caramel Set of 120	100.00	35.00	15.00
E122 American Caramel	135.00	40.00	20.00
E210 York Caramel	65.00	25.00	15.00
E224 Texas Tommy	850.00	300.00	125.00
E286 Ju Ju Drums	850.00	350.00	150.00
1914 Cracker Jack #69	1950.00	400.00	175.00
1915 Cracker Jack #69	700.00	325.00	150.00
D303 General Baking	225.00	85.00	35.00
D329 Weil Baking #116	225.00	100.00	35.00
M101-4 #116	65.00	30.00	15.00
M101-5 #114	95.00	35.00	20.00
M101-6	85.00	30.00	15.00
M116	725.00	250.00	100.00
Turkey Red (T3) #26	950.00	275.00	125.00
1940 Play Ball #235	225.00	75.00	35.00

William Boyd McKechnie

Elected HoF 1962 (manager). Bill McKechnie is one of the least known of all Hall of Famers. He did, however, have decent careers as both a player and manager. He did not, however, have great careers, and to a degree that is shown in his lack of cards. A tough card to find, but not many are looking.

	NM	EX	VG
T207	525.00	175.00	75.00
1940 Play Ball #153	110.00	40.00	20.00

Joseph "Ducky" Medwick

Elected HoF 1968. Ducky Medwick has average popularity and a slightly below-average number of cards. Don't expect big profits from Ducky's cards, but they should at least hold their own.

	NM	EX	VG
Diamond Star #66	125.00	50.00	25.00
1934 Batter Up #145	325.00	125.00	50.00
1938 Goudey #262	325.00	125.00	50.00
1938 Goudey #286	375.00	150.00	65.00
1941 Double Play #22	55.00	25.00	10.00

John Robert "Big Cat" Mize

Elected HoF 1981. Johnny Mize stands squarely between two generations of cards, so an above-average supply of cards exists for a player from the 1940s and a below-average supply for one from the 1950s. Translated into dollars, he's inexpensive and likely to stay that way.

	NM	EX	VG
1941 Double Play #39	125.00	50.00	25.00
1941 Double Play #99	65.00	30.00	15.00
1948 Bowman #4	110.00	45.00	17.75
1948 Leaf #46	95.00	35.00	12.50
1949 Bowman #85	95.00	35.00	12.50
1950 Bowman #139	55.00	17.50	8.50
1951 Bowman #50	55.00	17.50	8.50
1952 Topps #129	65.00	25.00	10.00
1953 Bowman (black and white) #15	100.00	35.00	12.50
1953 Topps #77	80.00	25.00	10.00

Joe Leonard Morgan

Elected HoF 1990. Joe Morgan was not only a great player on a Reds championship team, he has gone on to become a widely recognized broadcaster. There is demand for his cards and solid upward potential. This is especially true for his cards prior to 1975. (All other Morgan cards not listed are priced at under $1.00 in Near Mint condition.)

	NM	EX	VG
1965 Topps #16	185.00	75.00	25.00
1966 Topps #195	45.00	17.00	7.00

1967 Topps #337	28.00	12.00	5.00
1968 Topps #144	16.00	6.00	2.50
1969 Topps #35	12.50	4.00	1.50
1970 Topps #537	11.00	3.50	1.25
1971 Topps #264	12.50	3.00	1.00
1972 Topps #132	5.50	1.75	0.75
1972 Topps #752	50.00	17.00	6.00
1973 Topps #230	5.50	1.75	0.75
1974 Topps #85	5.50	1.75	0.75
1975 Topps #180	7.00	2.50	1.00
1976 Topps #420	4.50	1.50	0.50
1977 Topps #100	4.25	1.25	0.50
1978 Topps #300	3.25	1.00	0.35
1979 Topps #20	1.00	0.35	0.15
1980 Topps #650	2.50	1.00	0.25
1981 Topps #560	1.00	0.35	0.15
1981 Topps Traded #807	2.25	0.85	0.30
1983 Topps Traded #77	2.75	1.25	0.35
1984 Donruss #355	1.25	0.35	0.15
1984 Fleer Update #80	5.50	1.75	0.75
1984 Topps Traded #82	2.75	1.25	0.40

Stanley "Stan The Man" Musial

Elected HoF 1969. Stan Musial is one of the biggest names of the 1950s, and his cards are among the most difficult to get. He appears on very few cards and on no regular issues from 1954 to 1958. Compared to other stars of the 1950s, Musial cards are quite scarce. With very solid demand, Musial is one of the best buys from the 1950s.

	NM	EX	VG
1948 Bowman #36	900.00	375.00	150.00
1948 Leaf #4	775.00	275.00	125.00
1949 Bowman #24	535.00	185.00	80.00
1952 Bowman #196	625.00	175.00	75.00
1953 Bowman #32	550.00	175.00	75.00
1958 Topps #476	35.00	15.00	6.00
1959 Topps #150	160.00	60.00	20.00
1960 Topps #250	115.00	38.00	15.00
1961 Topps #290	85.00	30.00	10.00
1962 Topps #50	125.00	35.00	15.00
1963 Topps #250	110.00	30.00	10.00

Harold Newhouser

Elected HoF 1992. When the Hall of Fame added Hal Newhouser to the ranks, an immediate urgency for his cards was created. Newhouser was a star in the 1940s but was not on a card until 1948. By then his career was almost over, but the prices for his cards keep climbing.

	NM	EX	VG
1948 Leaf #98	550.00	200.00	100.00
1953 Topps #228	125.00	45.00	20.00
1955 Topps #24	35.00	15.00	7.50
1955 Topps Doubleheaders #109	45.00	17.50	7.50

Charles Augustus "Kid" Nichols

Elected HoF 1949. Kid Nichols is another one of those stars from before 1900 whose cards are very rare and nearly impossible to obtain. He has only a few cards, and none of them will come cheaply. In fact, most sellers are doing you a favor selling you a Kid Nichols at almost any price.

	NM	EX	VG
N172	1800.00	1000.00	750.00
N173	3500.00	1750.00	1000.00
N300	1500.00	600.00	375.00

James Henry O'Rourke

Elected HoF 1945. Orator Jim O'Rourke cards are slightly more common than those of Kid Nichols and some of the other pre-1900 stars whose cards are hard to obtain. There's very little price differential because the few sets in which he appeared are so rare. Like all the pre-1900 cards there's low purchase risk. If this overlooked era of cards ever gains in popularity, prices could skyrocket.

	NM	EX	VG
N172	1700.00	850.00	650.00
N173	3200.00	1500.00	900.00
N284 Buchner Gold Coin	275.00	125.00	50.00
N403 Yum Yum	1900.00	1000.00	750.00
N690 Kalamazoo Bats	2850.00	1300.00	650.00
E223 G&B Chewing Gum	2300.00	1000.00	600.00

Melvin Thomas Ott

Elected HoF 1951. Mel Ott was a huge star, but he didn't appear on as many cards as you might expect. Nor is he as expensive as you might think. Put those facts together and you get a good buy on an overlooked star.

	NM	EX	VG
Diamond Star #50	300.00	115.00	50.00
George Miller	450.00	175.00	75.00
1933 Goudey #127	375.00	150.00	65.00
1933 Goudey #207	430.00	165.00	75.00
1934 Batter Up #27	250.00	100.00	45.00
1935 Goudey	65.00	30.00	15.00
1939 Play Ball #51	200.00	85.00	35.00
1940 Play Ball #88	175.00	75.00	30.00
1941 Double Play #31	85.00	35.00	15.00
1941 Double Play #89	85.00	35.00	15.00
1941 Goudey #33	225.00	85.00	35.00
1941 Play Ball #8	350.00	125.00	50.00

LeRoy Robert Satchel Paige

Elected HoF 1971. Satchel's cards are among the most difficult to find and desirable to own of the 1940s and 1950s. Paige spent most of his years as a player in the Negro leagues. Thanks to his phenomenal longevity, he appeared in three sets before his retirement. Demand for Paige cards far outpaces supply.

	NM	EX	VG
1948 Leaf #8	2250.00	650.00	275.00
1949 Bowman #224	1400.00	450.00	200.00
1953 Topps #220	650.00	275.00	125.00

Jim Alvin Palmer

Elected HoF 1990. Jim Palmer, like Joe Morgan, was a star on a championship team who remains in the spotlight today. It's hard to predict when Palmer cards are likely to rise or fall in price, but you can usually count on prices rising. All Palmer cards not listed here are worth less than $1.00 in Near Mint condition.

	NM	EX	VG
1966 Topps #126	265.00	100.00	35.00
1967 Topps #475	95.00	35.00	15.00
1968 Topps #575	65.00	25.00	10.00

1969 Topps #573	41.00	17.00	7.50
1970 Topps #449	24.00	8.00	2.50
1971 Topps #570	37.00	11.00	3.50
1972 Topps #270	12.50	4.00	1.50
1973 Topps #160	11.00	3.50	1.50
1974 Topps #40	8.50	3.00	1.25
1975 Topps #335	9.50	3.75	1.25
1976 Topps #450	6.25	2.00	0.75
1977 Topps #600	5.50	1.75	0.75
1978 Topps #160	4.25	1.50	0.50
1979 Topps #340	3.50	1.25	0.35
1980 Topps #590	2.75	1.25	0.35
1981 Donruss #353	1.25	0.30	0.10
1981 Donruss #473	1.00	0.30	0.10
1981 Fleer #169	1.25	0.30	0.10
1981 Topps #210	1.75	0.60	0.20
1982 Topps #80	1.25	0.40	0.15
1983 Topps #490	1.10	0.35	0.10
1984 Donruss #576	3.50	1.25	0.35
1984 Fleer #16	1.50	0.35	0.10
1984 Topps #750	1.00	0.30	0.10

Herbert Jefferis Pennock

Elected HoF 1948. Herb Pennock does not appear on many cards, yet the sets he is in are common and easy to find. He has only average price-rise potential.

	NM	EX	VG
E120 American Caramel	85.00	40.00	20.00
E210 York Caramel #8	65.00	30.00	15.00
E220 National Caramel	125.00	50.00	25.00
Yuengling's Ice Cream #8	35.00	15.00	10.00
1933 Goudey #138	225.00	85.00	35.00

Gaylord Jackson Perry

Elected HoF 1991. Gaylord Perry proved that ability plus longevity can produce a Hall of Fame career. There are more than ample supplies for all but his earliest cards. (All other Perry cards not listed are priced under $1.00 in Near Mint condition.)

	NM	EX	VG
1962 Topps #199	225.00	75.00	25.00
1963 Topps #169	32.00	10.00	3.50

1964 Topps #468	43.00	17.00	7.50
1965 Topps #193	19.00	8.00	3.00
1966 Topps #598	275.00	125.00	40.00
1967 Topps #320	13.00	4.00	1.50
1968 Topps #85	11.50	3.75	1.25
1969 Topps (name in white) #485	70.00	25.00	10.00
1969 Topps (name in yellow) #485	9.50	3.00	1.00
1970 Topps #560	10.00	3.50	1.00
1971 Topps #140	9.00	2.50	1.00
1972 Topps #285	5.50	1.75	0.75
1973 Topps #400	4.50	1.50	0.50
1974 Topps #35	3.25	1.25	0.40
1975 Topps #530	3.50	1.25	0.40
1976 Topps #55	3.00	1.00	0.25
1977 Topps #152	2.25	0.75	0.25
1978 Topps #686	2.00	0.75	0.25
1979 Topps #321	1.75	0.75	0.25
1980 Topps #280	1.35	0.40	0.15
1981 Topps Traded #812	1.60	0.40	0.15
1982 Topps Traded #88	1.50	0.35	0.10
1984 Donruss #647	4.50	1.75	0.75

Edward Stewart Plank

Elected HoF 1946. Eddie Plank has the distinction of being on one of the most expensive of all cards — his T206. The publicity surrounding his T206 has increased demand for all other Plank cards. In addition, the supply is below average, as he did not appear with any regularity on tobacco cards. That leaves E cards if you want a Plank. High-grade Plank cards are very tough to come by.

	NM	EX	VG
T204 Ramly	3250.00	800.00	350.00
T206	42000.00	17000.00	10000.00
T208 Fireside	2300.00	750.00	325.00
T216	325.00	125.00	50.00
E90-1 American Caramel	950.00	325.00	125.00
E91 American Caramel Set A	250.00	100.00	40.00
E91 American Caramel Set B	250.00	100.00	40.00
E93 Standard Caramel	700.00	275.00	135.00
E95	700.00	275.00	135.00
E104 Nadja	325.00	125.00	50.00
E106 American Caramel	950.00	325.00	125.00
E107 Breisch Williams	625.00	250.00	100.00
E224 Texas Tommy	875.00	375.00	150.00

1914 Cracker Jack #6 .... 1850.00	325.00	125.00
1915 Cracker Jack #6 .... 800.00	325.00	125.00
D303 General Baking 250.00	100.00	45.00
M116 .... 950.00	300.00	100.00

Charles Gardner "Old Hoss" Radbourn

Elected HoF 1939. Old Hoss Radbourn was a special player. How many other pitchers won 60 games in a single season or 109 in two seasons? Do such legendary feats translate into the popularity one might expect? Hardly. In fact, Radbourn is generally forgotten. His cards are not cheap, however. They rank among the rare pre-1900 cards of other players. But can you buy the card of another single-season 60-game winner at any price?

	NM	EX	VG
N172 .... 1800.00	1000.00	750.00
N173 .... 3500.00	1750.00	1000.00
N284 Buchner Gold Coin 275.00	125.00	50.00
N526 Diamond S Cigars 1250.00	400.00	175.00

Harold Henry "Pee Wee" Reese

Elected HoF 1984. The popular captain of the Dodgers had his first card in 1941. It was not until after his service in World War II that he was featured on another card, in 1949. His cards remain popular and stable in price. Due to those years he spent in the military, he appears on fewer cards than many of the stars of the 1950s.

	NM	EX	VG
1941 Play Ball #54 .... 650.00	300.00	125.00
1949 Bowman #36 .... 225.00	110.00	50.00
1950 Bowman #21 .... 225.00	110.00	50.00
1951 Bowman #80 .... 140.00	65.00	30.00
1952 Bowman #8 .... 100.00	45.00	25.00
1952 Topps #333 .... 925.00	425.00	200.00
1953 Bowman #33 .... 450.00	250.00	100.00
1953 Topps #76 .... 185.00	90.00	40.00
1954 Bowman #58 .... 70.00	30.00	20.00
1955 Bowman #37 .... 65.00	25.00	15.00
1956 Topps #260 .... 135.00	55.00	30.00
1957 Topps #30 .... 75.00	35.00	20.00
1958 Topps #375 .... 50.00	20.00	15.00

Edgar Charles "Sam" Rice

Elected HoF 1963. Sam Rice is represented on most of the common issues of the period. The demand for his cards is average, so there's no reason to expect significant price movements.

	NM	EX	VG
Diamond Star #32	150.00	65.00	30.00
E120 American Caramel	95.00	40.00	20.00
E121 American Caramel Set of 120	90.00	40.00	20.00
E121 American Caramel Set of 80	75.00	30.00	15.00
E122 American Caramel	115.00	45.00	20.00
E210 York Caramel	75.00	30.00	15.00
E220 National Caramel	125.00	50.00	25.00
1933 Goudey #134	225.00	85.00	35.00

Wesley Branch Rickey

Elected HoF 1967. Branch Rickey is a player who didn't make it to the Hall of Fame. His selection was as an executive, probably due in large part to his involvement in bringing Jackie Robinson into the N. L. The demand for his cards is thus reduced, but there's not exactly a big choice for collectors of his cards.

	NM	EX	VG
1914 Cracker Jack #133	1550.00	225.00	75.00
1915 Cracker Jack #133	450.00	175.00	65.00

Eppa (Jephtha) Rixey

Elected HoF 1963. Eppa Rixey is like many other players from the 1930s. Overshadowed by the Ruths and Gehrigs of his day, he is not very common on cards, but there are ample supplies to meet the minimal demand.

	NM	EX	VG
E120 American Caramel	95.00	35.00	15.00
E121 American Caramel Set of 120	95.00	35.00	15.00
E121 American Caramel Set of 80	75.00	25.00	10.00
E122 American Caramel	125.00	45.00	20.00
E210 York Caramel	90.00	30.00	20.00
D329 Weil Baking #142	200.00	75.00	35.00
M101-4	65.00	25.00	15.00
M101-5	65.00	25.00	15.00
Yuengling's Ice Cream #16	35.00	15.00	10.00
1933 Goudey #74	225.00	75.00	25.00

Robin Evan Roberts

Elected HoF 1976. Robin is an underrated star of the 1950s. His cards are affordable and carry solid potential.

	NM	EX	VG
1949 Bowman #46	265.00	125.00	40.00
1950 Bowman #32	135.00	50.00	20.00
1951 Bowman #3	75.00	35.00	15.00
1952 Bowman #4	70.00	25.00	10.00
1952 Topps #59	135.00	50.00	20.00
1953 Bowman #65	78.00	30.00	10.00
1954 Bowman #95	35.00	15.00	6.00
1955 Bowman #171	27.50	10.00	3.50
1956 Topps #180	27.50	10.00	3.50
1957 Topps #15	22.00	7.50	2.50
1958 Topps #90	19.00	7.50	2.50
1959 Topps #352	16.00	5.00	1.75
1960 Topps #264	15.00	4.75	1.75
1961 Topps #20	9.50	3.00	1.25
1962 Topps #243	12.50	3.00	1.25
1963 Topps #125	9.00	3.00	1.00
1964 Topps #285	9.00	3.00	1.00
1965 Topps #15	7.50	2.50	0.75
1966 Topps #530	27.50	10.00	3.50

Brooks Calbert Robinson

Elected HoF 1983. Brooks Robinson set the standard at third base for a whole generation. Robinson has not been forgotten and his cards are still very popular, with higher-than-average prices. His continuing association with baseball keeps his early cards quite strong.

	NM	EX	VG
1957 Topps #328	375.00	150.00	55.00
1958 Topps #307	95.00	35.00	15.00
1959 Topps #439	60.00	25.00	10.00
1960 Leaf #27	40.00	15.00	5.00
1960 Topps #28	45.00	17.50	7.50
1961 Topps #10	32.00	13.00	5.00
1961 Topps #572	85.00	35.00	15.00
1962 Topps #45	45.00	15.00	5.00
1962 Topps #468	15.00	5.00	1.75

1963 Fleer #4	35.00	15.00	5.00
1963 Topps #345	37.50	12.00	4.00
1964 Topps #230	30.00	10.00	2.50
1965 Topps #150	23.00	8.00	2.50
1966 Topps #390	25.00	10.00	2.50
1967 Topps #600	175.00	75.00	25.00
1968 Topps #20	18.00	7.50	2.50
1968 Topps #365	7.00	2.00	0.75
1969 Topps #421	5.00	1.50	0.50
1969 Topps #550	17.50	7.50	2.50
1970 Topps #230	14.00	3.50	1.00
1970 Topps #455	5.00	1.50	0.50
1971 Topps #300	17.50	3.50	1.00
1972 Topps #498	1.50	0.50	0.10
1972 Topps #550	22.00	7.50	2.00
1973 Topps #90	5.50	1.75	0.50
1974 Topps #160	3.75	1.25	0.40
1975 Topps #50	5.50	1.75	0.50
1976 Topps #95	4.50	1.50	0.35
1977 Topps #285	3.00	1.00	0.25
1978 Topps #4	1.25	0.30	0.05

Frank Robinson

Elected HoF 1982. Considering his long career, Frank Robinson cards are fairly inexpensive. He has a lot of cards, but most are low priced compared to other Hall of Famers. His cards may have upward price potential. Cards not listed here are under $1.00 in Near Mint condition.

	NM	EX	VG
1957 Topps #35	285.00	125.00	40.00
1958 Topps #285	75.00	25.00	10.00
1958 Topps #484	19.00	6.50	2.50
1959 Topps #435	48.00	20.00	8.00
1960 Topps #490	50.00	22.00	9.00
1961 Topps #581	85.00	30.00	10.00
1962 Topps #350	55.00	20.00	8.00
1962 Topps #396	17.00	5.00	1.75
1963 Topps #400	40.00	15.00	5.00
1964 Topps #260	22.00	9.00	3.00
1965 Topps #120	24.00	10.00	4.00
1967 Topps #100	18.00	8.00	3.00
1968 Topps #373	6.25	2.25	1.00
1968 Topps #500	22.00	9.00	3.00

1969 Topps #250 .... 23.00	9.00	3.00
1970 Topps #463 .... 7.50	2.50	1.00
1970 Topps #700 .... 47.00	15.00	5.00
1971 Topps #640 .... 42.00	7.00	2.00
1972 Topps #100 .... 5.50	1.50	0.50
1973 Topps #175 .... 4.50	1.50	0.50
1974 Topps #55 .... 4.50	1.50	0.50
1975 Topps #580 .... 4.50	1.50	0.50

Jack Roosevelt "Jackie" Robinson

Elected HoF 1962. Jackie Robinson cards are not cheap. Considering his ground-breaking role in the game, the quality of his play, and the few issues on which he appears, it's not surprising. His card prices will probably rise even higher.

	NM	EX	VG
1948 Leaf #79 .... 675.00	250.00	100.00
1949 Bowman #50 .... 725.00	275.00	125.00
1950 Bowman #22 .... 675.00	250.00	100.00
1952 Topps #312 .... 925.00	300.00	135.00
1953 Topps #1 .... 700.00	200.00	85.00
1954 Topps #10 .... 315.00	100.00	40.00
1955 Topps #50 .... 265.00	110.00	40.00
1956 Topps #30 .... 140.00	40.00	15.00

Wilbert Robinson

Elected HoF 1945. The beloved "Uncle Robby" who managed some of the more unusual Dodger teams was also a noted player. That gives him cards in a couple of eras. His player cards are expensive, his manager cards more affordable. Take your pick.

	NM	EX	VG
N142 .... 4500.00	1750.00	1000.00
N172 .... 1800.00	1000.00	750.00
N173 .... 3500.00	1750.00	1000.00
N300 .... 1350.00	500.00	350.00
N690 Kalamazoo Bats 2250.00	1100.00	600.00
M101-4 .... 65.00	25.00	15.00
M101-5 .... 65.00	25.00	15.00
E121 American Caramel Set of 120 .... 95.00	35.00	15.00
E210 York Caramel #43 .... 65.00	25.00	15.00
D329 Weil Baking #144 .... 200.00	75.00	25.00

Edd Roush

Elected HoF 1962. Edd Roush is one of the overlooked stars of the 1920s. Roush was a great player and appeared on just a few cards. Card prospects, except in the E-card area, are bright.

	NM	EX	VG
E120 American Caramel	95.00	35.00	15.00
E121 American Caramel Set of 80	75.00	25.00	10.00
E121 American Caramel Set of 120	95.00	35.00	15.00
E210 York Caramel	90.00	30.00	20.00
E220 National Caramel	125.00	45.00	20.00
1915 Cracker Jack #161	625.00	250.00	125.00
D329 Weil Baking #146	200.00	75.00	25.00
M101-4	65.00	25.00	15.00
M101-5	70.00	25.00	15.00

Charles "Red" Ruffing

Elected HoF 1967. Red Ruffing is in the line of Yankee Hall of Fame pitchers. Ruffing, like Waite Hoyt and later Whitey Ford, was just overlooked in favor of his long-ball-hitting teammates. Consequently, prices for Ruffing are right on target due to modest demand.

	NM	EX	VG
Diamond Star #60	125.00	50.00	25.00
George Miller	350.00	150.00	65.00
1933 Goudey #56	275.00	100.00	35.00
1935 Goudey (See Bill Dickey)			
1939 Play Ball #3	115.00	40.00	20.00
1940 Play Ball #10	70.00	30.00	15.00
1941 Double Play #68	70.00	30.00	15.00
1941 Double Play #86 (See Hank Greenberg)			
1941 Play Ball #20	225.00	85.00	25.00

Amos Wilson Rusie

Elected HoF 1977. Amos Rusie is a player from the pre-1900s whose cards are fairly difficult to get. You can expect to pay a lot for his cards, but it's a secure investment as there will never be many of his cards around.

	NM	EX	VG
N172	1800.00	1000.00	750.00
N300	1250.00	600.00	275.00
N566 Newsboy	4000.00	2100.00	1000.00

George Herman "Babe" Ruth

Elected HoF 1936. The one and only: the Bambino, The Sultan of Swat, The Babe. They still call Yankee Stadium "The House That Ruth Built." Some argue that the Hall of Fame could be called "The Hall That Ruth Built." There are a lot of Babe Ruth cards, but not nearly enough. Extremely high prices are the rule for his cards. The few exceptions are weak issues most collectors are not interested in. Demand for the Babe's cards will remain high and prices will continue to climb.

	NM	EX	VG
E120 American Caramel	1750.00	750.00	450.00
E121 American Caramel Set of 120	1400.00	600.00	400.00
E121 American Caramel Set of 80	1400.00	600.00	400.00
E210 York Caramel	1000.00	350.00	200.00
E220 National Caramel	2250.00	850.00	400.00
M101-4	8500.00	4000.00	2500.00
M101-5	8500.00	4000.00	2500.00
Yuengling's Ice Cream #6	550.00	225.00	150.00
1932 U.S. Caramels	3300.00	1400.00	650.00
1933 Goudey #53	9500.00	2500.00	1000.00
1933 Goudey #144	7500.00	1500.00	750.00
1933 Goudey #149	8800.00	2300.00	1150.00
1933 Goudey #181	8800.00	2300.00	1150.00
1933 Sport Kings #2	4500.00	1750.00	750.00
1935 Goudey (See Rabbit Maranville)			
1948 Leaf #3	2500.00	850.00	350.00

Raymond William Schalk

Elected HoF 1955. Ray Schalk has been gaining some attention recently. He was a member of the 1919 White Sox, so some of the attention paid to Joe Jackson may be rubbing off on Schalk. There are still enough Schalk cards to meet demand, but they're going fast.

	NM	EX	VG
E120 American Caramel	95.00	40.00	20.00
E121 American Caramel Set of 120	90.00	40.00	20.00
E121 American Caramel Set of 80	75.00	30.00	15.00

E210 York Caramel	75.00	30.00	15.00
E254 Colgan's Chips	100.00	35.00	15.00
D329 Weil Baking #154	225.00	85.00	35.00
1914 Cracker Jack #61	1650.00	350.00	100.00
1915 Cracker Jack #61	450.00	150.00	65.00
M101-4	100.00	35.00	20.00
M101-5	80.00	40.00	25.00

Albert Fred "Red" Schoendienst

Elected HoF 1989. Red Schoendienst is a Hall of Famer whose cards are fairly inexpensive. His involvement with baseball put him on cards during four decades, so an ample supply of cards exists for today's demand. All other Schoendienst cards not listed are priced under $1.00 in Near Mint condition.

	NM	EX	VG
1948 Bowman #38	160.00	60.00	20.00
1949 Bowman #111	70.00	25.00	10.00
1950 Bowman #71	105.00	35.00	12.00
1951 Bowman #10	70.00	25.00	10.00
1952 Bowman #30	65.00	20.00	9.00
1952 Topps #91	85.00	27.00	10.00
1953 Bowman #101	85.00	27.00	10.00
1953 Topps#78	75.00	25.00	10.00
1954 Bowman #110	33.00	11.00	4.50
1955 Bowman #29	28.00	10.00	3.50
1956 Topps #165	27.50	10.00	3.50
1957 Topps #154	21.00	8.00	2.50
1958 Topps #190	17.50	7.50	2.50
1959 Topps #480	15.00	5.00	1.50
1960 Topps #335	12.50	4.00	1.25
1961 Topps #505	12.50	4.00	1.25
1962 Topps #575	44.00	15.00	5.00
1965 Topps #556	12.50	4.00	1.25
1966 Topps #76	3.50	1.25	0.50
1967 Topps #512	14.00	5.00	1.50
1968 Topps #294	3.00	1.00	0.25
1969 Topps #462	2.75	1.00	0.25
1970 Topps #346	1.90	0.60	0.20
1971 Topps #239	2.50	0.80	0.20
1972 Topps #67	1.15	0.30	0.10
1973 Topps #497	1.00	0.25	0.10

George Thomas "Tom" Seaver

Elected HoF 1992. Tom Seaver is the popular star of the 1969 Miracle Mets and a number of other teams over the years. His cards are among the most important and high priced of the late 1960s. Generations of modern collectors have grown up with Seaver, so demand for his cards will remain high, although with a long career reaching into the 1980s, Seaver cards will always be available at inexpensive prices. All other regular-issue Seaver cards not listed have a Near Mint value of 10¢ or less.

	NM	EX	VG
1967 Topps #581	1350.00	500.00	200.00
1968 Topps #45	225.00	100.00	45.00
1969 Topps #480	135.00	50.00	20.00
1970 Topps #300	95.00	40.00	15.00
1971 Topps #160	75.00	30.00	15.00
1972 Topps #445	25.00	10.00	3.50
1972 Topps #446	20.00	7.50	3.00
1973 Topps #350	22.50	10.00	3.50
1974 Topps #80	22.50	10.00	3.50
1975 Topps #370	25.00	10.00	5.00
1976 Topps #600	15.00	5.00	2.00
1977 Topps #150	7.50	2.50	1.00
1978 Topps #450	6.00	2.00	0.75
1979 Topps #100	3.50	1.00	0.50
1980 Topps #500	3.25	0.75	0.25
1981 Donruss #422	1.00	0.35	0.20
1981 Donruss #425	1.00	0.35	0.20
1981 Fleer #200	1.00	0.35	0.20
1981 Topps #220	1.50	0.50	0.25
1982 Donruss #148	1.00	0.35	0.20
1982 Fleer #82	0.75	0.30	0.15
1982 Topps #30	1.25	0.40	0.25
1982 Topps #31	0.55	0.15	0.05
1982 Topps #346	0.40	0.10	0.05
1983 Donruss #122	0.75	0.30	0.10
1983 Fleer #601	0.65	0.20	0.05
1983 Topps #580	0.95	0.35	0.10
1983 Topps Traded #101	7.50	2.00	1.00
1984 Donruss #116	3.50	1.50	0.75
1984 Fleer #595	2.50	1.00	0.50
1984 Fleer Update #106	17.50	7.50	3.00
1984 Topps #740	1.00	0.35	0.10
1984 Topps Traded #108	6.50	2.50	1.00

1985 Donruss #424	3.50	1.50	0.50
1985 Fleer #526	0.50	0.15	0.05
1985 Topps #670	0.35	0.10	0.05
1986 Donruss #609	0.75	0.20	0.10
1986 Fleer #216	0.50	0.20	0.10
1986 Topps Traded #101	0.25	0.10	0.05

Joseph Sewell

Elected HoF 1977. I dare you to find a better contact hitter anywhere at any time than Joe Sewell. Unfortunately, being the one of the greatest contact hitters does nothing for his card prices. His cards would have seen better demand if he struck out more and hit a few more home runs. Since his statistics won't change, it's unlikely that demand for his cards or prices will change much either.

	NM	EX	VG
E120 American Caramel	95.00	40.00	20.00
E121 American Caramel Set of 120	90.00	40.00	20.00
Yuengling's Ice Cream	35.00	15.00	10.00
1933 Goudey #165	225.00	85.00	35.00

Aloysius Harry "Al" Simmons

Elected HoF 1953. Al Simmons was a top hitter in his day. He appears on a lot of cards as a result of his popularity, and this has created some demand, but not enough to justify higher prices. His greatness as a hitter remains unchallenged.

	NM	EX	VG
Diamond Star #2	250.00	100.00	35.00
George Miller	350.00	125.00	50.00
1933 Tatoo Orbit	75.00	30.00	15.00
1933 Delong #2	300.00	125.00	50.00
1933 Goudey #35	550.00	175.00	65.00
1934 Batter-Up #34	375.00	150.00	50.00
1935 Goudey (See Mickey Cochrane)			

George Harold Sisler

Elected HoF 1939. George Sisler is one of the truly great hitters in baseball history. He never appeared on a widely collected card. He appears on some common cards, but none collectors really like. He should cost a lot more and would if he had only appeared on a card like a 1933 Goudey.

	NM	EX	VG
E120 American Caramel	165.00	75.00	35.00
E121 American Caramel Set of 120	125.00	50.00	25.00
E121 American Caramel Set of 80	75.00	25.00	10.00
E210 York Caramel	75.00	25.00	10.00
M101-4	95.00	35.00	15.00
M101-5	95.00	35.00	15.00
M101-6	80.00	25.00	10.00
Yuengling's Ice Cream	45.00	20.00	15.00
1940 Play Ball #179	165.00	60.00	25.00

Enos Bradsher "Country" Slaughter

Elected HoF 1985. Enos Slaughter is another of the stars of the 1940s and 1950s who had a career shortened by World War II. That means that a Slaughter card is slightly more difficult to find than average, even though his prices do not currently reflect that fact.

	NM	EX	VG
1948 Bowman #17	110.00	50.00	35.00
1948 Leaf #127	550.00	225.00	175.00
1949 Bowman #65	70.00	30.00	20.00
1950 Bowman #35	115.00	50.00	20.00
1951 Bowman #58	50.00	20.00	7.50
1952 Bowman #232	100.00	45.00	25.00
1952 Topps #65	125.00	50.00	30.00
1953 Bowman #81	85.00	40.00	30.00
1953 Topps #41	90.00	40.00	25.00
1954 Bowman #62	30.00	12.50	7.50
1955 Bowman #60	25.00	10.00	5.00
1956 Topps #109	25.00	10.00	5.00
1957 Topps #215	20.00	8.00	3.00
1958 Topps #142	25.00	10.00	5.00
1959 Topps #155	15.00	5.00	2.50

Edwin Donald "Duke" Snider

Elected HoF 1980. Duke Snider still ranks right up there with Mantle and Mays in popularity. He was the other center fielder from New York (for the Brooklyn Dodgers) during the 1950s and was bound to have a large following. He's not priced quite as high as Mays and Mantle, but his are sought-after cards.

	NM	EX	VG
1949 Bowman #226	1100.00	350.00	150.00
1950 Bowman $77	280.00	130.00	45.00
1951 Bowman #32	245.00	100.00	35.00
1952 Bowman #116	225.00	90.00	30.00
1952 Topps #37	285.00	115.00	45.00
1953 Bowman #117	575.00	175.00	75.00
1954 Bowman #170	145.00	45.00	17.00
1954 Topps #32	145.00	50.00	15.00
1955 Topps #210	540.00	175.00	60.00
1956 Topps #150	125.00	35.00	12.00
1957 Topps #170	95.00	35.00	10.00
1958 Topps #88	70.00	25.00	9.00
1959 Topps #20	62.50	20.00	7.50
1960 Leaf #37	43.00	16.00	5.50
1960 Topps #493	50.00	17.00	6.50
1961 Topps #443	42.00	15.00	5.00
1962 Topps #500	45.00	18.00	7.00
1963 Topps #550	60.00	20.00	7.50
1964 Topps #155	30.00	10.00	3.50

Warren Edward Spahn

Elected HoF 1973. When you consider his career, Warren Spahn cards are a steal at today's prices. He was quite a pitcher, winning 20 games in 13 separate seasons. His 363 career wins is fifth on the all time list. Should you run out and buy his cards? So far they haven't achieved superstar prices. Some day they should be more expensive, but it's hard to predict when.

	NM	EX	VG
1948 Bowman #18	285.00	125.00	50.00
1948 Leaf #32	225.00	100.00	35.00
1949 Bowman #33	165.00	70.00	25.00
1950 Bowman #19	185.00	75.00	30.00
1951 Bowman #134	115.00	40.00	15.00
1952 Bowman #156	95.00	35.00	15.00
1952 Topps #33	245.00	100.00	35.00
1953 Bowman #99	165.00	70.00	25.00
1953 Topps #147	135.00	50.00	20.00
1954 Topps #20	110.00	35.00	12.00
1955 Topps #31	75.00	25.00	10.00
1956 Topps #10	75.00	25.00	10.00
1957 Topps #90	70.00	22.00	12.00

	NM	EX	VG
1958 Topps #270	48.00	17.50	7.50
1958 Topps #494	17.50	7.50	2.50
1959 Topps #40	53.00	18.00	7.75
1959 Topps #571	33.00	10.00	3.50
1960 Topps #445	45.00	16.00	5.50
1961 Topps #200	32.50	9.50	3.00
1961 Topps #589	135.00	40.00	15.00
1962 Topps #100	35.00	10.00	3.25
1962 Topps #399	12.00	4.00	1.50
1963 Fleer #45	35.00	10.00	3.00
1963 Topps #320	30.00	10.00	3.00
1964 Topps #400	27.50	9.00	2.50
1965 Topps #205	21.00	6.50	2.00

Al Goodwill Spaulding

Elected HoF 1939. He played and managed for Chicago in the 1870s, well before the advent of baseball cards.

	NM	EX	VG
No cards			

Tristram "Tris" Speaker

Elected HoF 1937. Tris Speaker is one of the real premium cards from the tobacco era. Even though he was featured on a lot of cards, he's just a step below the likes of Ty Cobb and Walter Johnson for both popularity and price.

	NM	EX	VG
T201 Mecca	225.00	85.00	40.00
T202 Hassan	575.00	150.00	75.00
T205	850.00	200.00	85.00
T206	750.00	150.00	65.00
T207	1450.00	250.00	100.00
T213 Type 2	475.00	150.00	65.00
T213 Type 3	625.00	225.00	90.00
T215 Type 1	750.00	150.00	65.00
T215 Type 2	700.00	125.00	60.00
T216	600.00	150.00	75.00
E90-1 American Caramel	1550.00	450.00	175.00
E91 American Caramel Set C	325.00	100.00	35.00
E94	850.00	225.00	100.00
E106 American Caramel	925.00	325.00	125.00

	NM	EX	VG
E120 American Caramel	300.00	85.00	40.00
E121 American Caramel Set of 120	165.00	75.00	35.00
E121 American Caramel Set of 80	175.00	75.00	35.00
E122 American Caramel	135.00	50.00	25.00
E220 National Caramel	135.00	50.00	25.00
E224 Texas Tommy	1200.00	400.00	150.00
E254 Colgan's Chips	175.00	65.00	25.00
E270	195.00	70.00	30.00
E286 Ju Ju Drums	950.00	450.00	300.00
E300 Plow's Candy	925.00	325.00	125.00
D303 General Baking	350.00	150.00	75.00
1914 Cracker Jack #65	2350.00	325.00	100.00
1915 Cracker Jack #65	1000.00	300.00	100.00
M116	1650.00	350.00	150.00
Turkey Red (T3)	3500.00	1000.00	400.00
Yuengling's Ice Cream #28	75.00	30.00	15.00
1933 Goudey #89	500.00	175.00	75.00
1940 Play Ball #170	225.00	85.00	35.00

Wilver Dornel "Willie" Stargell

Elected HoF 1988. Willie Stargell remains a popular figure with fans nationwide. The only drawback to Stargell cards is that they are a fairly recent vintage, so they were heavily produced. Despite their cost, older Stargells are bound to be the better investment. All other Stargell cards nots listed are priced under $1.00 in Near Mint condition.

	NM	EX	VG
1963 Topps #553	260.00	110.00	45.00
1964 Topps #342	48.00	20.00	7.50
1965 Topps #377	24.00	8.50	3.00
1966 Topps #255	17.50	7.50	3.00
1967 Topps #140	18.00	7.00	2.50
1968 Topps #86	9.25	3.25	1.00
1969 Topps #545	12.50	3.75	1.25
1970 Topps #470	8.50	2.50	1.00
1971 Topps #230	11.00	2.50	1.00
1972 Topps #447	4.25	1.25	0.50
1972 Topps #448	2.25	0.75	0.25
1973 Topps #370	4.75	1.50	0.50
1974 Topps #100	3.75	1.25	0.35
1975 Topps #100	3.25	1.00	0.25
1976 Topps #270	2.75	0.85	0.20
1977 Topps #460	2.50	0.75	0.15

	NM	EX	VG
1978 Topps #510	2.50	0.75	0.15
1979 Topps #55	2.15	0.65	0.15
1980 Topps #610	1.50	0.50	0.10
1981 Topps #380	1.25	0.35	0.10

Charles Dillon "Casey" Stengel

Elected HoF 1966. Casey Stengel is a legendary figure. His colorful career started in 1912 and spanned most of baseball history. His quotes are quite special. Though he's remembered mainly for his accomplishments as a manager (which usually hurts demand), he's still a popular figure. Although some of his cards are fairly expensive, there are so many that just about anyone can afford at least one.

	NM	EX	VG
E220 National Caramel	325.00	135.00	50.00
D329 Weil Baking #169	200.00	75.00	35.00
M101-4	250.00	100.00	45.00
M101-5 #171	300.00	125.00	50.00
1940 Play Ball #142	175.00	60.00	25.00
1950 Bowman #217	135.00	50.00	20.00
1951 Bowman #181	95.00	35.00	15.00
1952 Bowman #217	135.00	50.00	20.00
1953 Bowman (black and white) #39	350.00	135.00	50.00
1959 Topps #552	27.50	10.00	3.50
1960 Topps #227	13.50	5.00	1.75
1962 Topps #29	16.00	6.00	1.75
1963 Topps #223	11.00	4.00	1.00
1964 Topps #324	13.50	5.00	1.75
1965 Topps #187	16.00	5.00	1.50

William Harold Terry

Elected HoF 1954. Bill Terry was a legitimate superstar of his time. His cards bring some premiums, but prices are probably not in line with his stature.

	NM	EX	VG
E210 York Caramel #46	85.00	35.00	15.00
Diamond Star #14	135.00	45.00	20.00
George Miller	425.00	135.00	45.00
Yuengling's Ice Cream	45.00	20.00	10.00
1933 Delong #4	350.00	125.00	50.00
1933 Goudey #20	475.00	150.00	50.00
1933 Goudey #125	325.00	125.00	40.00

1934 Batter-Up #6	185.00	65.00	30.00
1934 Goudey #21	235.00	75.00	25.00
1935 Goudey (See Travis Jackson)			

Samuel Luther "Big Sam" Thompson

Elected HoF 1974. Sam Thompson is a pre-1900 Hall of Famer whose cards are extremely tough to get. Buy him when you can, but expect to pay dearly for any of his cards.

	NM	EX	VG
N172	1800.00	1000.00	750.00
N284 Buchner Gold Coin	275.00	125.00	50.00
E223 G&B Chewing Gum	2300.00	1000.00	600.00

Joseph Bert Tinker

Elected HoF 1946. He was the start of the famous Tinker-to-Evers-to-Chance double-play combination. Joe Tinker is popular, but is heavily represented in all the cards of the era.

	NM	EX	VG
T202 Hassan	625.00	200.00	75.00
T204 Ramly	1250.00	400.00	150.00
T205	850.00	225.00	75.00
T206 (bat off or on shoulder)	500.00	150.00	50.00
T206 (hands on knees)	550.00	150.00	50.00
T206 (portrait)	625.00	150.00	50.00
T207	650.00	150.00	50.00
T213 Type 2	250.00	100.00	40.00
T213 Type 3	425.00	150.00	50.00
T214	1900.00	1000.00	750.00
T215 Type 1	850.00	225.00	90.00
T215 Type 2	425.00	125.00	50.00
T216	325.00	100.00	50.00
E90-1 American Caramel	575.00	125.00	50.00
E90-3 American Caramel	775.00	250.00	100.00
E93 Standard Caramel	575.00	125.00	65.00
E96 Philadelphia Caramel	575.00	125.00	65.00
E98	800.00	250.00	100.00
E101	450.00	100.00	50.00
E102	700.00	175.00	75.00
E105 Mello-Mint	400.00	100.00	45.00

E106 American Caramel	825.00	275.00	125.00
E254 Colgan's Chips	100.00	35.00	15.00
E270	100.00	35.00	15.00
E300 Plow's Candy	900.00	275.00	100.00
D329 Weil Baking #174	225.00	100.00	35.00
D303 General Baking	225.00	85.00	35.00
1914 Cracker Jack #3	1850.00	225.00	95.00
1915 Cracker Jack #3	650.00	200.00	75.00
M116	575.00	150.00	50.00
Turkey Red (T3) #35	950.00	275.00	125.00

Harold Joseph "Pie" Traynor

Elected HoF 1948. A lot of people think that Pie Traynor was the best third baseman to ever play the game. He should be enormously popular. The fact is, he isn't. He has a fair number of cards, but they have not saturated the market, so there should be some upward price potential.

	NM	EX	VG
E120 American Caramel	95.00	35.00	20.00
E210 York Caramel #14	110.00	40.00	20.00
Diamond Star #27	250.00	85.00	30.00
Diamond Star #99	650.00	250.00	100.00
Yuengling's Ice Cream #14	35.00	20.00	10.00
1933 Delong #12	275.00	100.00	35.00
1933 Goudey #22	435.00	165.00	70.00
1934 Batter-Up #14	165.00	55.00	25.00
1934 Batter-Up #100	375.00	125.00	50.00
1935 Goudey	90.00	35.00	20.00

Clarence Arthur "Dazzy" Vance

Elected HoF 1955. Dazzy Vance cards are about as tough to find as players from the 1930s get. Forget the modest demand. There are virtually no cards. One is a 1933 Goudey that is a condition rarity; another is the always unpopular 1935 Goudey. The pickings are slim for Vance. His cards are expensive and likely to get even more costly.

	NM	EX	VG
1933 Goudey #2	1450.00	350.00	150.00
1935 Goudey	125.00	50.00	25.00

Joseph Floyd "Arky" Vaughan

Elected HoF 1985. Arky Vaughan cards are readily available. In fact, as an investment, his cards are among the weakest of the 1930s players. There is minimal demand and more than ample supplies.

	NM	EX	VG
1933 Goudey #229 225.00	85.00	35.00	
1934 Batter-Up #21	100.00	35.00	15.00
1934 Goudey #22	225.00	85.00	35.00
1939 Play Ball #55	115.00	40.00	20.00
1940 Play Ball #107	90.00	30.00	15.00
1941 Double Play #34	55.00	25.00	15.00
1941 Play Ball #10	85.00	35.00	15.00

George Edward "Rube" Waddell

Elected HoF 1946. Rube Waddell was a top pitcher in the early 1900s. The problem is that he was not a Walter Johnson or Christy Mathewson, so the demand for his cards is not what it might be. That's balanced, however, by the fact that there are not that many Waddell cards. The Waddell of choice is one of his T206s.

	NM	EX	VG
T206 (pitching)	575.00	150.00	50.00
T206 (portrait)	600.00	150.00	50.00
E91 American Caramel Set A	175.00	75.00	30.00
E93 Standard Caramel	575.00	150.00	50.00
E107 Breisch Williams	650.00	175.00	60.00
E254 Colgan's Chips	100.00	35.00	15.00
E270	100.00	35.00	15.00
M116	725.00	175.00	75.00

John Peter "Honus" Wagner

Elected HoF 1936. People have a lot of strange ideas about Honus Wagner cards. The first is that his T206 is the rarest of all baseball cards. That's not even close to true. It is the most expensive baseball card at present, but there are hundreds of cards that are tougher to find. The other strange idea is that because he has one rare card all Wagners are rare. This belief, coupled with the heavy demand you would expect for someone like Wagner, produces very high prices for almost all Wagners, whether they deserve the lofty prices or not.

	NM	EX	VG
T206	425000.00	150000.00	55000.00
E90-1 American Caramel	1750.00	400.00	125.00
E90-2 American Caramel	2200.00	500.00	175.00
E91 American Caramel Set C	450.00	150.00	50.00
E92 Croft's Candy	1150.00	275.00	100.00
E92 Croft's Cocoa	1150.00	275.00	100.00
E92 Dockman	775.00	175.00	75.00
E93 Standard Caramel	1750.00	400.00	125.00
E94	1750.00	400.00	125.00
E95	2000.00	425.00	135.00
E98	2200.00	500.00	175.00
E101	1150.00	375.00	100.00
E102	1750.00	400.00	125.00
E103 Williams Caramel	3200.00	750.00	250.00
E105 Mello-Mint	1350.00	300.00	100.00
E106 American Caramel	2750.00	650.00	225.00
E107 Breisch Williams	2200.00	500.00	175.00
E224 Texas Tommy	2300.00	500.00	175.00
E254 Colgan's Chips	650.00	175.00	75.00
E270	650.00	175.00	75.00
E286 Ju Ju Drums	2500.00	1000.00	575.00
D303 General Baking	675.00	200.00	85.00
D304 General Baking	675.00	200.00	85.00
D329 Weil Baking #182	675.00	200.00	85.00
1914 Cracker Jack #68	5500.00	1250.00	500.00
1915 Cracker Jack #68	2500.00	800.00	400.00
M101-4 #182	425.00	175.00	75.00
M101-5 #184	450.00	200.00	75.00
M101-6 #86	650.00	250.00	100.00
M116 (blue background)	2750.00	1000.00	450.00
M116 (pastel background)	1750.00	750.00	300.00
1940 Play Ball #168	250.00	100.00	45.00
1948 Leaf #70	275.00	85.00	40.00

Rhoderick John "Bobby" Wallace

Elected HoF 1953. Bobby Wallace is one of the lesser-known players from the early 1900s. He was, however, on a fairly limited number of cards, so prices are average for the period even if the demand is not.

	NM	EX	VG
T201 Mecca	175.00	75.00	35.00
T202 Hassan	350.00	125.00	50.00

T204 Ramly	1000.00	350.00	100.00
T205 (with cap)	475.00	125.00	40.00
T205 (without cap)	975.00	350.00	125.00
T206	450.00	100.00	35.00
T207	475.00	100.00	35.00
E90-1 American Caramel	450.00	100.00	35.00
E92 Nadja	1200.00	450.00	200.00
E107 Breisch Williams	650.00	175.00	75.00
M116	575.00	150.00	60.00

Edward Augustine "Big Ed" Walsh

Elected HoF 1946. Big Ed Walsh was a big name in the early 1900s. Not as big a name as Walter Johnson surely, but he still retains solid popularity today. He is not on a lot of cards compared to other players of the era, but he's a solid bet.

	NM	EX	VG
T201 Mecca	200.00	80.00	35.00
T202 Hassan	525.00	150.00	65.00
T205	725.00	175.00	45.00
T206	675.00	150.00	50.00
E90-1 American Caramel	1350.00	500.00	175.00
E90-3 American Caramel	650.00	175.00	75.00
E98	750.00	200.00	85.00
E224 Texas Tommy	875.00	225.00	100.00
E270	100.00	35.00	15.00
E286 Ju Ju Drums	650.00	350.00	250.00
E300 Plow's Candy	825.00	200.00	100.00
D329 Weil Baking #184	225.00	85.00	40.00
1914 Cracker Jack #36	1650.00	300.00	100.00
1915 Cracker Jack #36	500.00	200.00	75.00
M101-4 #184	65.00	30.00	15.00
M101-5 #187	70.00	30.00	20.00
M116	750.00	250.00	100.00

Lloyd James "Little Poison" Waner

Elected HoF 1967. Lloyd Waner was clearly the less popular of the Waner brothers, which reflects in his card prices. The compensation for less demand is a slightly smaller number of cards than brother Paul.

	NM	EX	VG
Diamond Star #16	135.00	45.00	20.00
George Miller	350.00	125.00	50.00

	NM	EX	VG
Yuengling's Ice Cream #59	35.00	15.00	10.00
1933 Goudey #164	225.00	75.00	25.00
1934 Batter-Up #17	125.00	50.00	20.00
1934 Batter-Up #157	325.00	125.00	50.00
1935 Goudey (See Waite Hoyt)			
1939 Play Ball #89	115.00	45.00	20.00
1940 Play Ball #105	125.00	45.00	20.00
1941 Double Play #119	65.00	25.00	10.00

Paul Glee "Big Poison" Waner

Elected HoF 1952. There haven't been a lot of better hitters than Paul Waner. So far, however, his ability hasn't translated into higher card prices.

	NM	EX	VG
Diamond Star #83	225.00	75.00	25.00
George Miller	350.00	125.00	50.00
Yuengling's Ice Cream #45	35.00	15.00	10.00
1933 Goudey #25	385.00	125.00	35.00
1933 Tatoo Orbit	85.00	40.00	20.00
1934 Goudey #11	225.00	75.00	25.00
1935 Goudey (See Waite Hoyt)			
1936 Goudey	140.00	50.00	20.00
1939 Play Ball #112	125.00	40.00	20.00
1940 Play Ball #104	125.00	45.00	20.00
1941 Double Play #16	65.00	25.00	10.00

John Montgomery "Monte" Ward

Elected HoF 1964. John Montgomery Ward is one of the more common pre-1900 stars. Yet his cards are still very rare and quite expensive. It's worth noting that his cards are available. If it's a choice between a Radbourn or a Ward, the Radbourn will be tougher to find.

	NM	EX	VG
N28	950.00	350.00	175.00
N172	1650.00	800.00	450.00
N173	2750.00	1200.00	500.00
N300	1100.00	350.00	150.00
N338-2 S.F. Hess	2000.00	750.00	300.00
N566 Newsboy	2500.00	1250.00	800.00
E223 G&B Chewing Gum	2250.00	750.00	400.00

Michael Francis "Mickey" Welch

Elected HoF 1973. Mickey Welch cards are a bit tougher to find than Monte Ward's. He's a pre-1900 pitching star and trying to collect his cards can drive you crazy. There are Smilin' Mickey Welch cards out there, but they don't hit the market very often.

	NM	EX	VG
N172	1800.00	1000.00	750.00
N173	3000.00	1500.00	800.00
N338-2 S.F. Hess	2250.00	1000.00	400.00
N403 Yum Yum	2250.00	750.00	400.00
E223 G&B Chewing Gum	2250.00	750.00	400.00

Zachary Davis Wheat

Elected HoF 1959. Zack Wheat is one of the lesser-known players from the early 1900s. There are a reasonable number of Zack Wheat cards to be found in the tobacco and candy cards of the day, so the potential for much price movement in his cards is slight.

	NM	EX	VG
T201 Mecca	225.00	75.00	35.00
T202 Hassan	525.00	175.00	75.00
T205	675.00	125.00	50.00
T206	475.00	75.00	35.00
T207	575.00	75.00	25.00
T213 Type 2	225.00	75.00	35.00
T213 Type 3	375.00	125.00	50.00
T214	1750.00	1200.00	750.00
T215 Type 1	800.00	200.00	75.00
E120 American Caramel	125.00	45.00	20.00
E121 American Caramel Set of 80	125.00	45.00	20.00
E121 American Caramel Set of 120	100.00	35.00	20.00
E122 American Caramel	125.00	45.00	20.00
E220 National Caramel	125.00	45.00	20.00
E270	100.00	35.00	15.00
1914 Cracker Jack #52	1600.00	250.00	75.00
1915 Cracker Jack #52	525.00	225.00	75.00
M101-4	65.00	25.00	15.00
M101-5	65.00	25.00	15.00
M101-6	70.00	25.00	15.00

James Hoyt Wilhelm

Elected HoF 1985. Hoyt Wilhelm broke new ground for Cooperstown as a player who was basically a relief pitcher. He might represent a rare position for the Hall of Fame, but not one that brings big bucks, and that's unlikely to change anytime soon.

	NM	EX	VG
1952 Topps #392	575.00	225.00	100.00
1953 Bowman (black & white) #28	120.00	40.00	15.00
1953 Topps #151	75.00	25.00	10.00
1954 Bowman #57	23.00	10.00	3.50
1954 Topps #36	38.00	12.00	5.00
1955 Bowman #1	105.00	15.00	5.00
1956 Topps #307	32.50	13.00	5.00
1957 Topps #203	20.00	7.50	2.50
1958 Topps #324	14.00	5.00	1.75
1959 Topps #349	14.00	5.00	1.75
1960 Leaf #69	13.00	5.00	1.75
1960 Topps #395	14.00	5.00	1.75
1961 Topps #545	57.00	20.00	5.00
1962 Topps #545	60.00	20.00	5.00
1963 Topps #108	9.50	3.00	1.00
1964 Topps #13	7.50	2.50	1.00
1965 Topps #276	8.50	3.00	1.00
1966 Topps #510	14.00	4.00	1.25
1967 Topps #422	10.00	3.25	1.00
1968 Topps #350	5.50	1.50	0.50
1969 Topps #565	5.50	1.50	0.50
1970 Topps #17	4.50	1.25	0.40
1971 Topps #248	5.00	1.25	0.40
1972 Topps #777	19.00	6.00	2.00

Billy Leo Williams

Elected HoF 1987. Billy Williams is a recent Hall of Fame selection whose cards are still available at very reasonable prices. There may not be a lot of upward potential here, but the risks are slight.

	NM	EX	VG
1961 Topps #141	115.00	40.00	15.00
1962 Topps #288	35.00	15.00	5.00
1963 Topps #353	24.00	8.50	3.50

1964 Topps #175	14.00	4.00	1.50
1965 Topps #220	11.00	3.50	1.50
1966 Topps #580	90.00	30.00	10.00
1967 Topps #315	12.50	3.75	1.65
1968 Topps #37	8.50	3.50	1.25
1969 Topps #450	6.25	2.00	0.85
1970 Topps #170	6.50	2.00	0.85
1971 Topps #350	7.00	2.25	0.90
1972 Topps #439	4.50	1.25	0.50
1972 Topps #440	2.25	1.00	0.25
1973 Topps #200	3.00	1.00	0.25
1974 Topps #110	2.75	0.95	0.20
1975 Topps #545	3.25	1.00	0.25
1976 Topps #525	2.00	0.75	0.15

Theodore "Ted" Williams

Elected HoF 1966. Even 30 years of cards is not enough to meet the demand for the Splendid Splinter. With strong national and almost fanatical regional demand, don't expect Ted Williams cards to drop in price.

	NM	EX	VG
1939 Play Ball #92	2250.00	1000.00	600.00
1940 Play Ball #27	1900.00	850.00	350.00
1941 Play Ball #14	2300.00	900.00	300.00
1941 Double Play #57	650.00	200.00	90.00
1941 Double Play #81	650.00	200.00	90.00
1948 Leaf #76	825.00	300.00	125.00
1950 Bowman #98	725.00	225.00	100.00
1951 Bowman #165	575.00	225.00	100.00
1954 Topps #1	700.00	200.00	100.00
1954 Topps #250	775.00	225.00	100.00
1955 Topps #2	450.00	175.00	75.00
1956 Topps #5	310.00	125.00	50.00
1957 Topps #1	475.00	175.00	60.00
1958 Topps #1	425.00	125.00	45.00
1958 Topps #485	75.00	25.00	10.00
1969 Topps #650	12.00	4.00	1.50
1970 Topps #211	10.00	2.50	1.00
1971 Topps #380	7.50	2.50	1.00
1972 Topps #510	6.25	2.25	1.00
1976 Topps #347	5.00	1.50	0.50

Lewis Robert "Hack" Wilson

Elected HoF 1979. There's probably not another card like the 1933 Goudey of Hack Wilson that so perfectly captures the public feeling for the player. All other Wilsons (and there aren't many) pale by comparison.

	NM	EX	VG
E210 York Caramel	75.00	30.00	15.00
Yuengling's Ice Cream	35.00	20.00	10.00
1933 Goudey #211	525.00	200.00	85.00
1934 Batter-Up #73	275.00	125.00	50.00

George Wright

Elected HoF 1937. George Wright's seven year career ended in 1882 and there are no known cards for him.

	NM	EX	VG
No cards			

William Henry "Harry" Wright

Elected HoF 1953. Harry Wright's cards are among the toughest of all pre-1900 Hall of Famers to find. There is surprising demand.

	NM	EX	VG
N172	1800.00	1000.00	750.00
N173	3500.00	1500.00	900.00
N690 Kalamazoo Bats	2750.00	1300.00	850.00

Early Wynn

Elected HoF 1972. Early Wynn is an amazingly overlooked great pitcher of the 1950s. Pitchers with far fewer wins bring more money even though their cards are more common. Following the supply and demand concept, there is a surprising lack of demand for Wynn cards with no immediate interest in sight.

	NM	EX	VG
1949 Bowman #110	130.00	50.00	20.00
1950 Bowman #148	70.00	25.00	10.00
1951 Bowman #78	55.00	20.00	10.00
1952 Bowman #142	50.00	20.00	10.00
1952 Topps #277	180.00	75.00	25.00

1953 Bowman #146	130.00	40.00	15.00
1953 Topps #61	85.00	35.00	12.00
1954 Bowman #164	38.00	15.00	5.00
1955 Bowman #38	25.00	10.00	3.50
1956 Topps #187	32.50	10.00	3.50
1957 Topps #40	27.00	10.00	3.00
1958 Topps #100	25.00	10.00	2.50
1959 Topps #260	16.00	5.00	2.00
1960 Topps #1	45.00	15.00	3.00
1961 Topps #455	14.00	4.50	1.75
1962 Topps #385	22.00	5.00	2.00

Carl Michael "Yaz" Yastrzemski

Elected HoF 1989. Carl Yastrzemski is enormously popular. Fortunately, he has one of the largest and most diverse supplies of cards, spanning from 1960 to the mid-1980s. The situation for his cards is interesting, as current demand puts a lot of upward pressure on prices. Down the road, however, there has to be some question as to whether the demand will support the prices, especially of the later cards. All other Yastrzemski cards not listed are priced under $1.00 in Near Mint condition.

	NM	EX	VG
1960 Topps #148	325.00	135.00	50.00
1961 Topps #287	145.00	65.00	25.00
1962 Topps #425	250.00	110.00	40.00
1963 Fleer #8	80.00	25.00	10.00
1963 Topps #115	95.00	30.00	10.00
1964 Topps #210	75.00	25.00	10.00
1965 Topps #385	80.00	30.00	10.00
1966 Topps #70	43.00	17.00	7.50
1967 Topps #355	80.00	30.00	10.00
1968 Topps #250	35.00	15.00	5.00
1968 Topps #369	14.50	6.00	2.25
1969 Topps #130	27.50	12.00	3.50
1969 Topps #425	10.00	2.50	1.00
1970 Topps #10	35.00	10.00	2.50
1970 Topps #461	10.00	2.50	1.00
1971 Topps #530	50.00	15.00	5.00
1972 Topps #37	15.50	5.00	1.50
1972 Topps #38	8.50	2.50	1.00
1973 Topps #245	14.00	4.50	1.50
1974 Topps #280	11.00	3.00	0.85
1975 Topps #280	15.00	2.50	0.75

1976 Topps #230	8.25	2.25	0.75
1977 Topps #434	1.50	0.50	0.10
1977 Topps #480	6.50	1.50	0.50
1978 Topps #40	4.50	1.50	0.50
1979 Topps #320	3.50	1.00	0.25
1980 Topps #720	2.00	0.50	0.10
1981 Donruss #94	2.00	0.50	0.10
1981 Donruss #214	2.00	0.50	0.10
1981 Fleer #221	2.00	0.50	0.10
1981 Fleer #638	2.00	0.50	0.10
1981 Topps #110	2.25	0.75	0.15
1982 Topps #650	1.75	0.65	0.13
1983 Topps #550	1.25	0.40	0.10
1984 Donruss "Living Legends"	7.75	2.25	1.00
1984 Fleer #412	1.75	0.50	0.10
1984 Fleer #640	1.75	0.50	0.10

Denton True "Cy" Young

Elected HoF 1937. Cy Young is still the standard by which all pitchers are measured. With one of each year's biggest awards bearing his name, he remains a legend. Fortunately, he appeared on many cards over a long career, so most collectors can still afford his cards.

	NM	EX	VG
T202 Hassan	650.00	200.00	100.00
T205	1250.00	500.00	175.00
T206 (pitching)	850.00	250.00	100.00
T206 (portrait)	1300.00	350.00	125.00
T215 Type 1	950.00	250.00	100.00
T216	450.00	175.00	90.00
E90-1 American Caramel (Boston)	850.00	300.00	100.00
E90-1 American Caramel (Cleveland)	975.00	350.00	150.00
E92 Croft's Candy	975.00	275.00	150.00
E92 Croft's Cocoa	975.00	275.00	150.00
E92 Dockman	650.00	200.00	100.00
E92 Nadja	3000.00	1300.00	500.00
E93 Standard Caramel	1100.00	300.00	150.00
E94	1100.00	300.00	150.00
E97 Briggs	1650.00	550.00	200.00
E98	1100.00	300.00	150.00
E101	1100.00	300.00	150.00
E105 Mello-Mint	650.00	200.00	100.00

E107 Breisch Williams	1350.00	500.00	225.00
E254 Colgan's Chips	300.00	125.00	50.00
E270	300.00	125.00	50.00
D304 General Baking	450.00	175.00	75.00
M116	1250.00	325.00	150.00

Royce Middlebrook "Ross" Youngs

Elected HoF 1972. Ross Youngs isn't on many cards. Fortunately, the few he is on are rather easy to find, so prices are lower than they might otherwise be.

	NM	EX	VG
E120 American Caramel	125.00	50.00	25.00
E121 American Caramel Set of 120	125.00	50.00	25.00

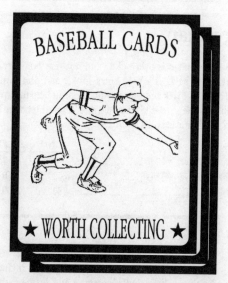

Major Modern Card Sets

A note about the listings

LISTED ARE VALUES of individual cards for common players and for complete sets. In some cases, values are separated into groups, which may differ slightly in value. In a few cases, values are also given for cards of scarce players within the set. Players not listed in either the Hall of Famers or Key Players sections are considered (at least for the purposes of card values) common. Find the year, manufacturer, and set of the card in question, and take the value for common cards of that set as the value of a card for a common player. In some cases, individual cards are actually worth less than 1¢: for instance, you could buy 10 for 5¢. However, due to rounding off and for consistency of the number format, these values appear as 0.01 in the listings. Of course, other factors, such as additional packaging, autographs, and so on may affect the value of any single common card.

1948 Bowman

The 1948 Bowman set is overlooked and not very popular. This set has some important cards, such as a Yogi Berra rookie and first cards of many Hall of Famers. The set is black and white, which doesn't help the investment, but then Babe Ruth's rookie card is black and white. The set tends to be eclipsed by the 1948 Leaf set, but it is still a solid set.

	NM	EX	VG
Common Player #1–36	17.50	7.50	2.00
Common Player #37–48	20.00	8.50	2.50
Complete Set	3800.00	1500.00	600.00

1948 Leaf

This set features more stars than Bowman's 1948 set, including Joe DiMaggio and Jackie Robinson. It includes common and scarce cards such as George Kurowski's, whose cards currently bring big bucks.

	NM	EX	VG
Common Player	27.50	12.00	4.00
Complete Set	32000.00	12500.00	5000.00
Scarce Player	275.00	125.00	50.00

1949 Bowman

This is not a very attractive set, but it does include Roy Campanella and Robin Roberts rookies. It's awfully expensive for a fairly modest list of stars.

	NM	EX	VG
Common Player #1–36	16.00	5.00	2.00
Common Player #37–73	17.50	6.00	2.50
Common Player #74–144	16.00	5.00	2.00
Common Player #145–240	75.00	25.00	10.00
Complete Set	17500.00	7500.00	3500.00

1950 Bowman

Bowman finally produced a set of attractive cards, but managed to do so in a set lacking any very important rookies. It's not very expensive and you get what you pay for in this case.

	NM	EX	VG
Common Player #1–72	55.00	20.00	7.50

	NM	EX	VG
Common Player #73–252	17.50	7.50	2.50
Complete Set	12000.00	4500.00	2000.00

1951 Bowman

This is the set the stars fall in — two rookies named Mantle and Mays. There is also a condition rarity rookie of Whitey Ford. This is one of the top sets of the 1950s.

	NM	EX	VG
Common Player #1–36	22.00	8.00	3.50
Common Player #37–252	15.00	7.00	3.00
Common Player #253–324	65.00	28.00	13.00
Complete Set	25000.00	11000.00	5500.00

1952 Bowman

This is a very pretty set featuring almost no rookies of any real importance, but it's not that expensive.

	NM	EX	VG
Common Player #1–216	20.00	8.00	3.50
Common Player #217–252	35.00	16.00	6.50
Complete Set	10000.00	4000.00	1850.00

1952 Topps

This is the most important, and most expensive, set of the 1950s. It's the first Topps set featuring the famous first Topps card of Mantle (#311). It's the same for Mays (#261), but no one seems to notice. This set runs about the same price as a new house, so in today's real estate market it looks overpriced.

	NM	EX	VG
Common Player #1–80	55.00	23.00	10.00
Common Player #81–250	27.50	12.00	5.00
Common Player #251–310	55.00	20.00	8.00
Common Player #311–407	190.00	80.00	35.00
Complete Set	100000.00	45000.00	20000.00

1953 Bowman

This is a very popular set despite a lack of any very exciting rookies. Some of the best pictures of the early 1950s make it a solid investment.

	NM	EX	VG
Common Player #1–112	33.00	12.00	5.00
Common Player #113–160	45.00	15.00	6.00
Complete Set	15000.00	5000.00	2000.00

1953 Bowman (black and white)

Black-and-white cards are never popular. Even a great Casey Stengel can't save this set.

	NM	EX	VG
Common Player	32.00	12.00	3.50
Complete Set	2600.00	1100.00	450.00

1953 Topps

This was a beautiful and popular set before Topps released its archives version. There aren't many rookies in the set, but it's got great cards of Mantle, Robinson, Berra, and many others.

	NM	EX	VG
Common Player #1–220	17.50	7.50	3.00
Common Player #221–280	55.00	20.00	8.50
Complete Set	16500.00	7200.00	2500.00
Singleprints #1–165	23.00	10.00	4.00
Singleprints #221–280	100.00	40.00	17.00

1954 Bowman

It's hard to believe that the same company that produced the 1953 Bowman set came up with this. It doesn't have quality, it doesn't have great rookies, but it does have two #66 cards. One was Jimmy Piersall. The other, which was quickly withdrawn, was Ted Williams — which is worth more than the set and has a better future.

	NM	EX	VG
Common Player #1–112	8.50	3.00	1.00
Common Player #113–224	11.00	3.50	1.50
Complete Set (#66 Piersall)	4300.00	2000.00	950.00
Complete Set (#66 Williams)	10000.00	4800.00	2350.00

1954 Topps

This is a nicely done set. It doesn't have Mantle, but it does have rookies of Banks, Aaron, and Tommy Lasorda. A real sleeper set.

	NM	EX	VG
Common Player #1–50	14.00	6.00	2.00
Common Player #51–75	32.50	12.50	5.00
Common Player #76–250	14.00	6.00	2.00
Complete Set	10000.00	4000.00	1700.00

1955 Bowman

This set is a true relic of the 1950s. The players are in color television sets with different-colored wood grain. It's no surprise it was Bowman's last set. It has a lot of stars, but no rookies worth mentioning. It does have umpires (including Hall of Famers not otherwise available), but it's still too bad the picture tube didn't blow.

	NM	EX	VG
Common Player #1–224	10.00	4.00	1.50
Common Player #225–320	28.00	11.00	3.50
Complete Set	5500.00	2200.00	1000.00

1955 Topps

This set helped to compensate for the 1955 Bowman set. It has only 210 cards, but features Clemente, Koufax, and Killebrew rookies. Despite the lack of a Mantle, it's a solid set.

	NM	EX	VG
Common Player #1–150	8.50	3.00	1.25
Common Player #151–160	17.50	7.50	3.00
Common Player #161–210	28.00	12.00	5.00
Complete Set	8000.00	3500.00	1500.00

1956 Topps

This is a very representative set of the 1950s. There are no great rookies except for Aparicio, but it has most of the major names of the golden era.

	NM	EX	VG
Common Player #1–100	7.50	2.50	1.00
Common Player #101–180	10.00	4.00	1.50

	NM	EX	VG
Common Player #181–260	17.50	7.50	3.00
Common Player #261–340	10.00	4.00	1.50
Complete Set	8200.00	3200.00	1300.00

1957 Topps

This is an excellent set for sleepers and Hall of Fame rookies. Start with Brooks and Frank Robinson. Add Don Drysdale and Bill Mazeroski, Whitey Herzog, Colavito, and Bunning, and you have a set with solid potential.

	NM	EX	VG
Common Player #1–264	7.50	3.00	1.00
Common Player #265–352	20.00	8.50	3.50
Common Player #353–407	7.50	3.00	1.00
Complete Set	8500.00	3400.00	1500.00

1958 Topps

This is the first set with all-star cards offering two cards of some stars. It included a number of sleepers such as Maris, Cepeda, and Pinson rookies.

	NM	EX	VG
Common Player #1–110	7.50	3.00	1.00
Common Player #111–440	5.25	2.00	0.75
Common Player #441–495	4.25	1.35	0.60
Complete Set	5500.00	2250.00	1000.00

1959 Topps

This is another solid set of the 1950s. It's top rookies are Bob Gibson and Sparky Anderson. It's not too expensive considering the players.

	NM	EX	VG
Common Player #1–110	5.50	1.75	0.50
Common Player #111–506	3.25	1.00	0.25
Common Player #507–572	17.00	5.00	1.00
Complete Set	5700.00	2200.00	1000.00

1960 Topps

Carl Yastrzemski and Willie McCovey headline this set, which returns to the horizontal format of the middle 1950s. That move apparently does not sit too well with today's buyers — despite better rookies it's cheaper than the 1959 set.

	NM	EX	VG
Common Player #1–370	2.30	1.00	0.20
Common Player #371–522	4.50	1.50	0.35
Common Player #523–589	26.00	10.00	3.50
Complete Set	6000.00	2500.00	1000.00

1961 Topps

The 1961 Topps set has the popularity the 1960 set lacks. The rookies aren't spectacular (Billy Williams and Juan Marachal), but this set includes MVP cards. Though the MVP cards may be a bit overrated, they add to the complete set price.

	NM	EX	VG
Common Player #1–370	2.30	1.00	0.20
Common Player #371–522	4.50	1.50	0.35
Common Player #523–589	26.00	10.00	3.50
Complete Set	6000.00	2500.00	1000.00

1962 Topps

This set has an innovative design, with a Gaylord Perry rookie plus a host of overpriced rookies among the last ten cards. Look for softness in price due to such inclusions as the $55 Jim Hickman rookies.

	NM	EX	VG
Common Player #1–370	2.25	0.80	0.20
Common Player #371–522	4.50	1.50	0.35
Common Player #523–598	14.00	3.50	1.50
Complete Set	5400.00	1800.00	750.00

1963 Fleer

This is not high on anyone's list of sets, although it certainly is a historic set. It's far less common than Topps sets for the same period. It has some major names, but no rookies. For the present it tends to have little or no demand or upward price pressure.

	NM	EX	VG
Common Player	6.25	2.00	0.75
Complete Set	1125.00	400.00	150.00

1963 Topps

This used to be dubbed "the set with the Pete Rose rookie." It still is, but Rose isn't quite as popular as he was seven or eight years ago. It has Rose and Willie Stargell and two cards that ought to get more attention—a Dave DeBusschere rookie and a Rusty Staub. It's a worthwhile, although slightly speculative, set.

	NM	EX	VG
Common Player #1–283	1.75	0.65	0.20
Common Player #284–446	3.25	1.00	0.25
Common Player #447–506	11.00	3.50	1.25
Common Player #507–576	7.50	2.50	1.00
Complete Set	5300.00	2000.00	800.00

1964 Topps

This set is more readily available than in previous years. It has no top rookies, but there are a few that give it potential, such as Tommy John, Lou Piniella, Richie Allen, and Phil Niekro. Other than the John card, which is around $200, there are some fairly cheap gambles that could move a set filled with big names.

	NM	EX	VG
Common Player #1–370	2.25	0.75	0.20
Common Player #371–522	3.25	1.00	0.25
Common Player #523–587	7.50	2.50	1.00
Complete Set	3250.00	1100.00	375.00

1965 Topps

This is a very soild set when you consider the rookies it contains, such as Carlton, Hunter, Joe Morgan, Tony Perez, and Tug McGraw. If you want to take a shot at a bunch of rookies in a set, this is a good one from the 1960s.

	NM	EX	VG
Common Player #1–522	2.25	0.75	0.20
Common Player #523–598	5.50	1.50	0.50
Complete Set	3750.00	1400.00	575.00

1966 Topps

This is another good set for rookies, with Jim Palmer, Don Sutton, Fergie Jenkins, and Roy White. It's a problem set, however, with high-priced commons in the last 75 cards. It's an overpriced set generally.

	NM	EX	VG
Common Player #1–446	1.30	0.35	0.15
Common Player #447–522	5.50	1.50	0.50
Common Player #523–598	17.50	7.00	2.50
Complete Set	4900.00	2000.00	900.00

1967 Topps

This is the set of the Tom Seaver and Rod Carew rookies. The price for this set is interesting as Seaver and Carew by themselves make up about one-third of the price of the complete set. The set rises and falls with Seaver and Carew.

	NM	EX	VG
Common Player #1–457	1.25	0.30	0.12
Common Player #458–533	5.50	1.50	0.40
Common Player #534–609	14.00	4.50	1.35
Complete Set	5200.00	2200.00	1000.00

1968 Topps

The Nolan Ryan rookie makes this set. There is a Johnny Bench rookie, too, but the Nolan Ryan rookie by itself accounts for almost 50 percent of the set price. Under the circumstances the price for the set will rise and fall with Ryan.

	NM	EX	VG
Common Player #1–533	1.25	0.35	0.12
Common Player #534–598	3.00	1.00	0.25
Complete Set	3250.00	1350.00	600.00

1969 Topps

Reggie Jackson dominates this set in much the same way that Nolan Ryan dominates the 1968 set. Reggie's rookie is about 25 percent of the price of the whole set, which also includes Rollie Fingers and Bobby Bonds. It's worth noting that the 1969 set still has a lot of stars from the 1950s, including the last regular Mantle card.

	NM	EX	VG
Common Player	1.25	0.35	0.10
Complete Set	2800.00	1200.00	500.00

1970 Topps

There are no dominating rookies in this set. The best rookie is Thurman Munson. Despite being slightly tough to find in top grades, this set has not caught anyone's fancy.

	NM	EX	VG
Common Player #1–546	1.00	0.25	0.10
Common Player #547–633	1.75	0.60	0.20
Common Player #634–720	3.50	1.25	0.50
Complete Set	2400.00	950.00	375.00

1971 Topps

This is one of the toughest sets to find in Near Mint or better condition. The cards in this set have black borders that show the slightest sign of wear. It may not have the best rookies, although Blyleven, Concepcion, and Ted Simmons aren't bad. In top grade this set is rare, but any less and it's very ordinary.

	NM	EX	VG
Common Player #1–523	1.00	0.30	0.10
Common Player #524–643	1.00	0.30	0.10
Common Player #644–752	3.50	1.00	0.25
Complete Set	2750.00	900.00	350.00

1972 Topps

If any set belongs in the 1960s it's this one. It could have been designed by the Grateful Dead. A lot of people don't like it, but it's also got more than a few defenders. The Carlton Fisk rookie and stars-in-action cards are well worth the investment.

	NM	EX	VG
Common Player #1–525	0.50	0.15	0.06
Common Player #526–656	1.15	0.30	0.10
Common Player #657–787	3.25	1.00	0.20
Complete Set	2100.00	900.00	350.00

1973 Topps

Topps changed its approach to design after 1972 and came up with a more conservative look. The look may not be exciting, but the Mike Schmidt rookie is, and his card comprises about one-third of the set's value. Interesting support rookies for this set include Dwight Evans, Bob Boone, and Rick Reuschel.

	NM	EX	VG
Common Player #1–528	0.50	0.15	0.06
Common Player #529–669	2.25	0.75	0.20
Complete Set	1350.00	500.00	200.00

1974 Topps

The winning rookie in this set is Dave Winfield. The sleepers are Bill Madlock and Dave Parker. Otherwise it's a very ordinary set. It's much more common than sets just a few years older. With very few exceptions the stars from the 1950s are missing, as they had retired by 1974.

	NM	EX	VG
Common Player	0.40	0.12	0.05
Complete Set	750.00	400.00	175.00

1975 Topps

This is probably the best set of the 1970s for rookies. Two sure bets are Robin Yount and George Brett. They have some good company in Gary Carter, Keith Hernandez, Jim Rice, and Fred Lynn. If you like rookies, this is a set you must have, and one with a lot of potential.

	NM	EX	VG
Common Player	0.40	0.12	0.05
Complete Set	1000.00	400.00	175.00

1976 Topps

This set has little or nothing to offer. Dennis Eckersley is about the only card of note. It will be a long-slow climb before there is much profit here.

	NM	EX	VG
Common Player	0.30	0.10	0.03
Complete Set	435.00	175.00	75.00

1977 Topps

The rookies in this set cause it have have some real ups and downs. The strong rookie is Andre Dawson. The up-and-down rookies are Mark Fidrych, Dale

Murphy, Jack Clark, and Denny Martinez. Currently the set is down, and that's probably where it will stay.

	NM	EX	VG
Common Player	0.25	0.08	0.03
Complete Set	410.00	165.00	70.00

1978 Topps

This set is similar to but slightly cheaper than the 1977 set. It doesn't contain as many disappointing rookies. Paul Molitor and Alan Trammell are featured on the same card, and that seems to be the top item. Jack Morris is also a nice addition.

	NM	EX	VG
Common Player	0.15	0.05	0.02
Complete Set	375.00	150.00	60.00

1979 Topps

There's not much in this set except for an Ozzie Smith rookie, which is eternally underpriced. Carney Lansford is probably the best of the rest.

	NM	EX	VG
Common Player	0.15	0.05	0.02
Complete Set	265.00	100.00	35.00

1980 Topps

This set has had its share of ups turned down. It's got Mike Scott and Jesse Orosco on the same card. Dan Quisenberry, Rick Sutcliffe, and Tommy Herr are big disappointments on the heels of their best years. The main rookie star of the set is Rickey Henderson.

	NM	EX	VG
Common Player	0.15	0.05	0.02
Complete Set	300.00	125.00	50.00

1981 Donruss

The first Donruss set, which is still waiting for an audience despite Jeff Reardon and Tim Raines rookies. This set is not an artistic or commercial success.

	NM	EX	VG
Common Player	0.07	0.02	0.01
Complete Set	65.00	25.00	10.00

1981 Fleer

This set suffers from the same things as the 1981 Donruss. Both had heavy production and struggle to stay present in today's market.

	NM	EX	VG
Common Player	0.07	0.02	0.01
Complete Set	65.00	25.00	10.00

1981 Topps

This set holds up better than either Fleer or Donruss for the same year. Reardon and Raines are the highlights here. It's the set of choice for 1981.

	NM	EX	VG
Common Player	0.10	0.04	0.02
Complete Set	115.00	40.00	15.00

1981 Topps Traded

Reardon and Raines are the featured players, along with a first card of Danny Ainge.

	NM	EX	VG
Common Player	0.12	0.05	0.20
Complete Set	45.00	15.00	5.00

1982 Donruss

All 1982 sets are dominated by the rookie card of Cal Ripken Jr. Lee Smith runs a distant second.

	NM	EX	VG
Common Player	0.07	0.02	0.01
Complete Set	95.00	35.00	10.00

1982 Fleer

This set rides the back of one player: Cal Ripken Jr. He accounts for about 75 percent of the price of this set. Actually, this set is on the rise, as Lee Smith finally got some attention. Other interesting rookies are Dave Stewart, Dave Righetti, and Steve Sax.

	NM	EX	VG
Common Player	0.07	0.02	0.01
Complete Set	95.00	35.00	10.00

1982 Topps

Like the two preceeding sets, this one is a showcase for Cal Ripken Jr. In the Topps set, however, his card is only worth about 50 percent of the value instead of 75 percent.

	NM	EX	VG
Common Player	0.09	0.03	0.02
Complete Set	175.00	75.00	25.00

1982 Topps Traded

Cal Ripken Jr. is a sure bet, but without his card this is a $30 set.

	NM	EX	VG
Common Player	12.00	0.05	0.02
Complete Set	300.00	125.00	50.00

1983 Donruss

This was a good year. The set includes Ryne Sandberg, Wade Boggs, and Tony Gwynn. Add Howard Johnson, Julio Franco, Frank Viola, and Willie McGee and you have a very good investment for your money.

	NM	EX	VG
Common Player	0.07	0.02	0.01
Complete Set	145.00	55.00	20.00

1983 Fleer

The 1983 Fleer set provides the same story as the 1983 Donruss in terms of rookies. An interesting footnote is that once the hottest rookie of 1983 was Ron Kittle.

	NM	EX	VG
Common Player	0.07	0.02	0.01
Complete Set	145.00	55.00	20.00

1983 Topps

This set has the same rookies as the other 1983 sets, but it is more expensive.

	NM	EX	VG
Common Player	0.09	0.03	0.02
Complete Set	190.00	65.00	25.00

1983 Topps Traded

	NM	EX	VG
Common Player	0.12	0.05	0.02
Complete Set	135.00	50.00	20.00

1984 Donruss

This may be the highlight set of the 1980s. It's loaded with rookies, but remember, not many of them will make the Hall of Fame. The set includes Strawberry, Mattingly, Andy Van Slyke, Tony Fernandez, and Joe Carter.

	NM	EX	VG
Common Player	0.13	0.06	0.03
Complete Set	425.00	170.00	75.00

1984 Fleer

This set is a poor second in popularity and price to Donruss. Nevertheless, it's got Strawberry, Mattingly, Fernandez, and Van Slyke.

	NM	EX	VG
Common Player	0.09	0.03	0.02
Complete Set	240.00	100.00	35.00

1984 Fleer Update

The jackpot in 1984 was not the regular sets, but the Fleer Update. Roger Clemens and Kirby Puckett are the top rookies, followed by Gooden, Langston, Saberhagen, Jose Rijo, Jimmy Key, and John Franco. It's not easy to top that list and not exactly easy to afford them, either.

	NM	EX	VG
Common Player	0.17	0.07	0.03
Complete Set	775.00	300.00	125.00

1984 Topps

The last year for which Topps was the most expensive of sets was 1983; in 1984 Topps dropped to third. The reason for the change was a lack of major rookies. Mattingly and Van Slyke are the most important rookies in the set. Strawberry is the most confusing rookie, since his card seems to set the price pace of the set.

	NM	EX	VG
Common Player	0.09	0.03	0.02
Complete Set	100.00	35.00	15.00

1984 Topps Traded

Topps missed a few names in its regular 1984 set, so this set is where you will find the first Topps cards of Saberhagen, Key, Langston, Gooden, and Rijo.

	NM	EX	VG
Common Player	0.12	0.05	0.02
Complete Set	115.00	45.00	20.00

1985 Donruss

The 1984 Donruss set was loaded with rookies, but it still missed a few. You'll find the ones it missed in the 1985 set, with the first cards of Tartabull, Franco, Gooden, Clemens, Eric Davis, Puckett, Rijo, Langston, Key, Hershiser, and Saberhagen. In good years those names represent most of the all-star team. In bad years there can be a lot of minus signs by their prices.

	NM	EX	VG
Common Player	0.09	0.03	0.02
Complete Set	195.00	75.00	35.00

1985 Fleer

This set is in large part a repeat of the 1984 Fleer Update, but with the first regular-issue cards of some big names. New names include Joe Carter, Eric Davis, Danny Tartabull, and Shawon Dunston. Some of these names could make this set fairly volatile.

	NM	EX	VG
Common Player	0.07	0.02	0.01
Complete Set	190.00	70.00	35.00

1985 Topps

This is a fascinating set. It has the first regular cards of the stars from the 1984 Traded set plus the first Topps cards of Clemens, Puckett, Howard Johnson, John Franco, Eric Davis, Carter, Hershiser, and Sid Fernandez. Add to them No. 1 draft picks including Dunston and the Olympic team with Mark McGwire.

	NM	EX	VG
Common Player	0.10	0.04	0.02
Complete Set	195.00	75.00	35.00

1985 Topps Traded

This set is a bust in terms of rookies. Vince Coleman is the big name?! This set is going nowhere.

	NM	EX	VG
Common Player	0.12	0.05	0.02
Complete Set	27.50	10.00	3.50

1986 Donruss

Fred McGriff, Jose Canseco, and Cecil Fielder are the big names in this set. Those names provide a lot of potential and a certain amount of risk at present price levels.

	NM	EX	VG
Common Player	0.07	0.02	0.01
Complete Set	225.00	85.00	37.50

1986 Donruss Rookies

Better late than never, Donruss jumped into the rookie game with a late-season set. Will Clark heads a good list of rookies that includes Bonilla, Bonds, Drabek, Kruk, Sierra, and Bo Jackson. There's enough talent in this set that even though Jackson is overpriced there is still room for price increases.

	NM	EX	VG
Common Player	0.17	0.07	0.03
Complete Set	70.00	25.00	10.00

1986 Fleer

Canseco, Fielder, and Benito Santiago are the headliners in this popular set.

	NM	EX	VG
Common Player	0.07	0.02	0.01
Complete Set	135.00	55.00	20.00

1986 Fleer Update

Bonds, Bonilla, Clark, Drabek, Sierra, Joyner, and Kruk are the featured new cards in this set. It has potential at current price levels.

	NM	EX	VG
Common Player	0.09	0.03	0.02
Complete Set	45.00	15.00	5.00

1986 Sportflics

This initial Sportflics effort to produce sets was reviewed positively, but the rest have never really taken off. The exception is a rare Robin Yount with a Yankee logo in this set. The Canseco, Greenwell, and Tartabull rookies were also once hot, but have cooled off with their careers.

	NM	EX	VG
Common Player	0.09	0.04	0.02
Complete Set	37.50	15.00	6.00

1986 Topps

This is not generally considered a great set, although it has been drawing more attention with rookies of Dykstra, Fielder, and Darren Daulton.

	NM	EX	VG
Common Player	0.06	0.02	0.01
Complete Set	27.50	12.50	5.00

1986 Topps Traded

First Topps cards of Bonds, Bonilla, Clark, Kruk, and Canseco top a good list.

	NM	EX	VG
Common Player	0.08	0.03	0.02
Complete Set	25.00	10.00	5.00

1987 Donruss

First Donruss cards of Maddux, Bo Jackson, Palmeiro, Duane Ward, McGwire, Bonds, Sierra, Larkin, Bonilla, and others make this a top set.

	NM	EX	VG
Common Player	0.06	0.02	0.01
Complete Set	65.00	27.50	12.00

1987 Donruss Rookies

Donruss didn't improve very much on the regular set with this rookies set. Top rookie card is also the first card of Matt Williams. There is also a John Smiley and a Fred McGriff.

	NM	EX	VG
Common Player	0.09	0.04	0.02
Complete Set	25.00	10.00	5.00

1987 Fleer

Sierra, Clark, Larkin, and Canseco lead this set, one of the top sets of the 1980s.

	NM	EX	VG
Common Player	0.06	0.02	0.01
Complete Set	95.00	35.00	15.00

1987 Fleer Update

First Fleer cards of McGwire, Matt Williams, McGriff, and Greg Maddux are the features. It's fairly expensive, but remember that Fleer was behind others in producing any cards with top names.

	NM	EX	VG
Common Player	0.06	0.02	0.01
Complete Set	18.00	7.50	3.00

1987 Topps

This set is probably a steal, with first cards of Sierra, Williams, Drabek, Swindell, and many $1.00-and-up early cards of young stars.

	NM	EX	VG
Common Player	0.06	0.02	0.01
Complete Set	27.50	12.00	5.00

1987 Topps Traded

This set is a yawn. Late, but first Topps cards of McGriff, Santiago, Williams, and David Cone.

	NM	EX	VG
Common Player	0.06	0.02	0.01
Complete Set	12.00	5.00	2.25

1988 Donruss

Roberto Alomar, Mark Grace, Roberto Kelly, and Tom Glavine top an otherwise ordinary set. Jack McDowell helps, but there isn't much of note to bring this set up in price.

	NM	EX	VG
Common Player	0.05	0.01	0.01
Complete Set	20.00	8.50	4.00

1988 Donruss Rookies

Take away Roberto Alomar and you could give this set away.

	NM	EX	VG
Common Player	0.09	0.04	0.02
Complete Set	22.00	9.00	3.50

1988 Fleer

Fleer discovered Matt Williams! Aside from the first Fleer Matt Williams, also featured are Tom Glavine, Ron Gant, and Roberto Kelly. Don't expect a lot from this set and you won't be disappointed.

	NM	EX	VG
Common Player	0.06	0.02	0.01
Complete Set	32.00	13.00	5.00

1988 Fleer Update

Roberto Alomar, John Smoltz, and Mark Grace complete this set.

	NM	EX	VG
Common Player	0.06	0.02	0.01
Complete Set	17.50	8.25	3.75

1988 Score

Tom Glavine and Ron Gant are the top rookies in this set, but you can get them in other sets for less money. It's not easy to justify the price for this set.

	NM	EX	VG
Common Player	0.05	0.01	0.01
Complete Set	23.00	10.00	4.50

1988 Score Traded

This set includes a lot of players (primarily Roberto Alomar) who didn't make the regular offering. If you want to pay $60 and up for a Roberto Alomar card, then this set is for you.

	NM	EX	VG
Common Player	0.09	0.04	0.02
Complete Set	105.00	40.00	17.50

1988 Sportflics

The rookies aren't great, but the set has held its value. It's expensive considering the names are less than fantastic.

	NM	EX	VG
Common Player	0.11	0.05	0.02
Complete Set	35.00	15.00	5.00

1988 Topps

This set contains the first card of Tom Glavine and not much else of note. Other rookies could take off, but none so far have shown active signs of life.

	NM	EX	VG
Common Player	0.07	0.03	0.01
Complete Set	20.00	9.00	4.00

1988 Topps Traded

This set features the Olympic team which is still quite speculative. The big names in the set are Abbott, Alomar, Benes, McDowell, and Ventura, but their popularity will probably change.

	NM	EX	VG
Common Player	0.07	0.03	0.01
Complete Set	45.00	20.00	8.50

1989 Donruss

A cheap set, especially with Ken Griffey Jr., Gary Sheffield, Felix Jose, and Sandy Alomar Jr.

	NM	EX	VG
Common Player	0.04	0.01	0.01
Complete Set	17.50	8.00	3.50

1989 Donruss Rookies

This set is the same price as the regular 1989 set, but why? The rookie is Deion Sanders, but what sport does he play?

	NM	EX	VG
Common Player	0.11	0.05	0.02
Complete Set	17.50	8.00	3.50

1989 Fleer

Ken Griffey Jr. is about all you need to know about this set, although Gary Sheffield is quite good, too.

	NM	EX	VG
Common Player	0.06	0.02	0.01
Complete Set	17.50	8.00	3.50

1989 Fleer Update

Robin Ventura, Joey Belle, and Deion Sanders are the lead cards in this set. There's not much else of note, and the set has limited potential.

	NM	EX	VG
Common Player	0.07	0.03	0.01
Complete Set	15.00	6.00	2.50

1989 Score

This set contains primarily ordinary players, with Gary Sheffield as the only player of note.

	NM	EX	VG
Common Player	0.04	0.01	0.01
Complete Set	17.50	8.00	3.50

1989 Score Traded

Better late than never with Ken Griffey Jr. and Jim Abbott.

	NM	EX	VG
Common Player	0.06	0.02	0.01
Complete Set	9.50	4.00	1.50

1989 Sportflics

There's nothing special in this set except rookie cards of Sandy Alomar, Greg Jefferies, and Gary Sheffield.

	NM	EX	VG
Common Player	0.11	0.05	0.02
Complete Set	32.50	14.00	6.50

1989 Topps

So far, this is one of the weaker Topps sets. Number-one draft picks help and so does Ramon Martinez, but more help is needed to raise its price.

	NM	EX	VG
Common Player	0.04	0.01	0.01
Complete Set	22.50	10.00	3.50

1989 Topps Traded

Ken Griffey Jr. and Deion Sanders top this list.

	NM	EX	VG
Common Player	0.05	0.02	0.01
Complete Set	10.00	4.00	1.75

1989 Upper Deck

This is the first issue from Upper Deck. It had enormous impact even though the rookies are fairly standard. Will it hold its tremendous premium? is a major question.

	NM	EX	VG
Common Player	0.09	0.04	0.02
Complete Set #1–800	125.00	50.00	20.00

1990 Bowman

Topps brought back a famous name from the past with this set. It's fun, but where does it fit?

	NM	EX	VG
Common Player	0.06	0.02	0.01
Complete Set	12.00	5.00	2.00

1990 Donruss

It's too early to predict the value for all 1990 sets. Right now Juan Gonzalez looks like the top name, but there are others with potential.

	NM	EX	VG
Common Player	0.06	0.01	0.01
Complete Set	20.00	9.00	4.00

1990 Donruss Rookies

The same tale applies to all 1990 sets: It's too soon to make any predictions.

	NM	EX	VG
Common Player	0.11	0.05	0.02
Complete Set	10.00	4.00	2.00

1990 Fleer

Juan Gonzalez is the current big name for this set, but it's too soon to make any predictions.

	NM	EX	VG
Common Player	0.06	0.02	0.01
Complete Set	20.00	9.00	4.00

1990 Fleer Update

Frank Thomas is the current favorite.

	NM	EX	VG
Common Player	0.06	0.02	0.01
Complete Set	12.00	5.00	2.00

1990 Leaf

Leaf is another new name in 1990. This set brings huge prices due to small production, but will it hold?

	NM	EX	VG
Common Player	0.30	0.10	0.04
Complete Set	325.00	125.00	50.00

1990 Score

This set is filled with errors, number-one draft picks, and whatever else might cause you to buy it.

	NM	EX	VG
Common Player	0.04	0.01	0.01
Complete Set	22.00	10.00	4.00

1990 Score Traded

As if the errors and draft picks weren't enough, try an Eric Lindros baseball card. Frank Thomas makes more sense.

	NM	EX	VG
Common Player	0.06	0.02	0.01
Complete Set	14.00	5.00	2.00

1990 Sportflics

There's nothing spectacular in this set, but it's a good price—and that's the usual Sportflics story.

	NM	EX	VG
Common Player	0.11	0.05	0.01
Complete Set	27.50	12.00	5.00

1990 Topps

Frank Thomas and Juan Gonzalez are the big names in this set, but that could easily change.

	NM	EX	VG
Common Player	0.03	0.01	0.01
Complete Set	22.00	10.00	3.50

1990 Topps Traded

There are no big name rookies in this set yet. Top prices are for Carlos Baerga, Travis Fryman, and David Justice.

	NM	EX	VG
Common Player	0.05	0.02	0.01
Complete Set	10.00	5.00	2.00

1990 Upper Deck

This set is not in the same class as the 1989 issue, although it is still very popular. It contains lots of rookies such as Deion Sanders, Robin Ventura, Steve Avery, and Carlos Baerga, to name a few. The numbers suggest that there are bound to be some winners, but also some busts. It's future price depends on both rookies and on the continued popularity of Upper Deck.

	NM	EX	VG
Common Player	0.07	0.03	0.01
Complete Set #1–800	55.00	25.00	10.00

1991 Bowman

If you liked the 1990 set you'll love this one, but its place in the hobby is not secure.

	NM	EX	VG
Common Player	0.06	0.02	0.01
Complete Set	17.50	8.00	3.50

1991 Donruss

This set has a first Donruss card of Frank Thomas.

	NM	EX	VG
Common Player	0.03	0.01	0.01
Complete Set	20.00	8.50	3.50

1991 Donruss Rookies

Jeff Bagwell and Ivan Rodriguez along with the widely heralded Todd Van Poppel are currently the big names in this set.

	NM	EX	VG
Common Player	0.10	0.03	0.01
Complete Set	7.50	3.00	1.00

1991 Donruss Studio

This is the 1991 Donruss addition to the limited-production-high-quality card market. It's future, like that of other issues of the type, is speculative.

	NM	EX	VG
Common Player	0.14	0.05	0.01
Complete Set	45.00	20.00	8.00

1991 Fleer

It's too early to tell whether the rookies in this set will take off. Phil Plantier was an early favorite.

	NM	EX	VG
Common Player	0.05	0.01	0.01
Complete Set	22.00	8.50	3.75

1991 Fleer Ultra

Fleer's high-priced entry.

	NM	EX	VG
Common Player	0.07	0.03	0.01
Complete Set	40.00	17.50	8.00

1991 Fleer Update

Ivan Rodriguez and Jeff Bagwell are the top priced rookies in this set at present, but it's too early to know what cards will matter in 1991 sets by a few years.

	NM	EX	VG
Common Player	0.07	0.03	0.01
Complete Set	7.50	3.00	1.00

1991 Leaf

Leaf's second attempt to enter the sets market is still holding at high prices.

	NM	EX	VG
Common Player	0.09	0.03	0.01
Complete Set	60.00	25.00	10.00

1991 Score

It's far too early to predict where this set will go in price.

	NM	EX	VG
Common Player	0.04	0.01	0.01
Complete Set	23.00	10.00	3.50

1991 Score Traded

The first Score cards of Jeff Bagwell and Ivan Rodriguez are currently the major features in this set.

	NM	EX	VG
Common Player	0.07	0.03	0.01
Complete Set	7.50	3.50	1.50

1991 Topps

There are lots of rookies in this set, but it's too early to tell about any of them.

	NM	EX	VG
Common Player	0.04	0.01	0.01
Complete Set	20.00	6.50	3.75

1991 Topps Stadium Club

This is the Topps addition to the high-quality, high-priced card competition.

	NM	EX	VG
Common Player	0.25	0.10	0.03
Complete Set	275.00	125.00	50.00

1991 Topps Traded

Jeff Bagwell, Ivan Rodriguez, and Team U.S.A. make this set an interesting buy. Somewhere in here there should be a future star.

	NM	EX	VG
Common Player	0.06	0.02	0.01
Complete Set	12.00	5.00	2.00

1991 Upper Deck

There are lots of rookies in this set, but the Upper Deck magic of 1989 is missing.

	NM	EX	VG
Common Player	0.07	0.03	0.01
Complete Set #1–800	45.00	17.50	7.50

1992 Bowman

This set just contains more of the same in an effort to market the Bowman name.

	NM	EX	VG
Common Player	0.07	0.03	0.01
Complete Set	35.00	15.00	5.00

1992 Donruss

So far, this set contains better-than-average rookies for a regular Donruss set.

	NM	EX	VG
Complete Set	40.00	15.00	5.00
Common Player	0.06	0.01	0.01

1992 Donruss Elite

This is a high-end, limited-production set. The future of such an expensive set is open to debate.

	NM	EX	VG
Common Player	80.00	35.00	15.00
Complete Set	1750.00	750.00	350.00

1992 Fleer

There are lots of rookies in this set, but it's too soon to predict which ones are the stars of tomorrow.

	NM	EX	VG
Common Player	0.04	0.01	0.01
Complete Set	27.50	13.00	5.50

1992 Fleer Ultra

Eric Karros and Pat Listach were the hottest new names in this continuation of the Fleer high-end set.

	NM	EX	VG
Common Player	0.14	0.05	0.01
Complete Set	68.00	27.00	10.00

1992 Fleer Ultra Award Winners

Fleer likes expensive sets, and so it keeps making sets that are more expensive than its last ones. With that guiding notion Fleer came up with this addition to their product line in 1992. Its future, like other sets of this type, is unknown.

	NM	EX	VG
Common Player	5.75	1.00	0.15
Complete Set	200.00	75.00	25.00

1992 Leaf

There's nothing new and exciting in this set except Karros and Listach, with Dave Flemming, Cal Eldred, and Juan Gonzalez also gaining attention.

	NM	EX	VG
Common Player	0.09	0.03	0.01
Complete Set	50.00	15.00	5.00

1992 Leaf Gold Bonus

This is the Leaf high-end set.

	NM	EX	VG
Common Player	2.25	0.75	0.10
Complete Set	90.00	20.00	7.50

1992 Score

This is Score's regular 1992 set.

	NM	EX	VG
Common Player	0.04	0.01	0.01
Complete Set	25.00	10.00	2.50

1992 Score Impact Players

This set is new from Score in 1992. So far it hasn't done much.

	NM	EX	VG
Common Player	0.20	0.05	0.01
Complete Set	35.00	15.00	5.00

1992 Score Pinnacle

Yet another expensive set.

	NM	EX	VG
Common Player	0.12	0.04	0.01
Complete Set	75.00	25.00	10.00

1992 Topps

This set is the regular 1992 Topps set.

	NM	EX	VG
Common Player	0.04	0.01	0.01
Complete Set	25.00	7.50	3.00

1992 Topps Stadium Club

This is another new Topps high-end-limited-production issue.

	NM	EX	VG
Common Player	0.15	0.03	0.01
Complete Set	125.00	35.00	10.00

1992 Topps Stadium Club Dome

This is one of the new Topps high-end-limited-production sets.

	NM	EX	VG
Common Player	0.25	0.05	0.01
Complete Set	50.00	15.00	5.00

1992 Upper Deck

As usual, this Upper Deck set is loaded with rookies.

	NM	EX	VG
Common Player	0.06	0.02	0.01
Complete Set	45.00	15.00	5.00

Player Index